THE
GOUFFÉ
CASE

Harper & Brothers
Publishers
New York

THE GOUFFÉ CASE

JOACHIM MAASS

Translated from the German by
MICHAEL BULLOCK

CONTENTS

PROLOGUE

During the fourth quarter of the last century, a man lived and worked on the Ile de la Cité in Paris whom French public opinion revered as the greatest detective the country had known within living memory. His name was Goron. Although not yet forty, he was already head of the Security Police; and since his appointment a ruthless and unremitting assault had been launched on the world of vice and crime, the effects of which made themselves felt everywhere.

Crime reports, which had hitherto been usual only in respect of exceptional or capital offenses, appeared with increasing frequency, until these brief, concise, and gripping items became an almost daily feature of the press. The papers spoke of innovations in the methods of the police, who suddenly began to attract the interest, and hence the co-operation, of the public.

The control of prostitutes and their protectors and parasites, the so-called *costels* or *marlous*, was intensified and extended—by means of a newly formed body of plain-clothes officers—to the undercover semiprostitution that operated on the highest levels of society; a form of prostitution aimed at blackmail, the exercise of subversive political influence or espionage, the practice of which frequently ended in the suicide of the victim. Police spies of a new type, known as "beaters," whose whereabouts were often unknown for weeks even to the authorities, were dressed in the clothing and supplied with the papers of bandits and men with serious criminal records and sent right into the dens of thieves, robbers, murderers, and blackmailers. They took part in all kinds of unsavory plots, and just before the crime was committed passed their brief warnings, couched in terms only the police could decipher, to the *indicateurs* of the Cité; they were arrested along with the accomplices they had tricked and disappeared with them into prison, still unmasked. Active everywhere, and everywhere passing for criminals among criminals, these men spread alarm and despondency and sapped the energies of the underworld in advance.

There were also rumors of psychological ruses to make particularly stubborn but promising prisoners confess and incriminate their confederates. The method finally proved to be astonishingly simple, and one to which not even the most humanitarian could take exception: after a prolonged period of confinement in darkness and on a meager diet, the prisoner was given a sumptuous dinner with wine. Curiously enough, this act of generosity rarely failed in its effect on even the most hardened evildoer. The maneuver quickly acquired such notoriety, especially in the circles it particularly concerned, that "Monsieur Goron's cookshop" became a byword; and it was said of anyone who had confessed that "He has been to dinner." As a reward for exceptionally valuable information, criminals condemned to hard labor for life were given permission to take their girls with them, if they were willing, and to marry them—an innovation against which there were many protests, but the effectiveness of which was so striking that there could be no question of revoking it. Gangs who had terrorized the city for years with their robberies, with violence and other bloody deeds, such as the Pilets and the atrocious Mother Berland, were ferreted out of their secret hiding places in the wooden warehouses on the banks of the Seine and in the Fortifications, the city wall; and the deportation ships for New Caledonia were full. The most-feared lone wolves, the *solitaires* as they are called in France, fell victim to the tireless vigilance of Goron's detective sergeants. The gates of La Roquette prison, in whose yard stood the guillotine, now opened to Ribot "the Weakling," Jeantroux "the Sardine," and "Fat Nose" Forgerit—celebrated figures in their own dark world, on whom no one would otherwise have dared to squeal for fear of their savage vengeance, and who were protected by an aura of invulnerability. "Monsieur de Paris," Deibler the executioner, became a busy man once more.

In the past, people had barely known who the chief of the Security Police was; but Goron's efficiency was so spectacular that his name was soon on everybody's lips. The public was proud of this master detective. They cherished his fame like a tenor's and it was typical of the situation that people said simply "la Cité" when they meant the Sûreté, the Security Police—ignoring the fact that a whole series of other police and legal departments, and especially the General Prefecture of Police, were housed on this island in the Seine.

Yet Goron himself never sought the limelight. No picture of him was ever published; official publications and reports occasionally referred to the head of the Security Police, but very rarely mentioned his name; and members of the public who were called to attend some interview or interrogation on the Cité had no idea that it was generally Goron himself they had been talking to. No one would have recognized him in the street. Whether this avoidance of publicity was due to professional precaution or to personal modesty, it certainly contributed to his fame; for one thing, it gave free play to popular imagination. A wiry man of medium height, his skin gathered in a strongly marked fold over the bridge of his nose; gaunt, clean-shaven, and pale-eyed; perhaps given to sudden jerky movements of the head such as characterize certain birds; cold, unerring, and quick to strike; a past master in assessing all the commonplace reactions of the human heart, all its hidden depths and anomalies—this, or something like it, was how the public doubtless pictured its mysterious favorite.

But just as great talent generally springs from other sources and manifests itself in other forms than those presupposed by the masses, with their love of the monumental, so this figment of the imagination bore no resemblance to the real Goron. He was a small, pot-bellied, short-winded man; his pendulous hamster's cheeks gave him a misanthropic look, and the scanty, short-cropped black hair that encircled his yellow bald patch stood up on the crown of his head in a series of uncontrollable tufts; in front of his not-very-mobile, round eyes, a pair of pince-nez with small, oval, rimless lenses were embedded firmly but askew in the skin on the bridge of his nose. He radiated a sense of ineradicable discontent, an unquenchable tendency to find fault with everything, even with himself. He was a grumbler of horrifying obstinacy, imbued with such pigheaded animosity toward the world as it was that he was compelled perpetually to tread on his own and other people's heels. He would race through the corridors and offices of the Cité issuing his impatient, carping comments and instructions, run up and down stairs, fling open the door of his room so that it banged against the wall, and drop onto the uncomfortable wooden chair at his desk; he would run his hand over his bald patch with a gesture of exhaustion, let it fall into his lap, and then, his mouth half open, stare fixedly into the void through his crooked pince-nez.

No doubt about it—this Goron was anything but a happy or agreeable man. Whatever he achieved seemed to him insufficient. "And yet—we're not getting anywhere"; this was one of the plaintive remarks, accompanied by headshaking and an expression of hopelessness, with which he disappointed his subordinates and threw them into a state of repressed rage and indignation when they reported notable successes perhaps achieved at the risk of their lives. What did he really want? To make life spotlessly clean? To rid the world of all vice and crime? That was silly, and the joyless fanaticism with which he pursued this mania and unrelentingly badgered his men made him appear to his colleagues both ridiculous and intolerable.

As a matter of fact, not even the oldest police officers could remember the Cité ever having had such an unpopular chief as Goron, this crossgrained crank from Brittany. But he himself was blind to all this. Sensitive and alert as he was in his dealings with crime and its representatives, he had little understanding for the guardians of civil order subordinate to him. In internal matters he was a wretched psychologist.

His knowledge of all his colleagues was on the same pattern. He knew the particular nature of their usefulness and their rank—no more; they were police officers; of the fact that they were also human beings with human weaknesses, animosities, and cupidities, and that they stood facing him across the desk with the greatest imaginable hostility, he took no notice, either because he really didn't see it or because it didn't interest him.

Whatever the personal motives behind the attitudes of his associates toward Goron, they would all have agreed on one thing: namely, that it was nothing but boundless and pathological ambition that spurred him on and made him so utterly unbearable. For there is nothing people find so hard to credit as that a man is genuinely concerned with the task in hand rather than with furthering his own interests. And yet this was, in fact, the case with Goron. With a singleness of purpose that could be looked on as the product either of a narrow outlook or of genius, or of both at once, his concern was with his task and nothing but his task.

Goron's task was to combat crime and protect society from its threat. His view of the matter was neither more superficial nor more profound than that. Evil was in the world, it must be removed from the world, its representatives must be rendered innocuous and if possible destroyed. Metaphysics or psychology had no place in his philosophy. That the world has its demonic depths did not interest him, he remained on the surface; that in the dark recesses of the human soul good and evil are inseparably commingled was unknown to him, he was a simple man. This simplicity was his strength—and it was to become his downfall.

Yet what brought him to disaster was, in appearance, an almost commonplace, though complicated, case—one among many others of its kind that he had already solved and settled through the application of his fanatical energy, aided by skill and good luck. But this time his adversary was of a different kind, and the scandalous events that snatched away his prey after he had secured it were beyond his comprehension. The detective understood nothing of the, so to speak, anonymous forces that rose up against him at the crucial moment and struck the weapon from his hand.

But that was not the end of the case. The same man who had brought it to Goron took it up again at the point where Goron was forced to drop it.

This man lived and operated in secret; and just as Goron's true picture was hidden from the public by the excessively glaring light of fame, so this man was concealed by the darkness of anonymity. Rumor knew of him, of course; but whereas in Goron's case it had imagined the sort of figure that appears on monuments, it pictured the other man in terms of an obscene caricature. As a matter of fact, it would have been impossible to conceive of a more complete antithesis to Goron: he was young, defenseless, and of a lethargic temperament. But one thing they had in common—an extreme degree of resolution. That the younger man should have had to take over the mission which the older had been unable to accomplish was no coincidence, but in full accord with a certain inner logic.

How good that it took place in secret! What would the world have said if it had known of the enterprise, of the young man's victories and defeats? The world, God be praised, never learns of the true struggles·of those who are called, whether they emerge victorious or perish.

BOOK ONE

❧❧❧❧❧❧❧

*"In my bedchamber dwells death,
and wherever I flee to,
there is death."*

GILGAMESH

1

THE CRIME

On July 29, 1889, the year of the Universal Exhibition, a Monday, a man named Edmond Jaquemar appeared on the Ile de la Cité and asked to speak to Goron, the chief of the Security Police, in person. On being informed by the officer on duty that an interview of this kind required a special pass, he replied, after some thought, that the matter he had come about was no less important to Goron than to himself and that he had been sent by Prefect Sallier.

Thereupon he was taken up to Secretary Guillaume, on the second floor, who straightaway showed him in to Goron. The latter was bending over a map of the city dotted with little flags, deciding how best to redistribute his forces between the various arrondissements; for the turmoil caused by the Universal Exhibition, with its considerable influx of foreign visitors, had provided a great stimulus to crime, although—as if by silent agreement with business interests, the Police, and the Press—the criminal elements were conducting themselves with a certain restraint, avoiding the most horrible crimes of violence and contenting themselves, even in the worst cases, with the so-called *coup du père François*, a trick in which the victim was lured into a thicket of the Bois de Boulogne or the Bois de Vincennes by some licentious beauty, subjected to a feigned threat of murder by desperadoes, and then stripped of his possessions while too terrified to resist.

The events reported by Goron's visitor, a frail, very quiet man of medium height and about thirty years old, did not at first sight appear in any way sensational. Goron listened to his calm and occasionally hesitant statement with some impatience, sitting on the edge of his wooden armchair as though ready to jump up at any moment, his pudgy little right hand clasping the knob of the armrest, the light reflected from the waters of the Seine glittering on the lenses of his pince-nez.

Jaquemar sat in a way that was somehow childish, with the whole of his thighs on the chair; as he spoke he kept glancing at a snowy white handkerchief he was holding in his lap, and from time to time he looked up with a questioning expression, revealing a face of fascinating ugliness. The opening and closing of his lips, which were marked above and below by a faint stubble, and twisted at intervals as though silently munching, made the face seem even more repulsive, while the slight cast in his pensive, almost melancholy eyes lent the young man an appearance of bewildered unhappiness whenever he looked his interlocutor full in the face. For all his quietness, however, there was a purposeful determination about him that gradually made itself felt; and the hesitant way in which he made his statement seemed due less to lack of confidence than to the desire to put into words only what was clearly thought out, to the point, and irrefutable. The case he reported to Goron concerned his brother-in-law, Alphonse Gouffé, and was briefly as follows:

While strolling along the Boulevard Saint-Michel at about 6 P.M. the previous Thursday, July 25, he caught sight of his brother-in-law Gouffé sitting with a mutual acquaintance, Madame Germaine Chottin, over an apéritif on one of the sidewalk terraces of the Café Véron. He went up to their table but walked on after exchanging a few words because, as he put it, he was "in a very strange mood." This was the last time he saw his brother-in-law. When he called at his office the following day to discuss an important matter with him, Dopffer, Gouffé's head clerk for the past fifteen years, inquired with some concern as to his whereabouts. Gouffé had failed to appear at the office, something that had never happened before without prior warning. According to a statement by the concierge Moumont, he had spent half an hour or so in the office the previous evening around 10 P.M.—that is to say, some four hours after his brief conversation with Jaquemar—but he seemed to have been in a great hurry, since as he left the building he did not answer Moumont when the latter called after him, but merely muttered inaudibly and dashed out into the street. This last fact, which had led the concierge to report to Dopffer, was particularly odd because Gouffé was known to everyone as a placid, exceptionally friendly, and polite man. As soon as Jaquemar heard Dopffer's story, he went around to his brother-in-law's apartment in the Rue des Ecoles, only to learn that he had not come home the previous night.

So matters had remained: Gouffé had not appeared either at the office or at his apartment, which was quite incomprehensible in view of the rather pedantic regularity of this forty-eight-year-old man's way of life. For this reason, on the previous Sunday Jaquemar had begun to make all sorts of inquiries, but without the slightest success; until a few hours ago (in the meantime he had paid several more visits to the Rue des Ecoles and the office) Prefect Sallier had referred him to Goron.

Goron, shifting irritably toward his beflagged plan of the city, remarked with a joyless little laugh that more men than his visitor had probably ever dreamed of disappeared without trace in Paris. Their families plagued and pestered the police unmercifully; then suddenly not another sound was heard from them, because the "missing man" had come home—either in the best of spirits from a trip into the country with some gay lady, or else dejected from one of the lockups that housed disturbers of the nocturnal peace, drunks or other people picked up in police raids on shady premises, until their identity and relatively clean record had been established. Perhaps Gouffé, too, had been "out on the town." No, contradicted Jaquemar with gentle obstinacy, Gouffé had not been "out on the town"; he was not given to dissipation. How was that? Didn't he like women, was he ill? Ill, answered Jaquemar, weighing his words, no—he wasn't ill, nor was he a misogynist; he was deeply in love with his wife, who died a year ago. There you are! cried Goron, raising both hands in the gesture of a conjurer. There you are! Why suppose that Gouffé should have been an exception, when "they all" carried on in secret with women? And Goron shook his head as though bitter over this wretched characteristic of men. But Jaquemar was unimpressed; he stared at the handkerchief he was holding in his lap and said in a low voice: "There is no innocent explanation for the disappearance of my brother-in-law Gouffé."

This utterance seemed to intrigue Goron more than anything that had preceded it. He looked at his visitor suspiciously, as though groping for something. So he thought there was crime behind it? Something bad anyhow, a mishap, an accident, and probably "something worse." Mishap, accident! cried Goron; that had nothing to do with him; Jaquemar should inquire at the first-aid posts, go to the morgue—perhaps Gouffé was there. No, he was not there; Jaquemar had made sure of that. Nothing was known of him at the first-aid posts, and Prefect Sallier's urgent inquiries at the police stations in every *arrondissement* had produced no result.

For a while neither of them spoke. Goron, now deep in thought, took a cigar from his waistcoat pocket and lit it; as he did so, the reflection of the match flickered in the lenses of his pince-nez. Then, as if overcoming his reluctance by a sudden act of will, he bit into his cigar with his eyetooth so that it stuck up in the air against his cheek, and with his right eye shut pulled a notepad toward him. Would Jaquemar please give him details about the missing man?

Gouffé's external circumstances were as favorable as could be. He was a well-to-do and perhaps wealthy man, with a regular annual income of some fifty thousand francs, which might have risen during recent years to sixty or seventy thousand, since, according to a statement by his head clerk, Dopffer, his office in the Boulevard Saint-Michel had a turnover of more than seven million. That is to say, he had recovered sums to this amount from his clients' creditors—for he was a so-called *huissier*, a notarial auditor, tax adviser, and debt collector.

To Goron's casual comment, "Aha, debt collecting makes people disliked," Jaquemar answered drily that his brother Gouffé was, on the contrary, very well liked, even by the debtors, whom he always treated with the greatest possible consideration, out of "chivalry" and humanity and also as a matter of business principle. Moreover, according once more to Dopffer, who was very well informed about the affairs of the office, no case had occurred recently that was particularly difficult or unpleasant, nothing that threatened to compromise, let alone ruin, the persons involved. Hence there was no visible reason why Gouffé should have gone off on a business trip. Goron asked whether anything had been missing on the morning following Gouffé's hurried visit to the office. On the contrary, he was told, nothing had been touched. In particular, the sum of eighteen thousand francs in bank notes, collected by Gouffé himself late that afternoon, was still in a cardboard box in an unlocked drawer of the desk, where it was the *huissier's* rather curious habit to keep such money.

This, then, was Jaquemar's statement; and as he had nothing more to add, Goron threw his little pencil on the notepad and stared in his turn into his lap, his right hand with the smoking cigar resting on the knob of the armrest. Finally he remarked, with a shrug of his left shoulder, that since none of this suggested any motive, either personal or material, for a crime, he could not see why Jaquemar insisted that there must be some "gloomy" explanation for his brother-in-law's "absence."

"Can you think of any other?" asked Jaquemar, after pausing to reflect and looking up at him. "Besides," he added after a while, in a much lower voice and as though speaking to himself, "we really know very little about another person, however well we think we know him, and I can well imagine a man of even the most regular habits being seduced into the dark back alleys of life."

"Seduced!" rejoined Goron in astonishment (for he had been considering such a possibility that very moment). "Whatever made you think of a thing like that?"

Jaquemar twisted his lips as though silently munching and murmured, almost to himself, that he was always thinking of "things like that. . . ."

"Aha," said Goron, with a rather absurd note of suspicion in his voice, and stood up. He would look into the matter, and by the way, what was Jaquemar's address? Hôtel des Mines, Rue de la Glacière, he scribbled on his pad at Jaquemar's dictation, bending over the desk, with one eye shut to keep out the smoke from his cigar. All right, he would get in touch. He stretched out his pudgy little hand to his visitor without looking at him; and Jaquemar, after gazing at Goron for a moment as though about to say something else, turned and made his way to the door leading into the next room. Goron glanced after him and observed with a fleeting sensation of surprise that this quiet, brooding man had a somewhat affected walk; it was not exactly mincing, but he set his feet down too carefully, in a way that was either inhibited or calculated, and the effect this had on the movement of his hips gave the young man in his very smartly cut, though rather shiny suit, a hint of effeminacy. A queer fish, thought Goron, as he shut the door behind Jaquemar.

The "Gouffé papers," after Secretary Guillaume had made a fair copy of Goron's notes, were passed on to Detective Sergeant Soudrais to deal with; for Goron's days were too hectic to allow him to cope with individual cases. He probably exaggerated his responsibility; after all, was it to be wondered at that as the number of visitors to the Universal Exhibition continued to increase the zeal and activity of the underworld should also have been intensified, till lawlessness was almost beyond control? The trouble was that while crimes multiplied, Goron's men remained the same in numbers and ability; and the most adroit strategy achieved less and less, especially as the adversary proved no less elastic, switching rapidly from one area to another and perpetually duping Goron, who almost always arrived on the scene after the birds had flown. There was no doubt about it: he needed more men.

But the authorities in general, perhaps more worldly-wise than the fanatic in the Cité, seemed perfectly satisfied with the state of affairs, and laconically dismissed the memoranda with which he bombarded them in quick succession and which were immediately followed by urgent requests that they should be attended to. The memoranda would be passed on to a "competent authority," "considered," and dealt with "as soon as possible"—it was like shooting at the air. Eventually the "competent authority," the Ministry of the Interior, reacted with a curt two-line note couched in terms of inquiry, addressed to the General Prefecture of Police, and passed on to Goron by Sallier without comment: if the Cité itself was dissatisfied with it, perhaps the security service should be made answerable to some new organization? Goron invited the leading figures of the Prefecture to a conference, which Sallier rendered more or less abortive by failing to attend himself and sending his secretary, the wiry Delattre, to represent him. The conference was a farce and Goron knew it. After half an hour's inconclusive talk he sprang to his feet, exclaiming that he had no time for "idle chatter" and: "The indolence of official bodies, messieurs, is a worse menace to public security than all the thieves in Paris!" With this, he ran out of the room, leaving the gathering in embarrassed silence. Inspector Latrille smiled beneath lowered eyelids and then exchanged a glance with Delattre.

Under these unhelpful conditions Goron slaved like a robot from early morning till late at night, at his desk, racing through the long corridors, or traveling to and fro between the police stations of the various *arrondissements* in his slow old carriage, whose scraggy chestnut with the long mane and sorrowful eyes Inspector Latrille had wittily nicknamed "Goron's Rosinante." But overworked though he was, the recollection of Jaquemar's visit came back to his mind now and then; and he once more saw in front of him the frail, brooding man with lowered head, a snowy white handkerchief in his hands, and an expression of bewildered unhappiness in his squinting eyes whenever he looked up. He had been so sure there was cause for alarm. Where had this Gouffé gone? Was there still no news of him? Had Soudrais discovered anything?

As a rule, he immediately forgot the matter again; the general turmoil sucked him in and swept him this way and that. Once, however, the memory of his quiet visitor grew so strong in him that he tore himself away from all his other preoccupations, sent for Soudrais, and demanded a progress report. But Soudrais, the boor, who, secretly egged on by Latrille, was showing his contempt for his chief more and more openly, found the whole affair ridiculous. He raised his hairy paw with the ingrown wedding ring and waved the matter aside: the chief would see; "the fellow" was thumbing his nose at all of them; one day he would turn up at home as merry as a cricket.

No theories! cried Goron, dismissing this remark with a movement of his head. He wanted facts, not theories! But there were no facts beyond those recorded in the papers on the case: Gouffé had spent half an hour in his office on the evening of July 25, the devil knows what for; he hadn't left anything behind or taken anything away with him, not a scrap of paper was missing; perhaps he simply wanted to use the lavatory, or to look up some date in the safe. What gave Soudrais that idea? There was a trail of dry tallow drops leading from the desk to the safe—nothing in the least out of the ordinary, added Soudrais with another dismissive gesture of the hand, as Goron looked up in surprise. Gouffé often burned candles; he had two standing on his desk in decorative candlesticks—"to create atmosphere, no doubt, for the private office is a positive boudoir." There was no money in the old-fashioned safe, to which both Gouffé and the head clerk had the key, but only papers; and Dopffer confirmed that none of these were missing. They consisted of judgments, pawn tickets, IOU's, and also a small iron—no, tin—cashbox containing personal papers: certificates of baptism, registration forms, birth certificates, and suchlike "unimportant stuff," and the cashbox had not been moved.

This was the whole outcome of Soudrais's investigations. His report was followed by a brief conversation, about which, as so often in conversations between these unequal partners, there was something peevish and futile; for after staring silently into space for a few minutes, Goron jumped up, strode to and fro, and complained bitterly that he must know more about this business of the candle. He just couldn't understand why Gouffé hadn't put the light on. It was probably too much trouble, commented Soudrais, shrugging his shoulders. No, that wasn't the explanation, it was no more trouble to light the gas than to light a candle—but it would have attracted more attention, the gaslight would have been visible from the street. And why not, rejoined Soudrais with a stupid little laugh, Gouffé was in his own home, so to speak.

At this Goron grew angry: Soudrais had no imagination, he was too superficial, too easily satisfied; perhaps Dopffer was lying, he should have questioned Dopffer unmercifully, and also Jaquemar, the concierge, and everyone employed in the office; he should have tried to find out what plans Gouffé had for the evening of July 25, what he was doing between 6 and 10 P.M., who he was with—in short (and as he said this Goron slumped down into his chair again and turned back to his plan of the city), Soudrais must begin his investigations all over again, and this time would he kindly do the job properly. All right, replied Soudrais, gazing up at a corner of the ceiling and giving vent to an exasperated grunt.

After this conversation, busy as his day-to-day affairs kept him, the feeling gradually insinuated itself into Goron that he was wasting his time and that all his activity was some kind of flight or evasion; and more often than before, the picture of Jaquemar sitting in front of him with lowered head forced itself upon him. He thrust the picture irritably aside; the uneasiness did not quite penetrate his intellect, but it remained somewhere inside him and grew.

Suddenly he could no longer ward off the feeling that he must intervene personally, and at once, in this "Gouffé case," if only because of the persistent Jaquemar, who refused to be fobbed off either in thought or reality—for, unknown to Goron, he had been daily calling on the indifferent Soudrais and had even paid a fresh visit to the Prosecution Department. In the middle of a conversation with Chief Inspector Jaumes and Latrille, Goron rose to his feet, stood for a second with head bowed and his two pudgy fists planted on the top of his desk, then took his black bowler from the hatrack and hurried off with a defensive "Do as you like!"

Jaumes stared after him uncomprehendingly. Latrille remarked perspicaciously: "It seems the Chief is making a new case for himself." And this witticism, far from the mark though it was, soon made its rounds through the Cité and was passed on and commented on with furtive laughter behind the desks and in the corridors: "The Chief is making a new case for himself."

This happened on a quiet rainy morning at the end of the first week of August, 1889, a fortnight after Gouffé had been seen for the last time and some ten days after Jaquemar's first call at the Cité. Goron passed down the Boulevard Saint-Michel in his ramshackle open carriage with the sadly trotting chestnut (they would never have dared to offer such a vehicle to any other high-ranking official). Holding in his right hand an open umbrella, on which the rain was softly drumming, occasionally spilling over in gathered drops, and with his left resting on his thigh, he sat leaning forward at an angle, staring out through his crooked pince-nez with the disgruntled, hamster-cheeked face that seemed quite incapable of smiling and which grew visibly tenser the closer he came to his destination.

The building that attracted his particular attention, and that he gazed at from the now-stationary carriage, stood facing the entrance to the Jardin du Luxembourg, its high iron railing with the gilded spikes overhung by heavy chestnut branches; through the rain-bespattered leaves an occasional glimpse could be caught of the gray stone figures inside the garden. On the builtup side of the Boulevard, more chestnut trees stood, and beneath the shelter of their trailing branches passed the traffic and the ladies with bustles, narrow waists, puff sleeves, and little tilted hats. So this was the district and this the building in which Gouffé had his office: 189 Boulevard Saint-Michel. It was a corner house (the side street was called Rue Soufflot), a spacious building dating from the forties, with the colorful display of a large bookshop on the ground floor, and above it five stories of plain gray wall, a long railing rather less than knee-high in front of the windows on each floor, and narrow shutters uniformly open everywhere.

Under his umbrella, Goron strode across the roadway and threaded his way awkwardly between hansom cabs, carriages, and bell-ringing horsedrawn buses—so that his umbrella kept colliding with other people's—through the passers-by to the entrance door of the building, which was rather inconspicuous and situated almost exactly at the corner of the Rue Soufflot. A cool dampness like that of a cellar seemed to rise up from the tiled floor and spread all over the visitor's skin the moment he entered. On the left, resembling a booking office, was the concierge's quarters with a man sitting inside reading a newspaper by the light of a lamp, for the hall was dim and the corners dark. Goron went straight to the small wooden door, tapped briefly on its glass pane with the four fingers of his right hand, and pushed it open.

Was he the concierge? Was his name Moumont? Of course, replied the man, looking up in surprise. He had round, stupid eyes, big protruding ears, and a little peaked cap of black prunella on his head. He watched Goron openmouthed as he pulled up a stool, sat down on it, tore the pince-nez from his nose and threw them on the table. Police, he explained casually in one word and began his interrogation. How could Moumont be sure that it was ten o'clock when he saw Gouffé enter the building on the evening of July 25? The post had been delivered a few minutes earlier, Moumont replied, the last post came at ten, he was about to call out "Monsieur Gouffé, your post!" but Gouffé had already passed; he hadn't been able to give him the post afterward either, because Gouffé hurried past too quickly and was already half out the door and only muttered unintelligibly when he called after him. Was he certain the man was Gouffé?

Now there developed one of those futile arguments into which Goron's interrogations were apt to degenerate. Moumont was sure the man was Gouffé, although "of course" he couldn't see his face in the light of the lamp, the only light in the hall; moreover, Gouffé had kept his head averted. But Goron demanded proof: how could Moumont have recognized Gouffé since he neither saw his face nor heard his voice? "I know Monsieur Gouffé!" rejoined the concierge. How could he fail to know Monsieur Gouffé after being concierge in the building for "half a lifetime"? Besides, Monsieur Gouffé was wearing his new hat! What kind of hat? Well, his new one, a black topper; he recognized it at once, because he was on the point of buying a new hat himself; the very day before, he had said to Madame Moumont, "A hat like Monsieur Gouffé has bought himself would be just right, it's so smart, such a modern style." All right, said Goron, now let Moumont imagine that the man who ran past him in the darkness, without showing his face or letting his voice be heard, was wearing a different hat—a gray felt hat, for example: would he still have recognized him as Gouffé? But this was too much for Moumont's powers of understanding. He stared Goron in the face with utter incomprehension (with the cap on his head and the round folds above his equally round eyes he now looked unmistakably like a cow). Well, it *was* Gouffé; Gouffé would never have worn a felt hat; and the concierge shook his head and laughed—the idea of Monsieur Gouffé in a felt hat!

"I just want you to *imagine* it," insisted Goron through clenched teeth, replacing his pince-nez on his nose and leaning over the table toward Moumont with both fists on the crook of his umbrella. Moumont suddenly went red in the face, breathed heavily, and shouted: "What nonsense! Monsieur Gouffé never wore a soft hat in his life! Fancy asking me to imagine it. I *can't* imagine it!" And he banged the table with his fist. Now they were both shouting, banging the table, and gesticulating. If anyone had looked in from outside he would have thought he was watching a violent quarrel, not a police inquiry. Finally Goron jumped to his feet with a disparaging gesture and, slamming the door behind him, ran up the stairs.

The entrance to the office he was looking for was on the third floor, directly opposite the stairs: a double door, and, extending above it, a translucent pane of frosted glass across which there ran diagonally, in fine black lettering encircled by artistic flourishes, the inscription "ALPHONSE GOUFFÉ—Huissier." As usual, Goron's entry aroused astonishment, a general raising of eyes and turning of heads at the desks. He strode straight through the antechamber and, uninvited and without a word of greeting, thrust open the low swing gate in the wooden barrier that separated it from the main office. Standing in the middle of the latter, with his hat still on his head, he looked around and asked which of them was Monsieur Dopffer. A tall man of about sixty, who had stopped in the doorway to the next room, which he was about to enter carrying a document in his left hand, now threw back his head and looked at the intruder calmly, but rather disapprovingly, through his horn-rimmed pince-nez, and after a while answered that his name was Dopffer. He bent his head forward, so that he was now looking over the top of his pince-nez, his lips parted in a well-bred smile beneath his handsome gray moustache: "You must be Monsieur Goron? May I ask you to step this way?"

Goron joined him in the next room, and observed at once that this was not Gouffé's office—it did not contain a safe. Dopffer took a key ring from his trouser pocket and unlocked the door into the next room, explaining that he had not wanted Monsieur Gouffé's office to be used. Holding the door open, he invited Goron to enter; and the police officer found himself in Gouffé's sanctum.

He was almost inclined to agree with Soudrais's description of the room as "a positive boudoir." Neither the cosily subdued light nor the luxurious furniture (not even the old-fashioned safe in the window corner) was in the least suggestive of an office; in particular, the sprays of peacock feathers and artificial flowers on the consoles flanking the divan, the silk armchairs, the plush stools, and the occasional tables gave it the appearance of a drawing room. On one of the longitudinal walls, close to the windows, hung a heavy velvet cloth (matching the draped curtains), the richly folded headpiece of which was transfixed and held in place by a slanting lance.

In front of this stood Gouffé's now-abandoned workplace: a re-volving chair of quilted and buttoned leather and a desk with elegant legs and all sorts of ornaments on it, among them two china candle-sticks with half-burnt candles and numerous daguerreotypes. The walls, too, were almost completely covered by daguerreotypes inter-mingled with small gilt-framed oil paintings, decorative plates, and mirrors in frames of violet plush, while from the ceiling a low gas chandelier was suspended, the cut-glass pendants of which tinkled slightly as Goron—his footsteps deadened by the thick carpet—walked over to the velvet hanging. He raised it, peered into the small washroom and cloakroom behind it, and turned to the desk, muttering "a queer office" and briefly shaking his head. That, re-marked Dopffer with a smile, had to do with the type of client who called on a *huissier* in the Boulevard, although (he said this as if making an admission) it was also Monsieur Gouffé's taste, especially because, since Madame Gouffé's death, he had virtually looked on this as his home and spent many hours here in the evenings as well.

Coming closer, he pointed with the document, which he was still holding in his hand, to the daguerreotypes on the desk. All these, he said, were pictures of Madame Gouffé—as a child, as a young girl, and in later years; it had been a very happy marriage. No, replied Goron promptly, picking up a picture; this was someone else. Really? answered Dopffer, frowning slightly and looking over his shoulder. Oh, that was Madame Chottin . . . also a client. Why "also" a client —a client whose portrait stood on the desk? Exactly, rejoined Dopffer with his well-bred smile, that was why he said "also." Monsieur Jaquemar had brought her along in connection with some trifling business matter; he thought Monsieur Gouffé had taken an interest in her. Obviously; was she his mistress? Dopffer, offended, took the picture away from Goron and put it back on the desk. Madame Chottin, he said, was a young lady of unblemished reputation; she had divorced her husband because of his disreputable habits during the first year of their marriage. He considered Goron's question out of place. So she wasn't his mistress! Who was his mistress, then? Dopffer answered drily that Goron misunderstood his position, he was not Monsieur Gouffé's *maître de plaisir*, but his head clerk. Goron turned his hamster-cheeked face to him irritably and replied: "Listen, Gouffé has been missing for a fortnight—no news from him, not a sign of life, nothing. It is probable that he has been a victim of a crime. I should be grateful if we could dispense with formalities."

Dopffer straightened up, removed his pince-nez, then lowered his head, nodded thoughtfully, and said: "I think you are right, Monsieur Goron. It was just your rather—robust way of asking questions that provoked me. I am entirely at your disposal."

With a slight grunt, Goron sat down in the revolving chair at the desk. From this moment on, the conversation proceeded without friction. With pauses for reflection, but quite freely, Dopffer, a man who inspired confidence, gave Goron all the information that was in his power to give.

Monsieur Gouffé was very reticent; he knew almost nothing about his private life apart from the fact that after his wife's death he had felt very lonely, enjoyed little or no social life, and, as far as Dopffer knew, saw no one regularly but his brother-in-law, Jaquemar. Relations between the two brothers-in-law were exceedingly cordial and free from any discord worth mentioning. Free from any discord "worth mentioning"? Well, Monsieur Gouffé worried about Monsieur Jaquemar's future; although already thirty he had not yet settled down to any profession; Monsieur Gouffé had frequently discussed the matter with him, Dopffer. What did Jaquemar live on, then, if he had no profession—did Gouffé give him money? Dopffer couldn't say. Had the picture on the desk suggested to Dopffer that Gouffé was interested in Madame Chottin? Yes, indeed, and besides, Gouffé himself had once hinted as much. "He stood there in the doorway gazing after Madame Chottin, who had just left. He smiled and said: 'A pity, Dopffer, she is a charming little woman.'" A pity—why? Oh, he probably felt he was too old (Madame Chottin was just twenty-five), and perhaps he also thought it might not please Monsieur Jaquemar —here Dopffer quickly pointed out that this was only conjecture on his part; he simply had the impression that Madame Chottin and Monsieur Jaquemar were fond of each other.

"What did he actually look like—Gouffé?" asked Goron, scanning the daguerreotypes in front of him and picking one up. "Is this him?"

The picture showed a smiling lady with a little boater tilted to one side, sitting on an artificial tree stump in front of a backcloth representing a landscape with trees and a spring. Beside her stood a gentleman in a short gray frock coat, a bowler of the same color in his right hand and a walking stick hooked over his bent left forearm. The gentleman was also smiling, but his excessively heavy forehead formed a somehow painful contrast to the healthy appearance of the face with its waxed moustache and the unsophisticated style of the hair, which was pomaded, brushed flat, and parted in the middle.

Yes, confirmed Dopffer, looking at the picture, that was Monsieur Gouffé—Monsieur Gouffé and his wife, or rather fiancée, for at the time (about five years ago) they were still engaged. But Gouffé had changed very little since then, merely putting on a little weight perhaps; he was a perfect example of what people call "a fine figure of a man. . . ." Here Dopffer broke off, stared into space, took a large multicolored handkerchief from his pocket with a slight shake of the head, and wiped his brow.

Goron, feeling awkward, replaced the picture. Dopffer had said that the boudoirlike furnishing of the room was connected with the type of clients Gouffé had—what sort of clients were they? Naturally, replied Dopffer, straightening up and raising his eyebrows reflectively, they had clients from all classes and especially middle-class people: doctors, lawyers, large and small commission salesmen, but also retailers and private individuals, landlords of apartment houses, *rentiers,* for all of whom they collected outstanding debts. Inevitably, however, the other side, the debtors, were also their clients in a sense, particularly as Monsieur Gouffé made a point of avoiding any impoliteness or harshness and was very nearly as friendly and helpful in his dealings with the debtors as with the creditors. Among the latter, as Dopffer had said, there were many retail shopkeepers, and in particular all the smart boulevard shops, the jewelers, perfumeries, and ladies' tailors, such as Mademoiselle Picaut's, for example; hence their clients were also Gouffé's. He meant the "ladies of the boulevard"? Hm—yes, replied Dopffer, nodding his head with an almost imperceptible smile; as a matter of fact, they never had any trouble with the ladies, many of them were—well, almost stuffily respectable.

And there was no particularly unpleasant affair, said Goron, opening the drawer of the desk and rummaging through its insignificant contents, there was definitely no particularly unpleasant affair at hand, nothing that might have ruined anyone, shown someone up, or caused a scandal? He looked up at the chief clerk and asked him to think carefully—was there perhaps something Gouffé had not told him about? That was conceivable, replied Dopffer, but most unlikely; it had never happened before. No, there was absolutely nothing of consequence at hand.

Goron shook his head briefly, shut the drawer again, stood up, and asked Dopffer to open the safe for him. They walked together to the almost square little armor-plated safe; and Dopffer, after turning a small disc, selected a key from the many on his key ring, unlocked the safe door, and held it open for Goron. All sorts of account books with brown leather backs bearing red title panels printed over in gold lettering; documents, some of them in folders, others bearing big notarial seals; and a few bundles of securities tied with string were stacked with pedantic tidiness between the thick, smooth walls of the various compartments; among them was the lead-colored cashbox referred to by Soudrais. Goron carried it to the desk, fiddled with it for a while, then took a bunch of long skeleton keys from his trouser pocket and poked about for a moment in the lock, which almost at once sprang open with a faint click.

He emptied the contents out on the desk—a collection of official documents: Gouffé's *huissier's* certificate; his birth, registration, and baptism certificates; Madame Gouffé's death certificate; and finally a medium-sized, thick, yellow envelope bearing in vertical, excessively neat handwriting the words *NOT TO BE OPENED TILL AFTER MY DEATH! Alphonse Gouffé*. Did Dopffer know about this, asked Goron in amazement. No, Dopffer only knew in a general way that the cashbox contained private papers—not very important ones, incidentally, since Monsieur Gouffé kept these in his safe at the bank. They both stared at the ominous envelope—Goron, having removed his pince-nez, with clouded, unhappy eyes. He gazed at it for a minute or two, suddenly threw back his head with an obstinate gesture, and slipped the envelope into his breast pocket with a muttered "No, not yet."

Goron stood up. He would send Latrille; Dopffer and Latrille together were to draw up an exact and complete list of all Gouffé's clients, with brief notes on each of them: debtor or creditor, the sum involved, a good or bad payer, peculiarities, and, as far as possible, personal circumstances. And once again: did Dopffer find nothing odd about Gouffé's visit to the office on the evening of July 25? Hm—no, not in the visit itself, but rather in the attendant circumstances. The rude way in which he hurried past the concierge Moumont was not in keeping with Gouffé; it almost looked as though Monsieur Gouffé had something definite and urgent to do, but he had absolutely no idea what it could have been. His use of the candle was also extremely strange, particularly strange in view of the fact that he went to the safe with it and yet did not take anything from the safe away with him, unless it was from the private cashbox (Dopffer was perfectly certain there was nothing else missing).

Goron nodded thoughtfully, shrugged his shoulders, and moved off, followed by Dopffer. Well, then, the list of clients, please, complete, accurate, and as quickly as possible. Latrille would be along that same afternoon, and by the way, what was Madame Chottin's address? They were back in the main office; each clerk at his desk squinted at the famous Goron from behind one arm, and one of them, addressed by Dopffer as Martineaux, eagerly turned the pages of a thick book, wrote something down on a piece of paper and brought it to Dopffer, who held it at arm's length and read it over the top of his pince-nez. "Yes, that's right: No. 5 Rue de l'Arbalète, it's quite near the Val-de-Grâce hospital, less than ten minutes from here." Goron looked at Dopffer comparatively benevolently through his pince-nez, thanked him for his help, turned on his heel, and let the door click shut behind him. Dopffer, after straightening up and expanding his chest in a manner peculiar to him, walked with a smile on his lowered face through the main office and back into his own room.

Goron descended the stairs lost in thought. On reaching the bottom, he cast a malevolent glance at the concierge's quarters, where Moumont was still sitting reading the paper. He went resolutely to the room and pushed the door open. Did he recognize the man who ran past in the dim light as Gouffé by anything else besides the hat, demanded Goron, or was it only the hat? "My God!" cried Moumont. "You again, what do you want now?" "Was it only by the hat that you recognized Gouffé?" "It was Gouffé, I told you, it was Gouffé!" And Moumont pulled angrily at the peak of his cap. Was he wearing the same coat or the same suit as usual? How could he tell, by that dim light? What, he had no opportunity of recognizing either the face or the voice, either the suit or the coat, and yet he was sure it was Gouffé? But of course! Really absolutely sure, so sure that he would swear to it? "Yes, yes! Devil take it, yes!" "Very well, raise your hand."

Moumont stared at Goron in perplexity, with his round eyes and the heavy round folds above them. What was he to do? To raise his hand; he was to swear an oath. Moumont remained silent and his face slowly turned red. No, he said at last, he wouldn't do that. Oh, and why not? He wouldn't swear an oath, no, he wouldn't do that. He wasn't so certain after all, then? Did the man behave like Gouffé, was it natural for Gouffé not to have answered his greeting, the greeting of someone he knew so well? Was it Gouffé's habit to keep his head turned to the wall? What was there to see on the wall, anyhow? Moumont looked stupidly through the glass pane at the wall of the entrance hall, then back into Goron's face. "Nothing," he said, shaking his head. He hung on the eyes of his inquisitor, who stood bending over him, on those sharp eyes like buttons behind the pince-nez. "The man behaved like someone who didn't want to be recognized, isn't that so? Was there any reason why Gouffé should not want to be recognized?" Again Moumont shook his head. "None at all," came the belated answer. "No, none at all," repeated Goron, straightening up. He seemed to have forgotten the man he was questioning; he stared into the light of the lamp, swung round on his heel, and walked quickly through the hall and out of the building, while Moumont gazed after him openmouthed, leaning out of the door of his cubbyhole to do so.

The house at No. 5 Rue de l'Arbalète, in which Madame Germaine Chottin lived, was no ordinary house. Long and only two stories high, it stood at right angles to the street, from which it was separated by a brick wall overgrown with creepers and pierced in the center by a round-arched doorway that opened onto a fine courtyard with old trees and a dreamily plashing fountain. Like a good many of the houses near the Val-de-Grâce it had once been a convent, an Ursuline convent, and some residue of the unworldly tranquillity of those days still clung to it; as he shut the gate behind him, deadening the sound of the traffic outside, the visitor suddenly felt himself far from the world, especially when, as today, the rain was pattering dully and regularly on the foliage and washing the flagstones of the courtyard black with a barely audible splash.

Goron felt even more moved by the person of the young Madame Chottin than by this sense of idyllic remoteness. In response to his impatient tugging at the bell rope (which produced a thin tinkle somewhere in the distance), an amiable old woman servant led him through a series of well-furnished rooms of strikingly similar shape, opened a glass door that occupied almost the whole width of the room, after a brief, unceremonious knock, and announced: "We have a visitor, Madame." Goron, entering at once, saw the young lady sitting by the window, which came down level with the floor, occupied with some delicate sewing, from which she looked up unhurriedly through large horn-rimmed spectacles. Goron, his wet umbrella over his left arm, his hat in his right hand, rather clumsily introduced himself: he was Goron, from the police, there was no cause for alarm. Calmly laying aside her work—and obviously in no need of any such reassurance—she rose and came toward the visitor, holding out her hand with a frank and charming smile, a finely shaped, weightless hand. Edmond—she meant Monsieur Jaquemar—had told her about him, she had been expecting him, and "Shall we sit down?"

She was distinctly pretty, but it was her winning charm that struck the observer at first glance, for there was nothing disturbing about her great attractiveness; she seemed rather to radiate something soothing and encouraging, a certain motherliness that was in delightful contrast to the unblemished youthfulness of the gentle face with the tiptilted nose, the smiling mouth, and the very quiet, clear eyes. The latter were pale blue, and the curved lashes closed over them without coquetry—or coquettishly in an engagingly frank manner—when, with slightly raised brows and the trace of a pout on her lips, she made the persuasive little remarks with which she punctuated her speech: "Don't you agree?" or "Why shouldn't I admit that?" Her hair was chestnut brown with strong golden lights in it and she had the slight, flowerlike body of a young girl. Her feet and ankles beneath the crinoline skirt were delicately trim, and delicately pointed were her small breasts in the gathered blouse; her neck, encircled by the tulle collar stiffened with whalebone, was slender.

They sat facing one another by the window, which was bordered along its lower edge by leafy plants standing on the tiled floor. Goron was sitting a little nearer the center of the room and in such a way that what light the rainy gray day and the thick foliage of the trees in the courtyard allowed to enter was reflected with a greenish shimmer in his crooked pince-nez. Madame Chottin spoke of her last meeting with "poor Monsieur Gouffé"; she had been waiting for Goron to call, so that she could tell him about it. Edmond had urged her to go and see him herself at the Cité, but she had felt sure he would come to see her—he could understand that, couldn't he?

Not that anything out of the ordinary had happened on the evening of July 25. She really had a dinner appointment with Monsieur Gouffé, but then she had an unexpected visitor from out of town and had only been able to spare him an hour. She was afraid she had bitterly disappointed poor Monsieur Gouffé, for she had an idea he had invited her for a particular purpose: in order to make her a proposal, in his own honorable way, of course. But perhaps she didn't really want to hear his proposal. Otherwise she would no doubt have sent her visitor to the opera.

Anyway, they sat chatting over an apéritif outside the Véron. Edmond (Goron should please forgive her for referring to Monsieur Jaquemar thus, it came to her more naturally since they were old friends)—Edmond came over to them and stood for a few minutes by their table, but he refused to sit down. "No, don't bother, Gouffé," he said (he always addressed his brother-in-law by his surname), "I don't want to disturb you. I'm not in the mood, in any case." "Oh, you and your moods!" retorted Gouffé with a laugh, whereupon Jaquemar gave him a profound, veiled look and answered after a pause: "Yes, I'm in a very strange frame of mind this evening." He stood beside them for a while longer, lost in thought, then glanced around, nodded to them, and said: "Well, my children, I wish you bon appétit—and good night." At this he left.

After he had gone, Monsieur Gouffé spoke indignantly about his brother-in-law in his good-natured way—wasn't he really too crazy, sometimes he felt really worried about him. "He's cracked," he commented, shaking his head. But when the time came to say good-by, he made a remark that had frequently occupied her thoughts since, because it sounded now almost like a gloomy prophecy. He sighed slightly (but not tragically; he was such a calm, sensible man) and said: "And I thought perhaps my fate would be decided today." He shrugged his shoulders and added: "And now it's going to be just another empty evening."

ed just as
talking too
."

longer con-
o him. Just
dealt with
in a whole-
it, but the
mar didn't
high (in
lack side).
the sum
was all.

escritoire
a sheet of
again and
"Was he
from the
ten sheet
No, she
pale blue
osed the
Madame
n in her
sive ex-
ourtyard
door in

n really
se. The
ad any
ith the
s been
than a
weeks
into a

—and she thought he understood that
looked at her and said: "Never mind,
She left; after making a purchase in a
again; he was reading a letter or docu-
from the briefcase lying on the chair at
waved to her.

that, in the course of his brief comments
ne to speak about his own very quiet and
other remark that now sounded ominous;
I sometimes feel like jumping into the
r believe it."

en the two brothers-in-law, which Goron
it, was the most cordial imaginable; they
o one another as a pair of lovers," although
plaints to make about each other. In par-
tually racking his brains as to how he could
to lead a "steadier" life, and by a steady life
fession, earning money, marrying, and having
ch appealed to Edmond. 'He wants to make
—heavens above!' he protested. For Edmond
re always forgetting about life in their concern
id he had no time to waste on such childish
what did he do, what did he live on—did
Chottin, give him money? Yes, both had.
anything out of the way in it; he frequently
thing.

was that it must be a pleasure to have him for
safest investment in the world." As a matter of
s exceedingly fussy about money matters and
orrowed on the dot and to the last centime; he
lazy man, only what he did—reading, writing,
ilar vague things—were of no practical use and,
usinessman like Gouffé had no sympathy with
w that Gouffé was interested in you?" "Oh, yes,
it. . . ." "Was he jealous?" Madame Chottin
l said: "No, I'm afraid not, Monsieur Goron."
and looked at her fixedly through his pince-nez.
put out by this suspicious gaze, or by the turn the

conversation had taken (though her expression remai
friendly); in any case she stood up and said: "I think I'm
much. Forgive me. It comes from sitting alone such a lo

Goron, feeling cheated because he had anticipated a
versation, likewise rose and shook the hand she held out t
one more thing—what was the business matter that Gouffé
for her? Oh, nothing really; she had invested a small sum
sale business, or rather her divorced husband had invested
money was awarded to her in the divorce settlement. Jaque
consider it a safe investment, the rate of interest was to
such things "too" he was terribly inclined to look on the b
Anyhow, he took her to Monsieur Gouffé, who withdrew
from this business and invested it for her elsewhere; that

Goron left, and Madame Chottin sat down at the little
standing against the wall with its flap lowered; she took
paper and dipped her pen in the ink. The door opened
Goron, now with his hat on, poked his head into the room.
wearing an overcoat?" Madame Chottin turned half around
waist—and saw Goron's buttonlike eyes glued on her unwri
of paper. Monsieur Gouffé, he meant, outside the Véron.
didn't think he had a coat with him; he was wearing a
suit with a white cravat. "Thank you," said Goron, and c
door. As he strode out through the succession of rooms,
Chottin stared at the blank sheet of paper, rose with her p
hand, and sat down on one side of the window; with a pe
pression on her face she watched him hurry across the c
under his black umbrella and make off in the direction of the
the wall.

It was only after this visit to Madame Chottin that Goro
began a systematic and planned investigation of the Gouffé ca
plan he adopted was to see and talk to every person who
business, any human and especially any amatory contact w
missing *huissier*; and no sooner had the list of Gouffé's clien
drawn up by the good Dopffer, with Latrille's assistance,
series of interviews began that filled the Cité for a period of two
with a milling throng of visitors and turned the Gouffé case

cause *célèbre*—too early, some people thought, and in a curiously misleading way, as any objective observer was bound to admit.

The list of clients comprised nearly four hundred persons, about half of them women and these without exception of doubtful reputation—the customers of the smart boulevard shops referred to by the head clerk, the "women of the boulevard," who now filled the Sûreté building with their rustling dresses, enticing glances, and alluring perfumes as they came and went or waited; inevitably, they made a considerable impression on the gentlemen who had also been called for interviews, so that people were soon saying what an exceptionally attractive clientèle Gouffé had—and there would have been something wrong if the missing *huissier*, a normal, healthy man, had not taken advantage and enjoyment from the fact! It was true that some of these beauties had eventually become his clients in a positive sense: having originally come into contact with him as debtors; and then, having made money by the exercise of their profession, they had appointed the friendly *huissier* to administer their capital. But for the overwhelming majority he had been the notarial debt collector, a dangerous person to be treated with respect, upon whose good will they were more or less dependent; and what in the world could have been more natural than to try and gain his favor by making their favors immediately available to him at any time?

The curious thing was that this obvious assumption was completely contradicted by the facts, as Goron came to know them (and he came to know them thoroughly). It seemed to have been a basic principle with Gouffé to keep business and private affairs strictly apart, as strictly as we expect of a conscientious doctor or civil servant. Only in one instance, about six months ago, had he infringed on this principle. The case involved Mademoiselle Georgette S., a woman who held a particular interest for Goron, since she was not only one of the most famous *demimondaines* of the Latin Quarter, but also the mistress of the (married) Prefect of Police, Sallier, as she revealed almost unasked and not without smiling self-satisfaction. Also with a smile, but to the accompaniment of an urgent request for secrecy, she stated that as regards an alibi for the night of July 25 to 26 she could invoke, not of course the rigorously official person of Sallier, but his secretary Delattre, who had called on her that morning with a bouquet of flowers and a message from Sallier, had gained her good will, and the same night enjoyed her favors.

Piquant as this anecdote was, it contributed as little to the solution of the riddle of the vanished *huissier* as the totally fruitless interviews with the rest of Gouffé's male and female clients. The only thing this exhausting fortnight produced was confirmation of Dopffer's assertion that, as far as could be seen, there was no potentially disastrous case among the missing man's current business. Even the possibility that Gouffé was holding documents for an unidentified friend or acquaintance which might have been compromising or otherwise dangerous to an equally unknown third party—though it could not be dismissed entirely—was unlikely, because papers of such importance would not have been kept in the office but deposited in the safe at the bank. In short, if Gouffé's disappearance was attributable to a crime (as Goron had come firmly to believe), there was absolutely no discernible motive for any such crime. This was particularly irritating and disappointing for Goron, because he had become secretly convinced that the man who called at the *huissier's* office on the night of July 25 was not Gouffé, but some person unknown, probably with Gouffé's hat on his head—someone whose visit now seemed completely inexplicable, since he had obviously not been out for robbery.

What now? No clue remained to suggest how and where the missing man might be sought; there was no further possibility of direct action. The measureless field of speculation opened out before Goron. So he decided, with a feeling of inner reluctance which he himself found exasperating and inexplicable, to make his first public announcement in connection with this mysterious case. Some four weeks after Jaquemar's first call at the Cité, it appeared in all the Paris dailies and the larger provincial papers. It read as follows:

Missing since 8 P.M., 25 July: the authorized *huissier* Alphonse Gouffé (official address: 189 Bld Saint-Michel, Paris). Height 5 feet 10 inches; age 48, appearance younger, looks about 40; hair brown, cut short, parted in the middle, brushed flat; short, waxed mustache. Light blue summer suit (maker's name probably Chevalier); white cravat; underclothes marked A.G. On the middle finger of the right hand a gold ring with a large sapphire encircled with brilliants. Special marks: a scar on the left ankle. Any information to the Chief of the Security Police: Goron, Ile de la Cité, Paris.

Sallier immediately conveyed his disapproval in a letter. The Prefecture would prefer to see the Security Police work rather less conspicuously; a public announcement of this kind was calculated not only to perturb visitors to the Universal Exhibition, but also to embarrass the missing person, if he should return. To this Goron replied drily that, according to the experience of the Security Police, the question of embarrassment was of no further significance after such a long disappearance. He sent copies of both letters to Carnot, the Senior Examining Magistrate, who replied that, contrary to the Prefecture, the Prosecution Department considered the announcement belated rather than premature, but was confident that the Sûreté had treated this case, as so many earlier ones, with all the requisite dispatch.

Actually, Goron had little hope of any immediate result from his advertisement; he knew better than anyone that personal descriptions of this kind rarely served any purpose unless, like a lasso cast at random, they happened by sheer chance to encircle the culprit.

The Press, its appetite whetted by the widespread rumors about mass interviews in the Cité, and further stimulated by supposedly confidential information, promptly turned Gouffé's disappearance into a major scandal. Goron himself observed the activities of the Press with some disgust, but not without satisfaction, because in the last resort it was in line with his desire for the active collaboration of the public that the Gouffé case, in however distorted a form, became a cause célèbre.

Nevertheless, Goron made no progress. His arms crossed over his fat chest, chewing his black cigar, he stood at his office window and stared ill-temperedly at the flowing waters of the Seine bathed in the afternoon light. A cause célèbre, certainly, but on the other hand a crime that could not even be proved really to be a crime—a crime with no motive and no concrete evidence, about whose victim nothing was known beyond the fact that he had been missing without trace for over a month. How was the problem to be tackled, where and to whom could he turn for some clue and for deeper insight?

Goron turned to Jaquemar, the only one who shared his conviction that there was no "innocent explanation" for Gouffé's disappearance. While the mass interviews were in progress on the Ile de la Cité,

Jaquemar had called to see him once or twice; but not since then, probably because he did not wish to be a nuisance—or was there some other reason?

The hotel in which Jaquemar lived—a very plain building in the pseudoclassical style, outside which summer trees were rustling and across the front of which, between the windows of the first and second floor, the words *Hôtel des Mines* ran diagonally in noble black and gold letters—stood on the corner formed by the Rue de la Glacière and the Boulevard Arago. Almost the whole of the ground floor was occupied by an extensive bistro; all its French windows were open, so that the people inside, touched by the warm wind, were sitting half out of doors, and anyone on the pavement could feel himself half inside. Goron, seated in his old carriage, saw the marble tables on the tiled floor; the hurrying waiters, enveloped in white aprons reaching to their feet, carrying bottles, spurting soda water into glasses from blue siphons; and the throng around the semicircular bar in the background: workmen in blue overalls, dandies leaning negligently on canes, bohemians in velvet jackets and berets, and among them young women in long frilly dresses and little tilted hats—all of them surrounded by an aura of carefree gaiety, gesticulating, laughing, with dripping glasses in their hands; for it was the hour of the apéritif, of titillation, and perhaps of love.

On the right-hand side, an entrance shared by both the bistro and the hotel led into a stone passage, at the end of which a spiral staircase with smooth cement steps and rough iron banisters spiralled its way upward, within the quadrilateral shaft formed by the walls, so steeply that Goron, panting as he clambered aloft, felt as though he were climbing a tower. On the second floor, after a brief search, he found the door of Jaquemar's room not far from the staircase; barely legible in the dim light on the landing, it bore the number 12A, no doubt to avoid having a room number 13 in the hotel. For a while Goron stood outside listening, staring through his pince-nez at the doorknob. Inside, a woman was speaking or reading in a mellifluously monotonous voice, which he recognized. Its unexcited, distinct tones made the listener feel the soundless, expectant silence around about him, although there was not the slightest ring of loneliness, apprehension, or melancholy in the voice itself, unlike the grave words that he heard without fully understanding: "Were I to tell thee the order of the earth that I saw, thou wouldst sit down and weep."

Goron knocked, the reading stopped, and he had to wait till Jaquemar's voice replied with a questioning "Yes?" He opened the door; the room before him was large, clean, and almost devoid of furniture apart from a few pieces around the painted walls and a threadbare, faded carpet in the wide expanse in the center of the room. Over by the window Jaquemar was half reclining in a large armchair, propped up on his elbows, his feet stretched out in front of him on a stool; he looked at the guest with his squinting gaze full of bewildered unhappiness. Young Madame Chottin was seated on a silk pouffe at his feet, a book in her lap, and the big, clumsy horn-rimmed spectacles on her delicate nose; she too looked at Goron, but with friendly attention.

Jaquemar rose and welcomed the visitor; and as he came toward him, Goron noticed that this slender-limbed young man with the rather overlarge head possessed strikingly beautiful hair, of a dark, metallic brown, which was brushed back on the left in a fine sweeping curve and on the right, next to the side parting, carefully cut short; in some way difficult to define, this gave him a well-to-do and aristocratic look, especially in conjunction with the snowy white, baggy shirt he wore, with the collar comfortably open, instead of a jacket; for the rest, he was wearing dark trousers and patent-leather pumps. With his rather too dainty walk he led his guest to Madame Chottin, who, without rising from her seat, smiled entrancingly and offered him her hand. She was glad to see him, she said, but she would leave at once in order not to be in the way. Goron, repudiating this with a "Not at all" and "On the contrary, Madame," was conducted to an armchair, on which he sat uncomfortably, right on the edge, while Jaquemar himself dropped to the footstool beside his lady friend.

There, with knees drawn up and head frequently lowered, he listened to the police chief's statement regarding his lack of success in the case of the missing Gouffé. True, he planned to set in motion a new intelligence service to gather information about all incidents throughout the country that might have some connection with Gouffé's disappearance; but there were so few facts to go on and nothing to indicate a possible line of inquiry. And now that the mass interviews at the Cité had led nowhere, a closer insight into the vanished man's circumstances, mental make-up, and emotional state seemed necessary. Here Jaquemar glanced up, looked for a second into the flashing pince-nez of the now-silent Goron, and, after an almost imperceptible shrug of the shoulders, stared down into his lap again. Certainly, said Goron with a joyless little laugh as though conceding a point, certainly he too would have preferred a more down-to-earth, methodical procedure—an attempt to guide public interest, which had been so irresponsibly whipped up, into useful channels by the offer of a high reward, as had long since become customary in Austria, Germany, and particularly the United States. But this was impossible on account of the "shameful" poverty of the Paris police; for naturally the reward would have to be no less sensational than the scandalous smear campaign in the Press, say at least ten thousand francs—a small fortune they would never expend "in this country," even if it was the Emperor of China they were looking for.

Again Jaquemar looked up, this time toward the doorway, into which, after the door had silently opened, a tall, emaciated man had stepped, unnoticed by anyone. He wore clothes that were far too tight and short, had a very small head, a face that was somehow puckered up, and dangling hands that looked large and raw because the sleeves of his frock coat were too short; and he stood there motionless, gazing sternly with dark bird's eyes from behind his spectacles at the group by the window. "You're disturbing us," said Jaquemar, without making the slightest impression on the newcomer. The latter, after an almost imperceptible shake of the head, went over to the screen —a flowered material, badly torn, in a white wooden frame—that divided off the far corner of the room, disappeared behind it, and reappeared a few moments later with a summer coat over his arm.

Young Madame Chottin watched him with silent amusement as he now walked up to Jaquemar, stretched out his large red hand, and said in a dry tone: "Ten, if you please." "No," replied Jaquemar; and the stranger, without taking his hand away, retorted in an equally laconic voice: "Five, then." And as Jaquemar took his purse out of his pocket, the bird-eyed man met Goron's uncomprehending stare, drew in his cheeks so that his lips protruded in a point like a beak and opened and closed them with a twittering sound, which increased his resemblance to a bird to an extent that was quite grotesque

—Goron could not believe his senses. But the stranger turned his now-unmoving, puckered face away and looked attentively at his outstretched hand, on which Jaquemar was just counting out five franc pieces. As he plunged the money deep into his tight trouser pocket, he muttered: "Always these difficulties." Shaking his head slightly, he walked over to the door, but turned around once more, raised his arm, and cried: "The Sublime One salutes the community of mendicant monks, overcoming his disgust at their disgraceful manginess."

The door shut behind him, and young Madame Chottin laughed, evidently on the point of giving a rational explanation of the man's queer behavior; but she changed her mind, because Jaquemar, once more lowering his head thoughtfully, returned to Goron's previous remarks as though nothing had happened. A closer insight into his brother-in-law's life? Yes, that might be worth following up; he would see to it and get in touch with Goron. As to the reward—well, why not? And as Goron, raising both hands impatiently, opened his mouth to object, he looked up and continued: "I shall send you a check." Goron's mouth remained open; he stared at him through his pince-nez. It was on the tip of his tongue to retort "How can you, since you barely have a centime yourself?" But he choked back the remark; and Madame Chottin, as though the two men needed a gently maternal reproof, commented that it seemed only right that Edmond should shrink from no sacrifice, for "we must really do everything possible to find poor Monsieur Gouffé, mustn't we?" Goron made no reply to this, but Jaquemar looked into her face with the hint of a smile, very calm and quite undisturbed by the presence of Goron, who, since there was nothing further to be done here and now, immediately rose to go with his usual abruptness.

The other two also rose, and while Goron offered to take Madame Chottin home in his carriage (it was almost on his way), Jaquemar stood pensively by, staring at the toe of his shoe, which he twisted around as though boring into the bedraggled fringe of the threadbare carpet; then, rather suddenly, he crossed the room with his dainty gait, disappeared behind the screen, and came back with a gray silk tippet, which he placed over the pretty young woman's shoulders without even a friendly smile. He kissed her hand, raising it to his lips and inclining his head only slightly. "See you soon," he remarked; but it was not clear whom he was addressing, since at that moment he was shaking hands with Goron. He saw them out and, leaning against the doorpost, watched them move away in the dim light of the landing.

The day after next there lay on the desk in the Cité a thick envelope, unstamped and hence no doubt delivered by hand, containing a check for ten thousand francs in favor of the Paris Sûreté, and also the following:

DEAR MONSIEUR GORON,

Since you left me a few hours ago, I have lain on my bed thinking. You want to know more about my brother-in-law Gouffé—what kind of man he was and how he lived. Well, that is more easily asked than answered. What do I really know about him, apart from the fact that he has vanished for over a month, vanished without trace, God knows why or where, and that I am filled with foreboding? This traceless disappearance makes me feel as though blinded by the vapors rising from a chasm—I tremble for my brother-in-law Gouffé.

But what else? What does one person know of another? Yet this man was close to me; I have shared experiences and talked over many things with him. If there is still not much I can tell you, you must bear in mind that I have not known him long.

I made his acquaintance only a little over three years ago; for when he married my sister Eugénie, I was not in Paris. They lived in the Rue des Ecoles, in the apartment you already know. Just as you must often have done recently, I frequently used to search this apartment for something interesting, something spiritually interesting, I mean; but I never found anything. It was an utterly impersonal apartment: the heavy carpets, the cut-glass chandeliers, the silk-upholstered armchairs, the étagères and the glass showcases for knickknacks, the fancy vases on the ebony console tables and the glass doors between the rooms, the thick curtains in front of the windows and the bouquets of gaslamps on the walls—thousands of our well-to-do married couples live in such apartments; even the pictures on the carved easels and the many bronze-framed daguerreotypes on the ornamental tables are indistinguishably alike. The marriages, too, are indistinguishably alike.

But my brother-in-law Gouffé was a particularly good husband. I didn't altogether like it. My sister was rather pretty, many people thought her beautiful, and she was very proud of the age and eminence of our family; we possessed nothing, but we could prove that it had been the same for several centuries; for this reason, she rather looked down on her husband. But he was a very good-natured man; perhaps he actually enjoyed it—anyhow I never once saw him annoyed about it. On the contrary, he always behaved rather like a suitor. Every single evening he brought her a small present—a bunch of flowers, a comfit box, a piece of Brussels lace; and every time I was present I was angered by the way she received these marks of attention—with a certain exaggerated surprise, the way conventional adults accept a child's paintings brought to them as a gift, because it never so much as crosses their minds that even a child's soul may have something it wants to express. (I am probably unjust toward my sister—I was one of those people who thought her beautiful, especially in my childhood, when I was ten or eleven and she a much-courted young miss: I used to stand forgotten and dejected in a corner of the drawing room.)

As I have said, my brother-in-law Gouffé never seemed to feel put out by my sister's behavior. He was full of her. Although opportunities forced themselves on him, I don't believe he was once unfaithful to her. She was almost a pleasant obsession with him. But there was nothing slavish about this attitude; this was particularly manifest in his behavior toward me. Eugénie and I had occasional disagreements. I was originally supposed to become a merchant, but I had finally realized that I was not cut out for this occupation. I didn't know, however, what I was cut out for—I don't know even now. My sister had a tendency to lay down the law where I was concerned, a habit left over from our childhood no doubt, and she was very dissatisfied with me for giving up what she called my "profession."

"My dear Edmond," she said, "earn money, acquire a position—then do what you like!" I sat on the sofa and stared into space and said: "Don't worry about me. I know what I'm doing." "No, no," she cried, "that's just it! You haven't the slightest idea what you want!" Then my brother-in-law laughed, slapped me on the back, and said: "At all events, he knows what he *doesn't* want. That's something!" He admired his wife's quick intelligence, but he was fundamentally much wiser and also more kindly than she.

When he showed me to the door, he would whisper as he said good-by: "Come and see me in the office tomorrow." There he would give me money, two hundred francs, three hundred francs—he used to take the money out of the safe, make a note, and hand it to me. "There," he said once. "Now listen, my dear fellow—you mustn't misunderstand Eugénie; she worries about you, she is only thinking of your well-being." I looked at the notes and answered: "Worrying won't help me. I can do that for myself." "Yes, yes," he said, linking his arm in mine to show me out. "But now tell me seriously: what do you really want?" "I don't know, Gouffé," I replied. "Perhaps I shall never know." "Do you want to become a poet?" he asked. I shrugged my shoulders. "I'm searching for something, Gouffé."

We were standing at the wooden barrier in the main office, he on one side, I on the other, looking into each other's face. "What are you searching for?" he asked. "I can't just live," I said (I found it very hard to explain myself, but I should have liked to explain to him). "It's all so unreal, everything passes so quickly—yesterday we were still children, to-day we're in love with a woman, tomorrow we may be dead. Is that all? Do you believe it is?" He asked with a baffled little smile: "Are you searching for eternal youth?" "Perhaps," I replied, "perhaps I'm also searching for eternal youth. I want to see *reality*." "Well," he said, and there was a trace of suspicion in his face, which at once gave way before his essential friendliness toward me, "that's your affair, Edmond. I won't poke my nose into it. Anyhow, don't worry. I shall always be here when you want me. You know that!" He slapped me on the shoulder and went back into his office.

Our relationship was, and remained, like this as long as Eugénie was alive. But her death changed everything. Her illness must have been silently preparing itself for years, but to us it seemed almost incomprehensibly sudden: it attacked quite unexpectedly, worried, rent, and pierced its victim as though in a frenzy, and let her fall back on the bed emptied and lifeless. It took only six weeks, this vengeance of a power that felt itself ignored. My brother-in-law Gouffé was beside himself with horror and apprehension. He couldn't stay in the room for more than half an hour at a time; day and night he paced aimlessly to and fro in the apartment. It was quite obvious that he was trying to flee from the hour that would say to him "You are alone." But I sat with my sister the whole time; she wanted it so. In the short pauses which the pain allowed her, while it gathered fresh fury, she used to look at me with her big, dark blue eyes that seemed to be growing larger and larger in her shriveling face. She was nothing but skin and bone now, and her head was turning into a skull. My brother-in-law Gouffé looked from one to the other of us—everything was becoming more and more incomprehensible to him.

Two days before her death she beckoned me over from my chair. I sat down on the edge of the bed, my hands in my lap and my face turned toward her; her ghostly pain-filled eyes rested on mine. "Edmond," she whispered, "you have always been so outspoken, most people couldn't stand you because you were so outspoken, Edmond, my little brother. Now I want to ask you something, and please answer me. Do you believe in God?" "Not in the Father in Heaven," I said. A little twitch ran through her fair eyebrows and she repeated impatiently: "Do you believe in God?" "How could I not believe in Him?" I replied. "Is he good?" she asked. "No," I said, "he has no human qualities." "Do you believe in Christ?" "With my whole soul," I said, "I believe in Christ." "Is life good?" "Yes," I answered, and she closed her eyes, "Life is marvelously beautiful." "And where I am going," she whispered, "death—is death bad?" "Only for the living," I said. "Don't be afraid."

She lay there with closed eyes, and two tears trickled into the deep hollows of her cheeks; her lips moved and she whispered: "Edmund, my little brother." During this strange dialogue my brother-in-law stood at the foot of the bed; I could feel how his gaze rested on whoever was speaking, now on my sister—this child with a skull for a head, who had once been his joy—now on me; I could feel his staring eyes on the back of my neck. Then I felt a tremendous pity for him. I turned and said: "She can't even bear to think of you, Gouffé." He nodded, but I knew how he felt: without being able to put it into words, it was as though he had caught us in flagrante, he felt shut out—he was alone.

It was a fine, hot summer's day when we buried my sister. Afterward, we sat in the carriage and drove back through the many columns, crosses, and statues of angels. "Did you hear," he asked, "how the earth fell on her coffin?" "Yes," I answered, "it is unforgettable. But it sounds the same on all coffins." He made no reply to this. After a while he asked: "Where shall we drive to now?" "Home," I said, and looked at him. "Rue des Ecoles." "Oh," he said, "there?" "We can drink cognac," I went on, in order to make some sort of suggestion. "Yes, that's true," he answered. "But it won't help much," I said, and he mutely shook his head. We reached his house and went in. His key was already in the door of his apartment, when he turned and said: "You know—I'd rather go in alone. Come back later, in two or three hours—come back this evening." "Won't it be hard for you to be alone?" I asked. He shook his head again. But all at once he was close beside me; he pressed himself against me and whispered: "Terribly hard! Terribly hard!" The door shut behind him. I stood for a long time on the landing, looking at the door and thinking.

In the evening, the two of us drank a bottle and a half of Hennessy. We were both drunk; it was the only time I have ever seen my brother-in-law drunk. "Yes, Edmond," he shouted with a laugh, and the tears were running down his cheeks, "this is a proper wake we're having! We're as drunk as penguins—let us be frank (Génie says you're so frank!): we're itching to play at the beast with two backs! You had a beautiful sister, Edmond! Where is she now? Where has she got to?" "Did you intend to hang yourself this afternoon?" I asked. He looked at me in astonishment (but I was just as drunk as he). "How did you know?" he demanded. "Yes, I intended to hang myself—you're quite right. But I was too cowardly." "No," I replied, "it wasn't that." "Do you know that too?" he cried. "Edmond, you're a dangerous man! No, it wasn't that. But when I held the rope in my hand (it was the cord of Génie's dressing gown), I thought to myself: What's the use? You don't even feel any real pain! The meanness of man is boundless—even now I don't feel any real pain, not at all—I could bite my own hand, just so as to feel pain! Why are you looking at me so queerly, Edmond? Don't you believe me?" "Wait," I said, "your pain is still a baby; it can't express itself properly yet. It will grow older. Keep your eye on it, Gouffé. I'm afraid it will wreak havoc with you."

Perhaps my brother-in-law felt ashamed of our unconstrained and drunken conversation that night; anyhow, a change took place in his behavior toward me. I had the feeling that he was avoiding me. Formerly, I used to call at the Rue des Écoles several times a week; now I scarcely ever saw him at home, and for various reasons I didn't want to go to the office. But one day a point came when I simply had to go again. I was rather surprised to find his room in the office so changed (for he had arranged it like a drawing room), but I thought I knew why. He received me with all his usual warmth and friendliness—he was a simple, kindly man and the inner motives for his own behavior were seldom known to him.

"So you've dropped in again at last!" he said. "That's nice, my dear fellow. I'm glad to see you." "Yes?" I answered thoughtfully. "Are you glad? I've been to you several times. You could have come to me for a change." "Well," he rejoined in some astonishment, "isn't it strange: I never thought of that." "Do you spend most of your time here nowadays?" I asked, looking around. "Yes," he answered and sighed. "Oh, Edmond—my apartment is too large." "Do you suffer from claustrophobia?" I asked. "What words you use! Claustrophobia? I have lost what I loved most in life!" "Yes, anxiety isn't exactly cheerful." "But I don't feel any anxiety! No, it's not that. It is only that it's torture to be in a place where I was so happy and that is now so terribly empty. Oh, you were right that night: pain is wreaking havoc with me." "Move out." "No. I can't tear myself away. You see, there at least everything means something: the chair in which she sat, the table at which she ate, the bed in which she slept." "Do you sleep in the same bed? In your marriage bed?" "Every night it costs me an effort to lie down on it—I loved her very deeply, Edmond." "You shouldn't sleep with death. It will poison you."

He nodded bitterly to himself. "Yes, those are just words to you—but there's some truth in what you say. Do you know, I hardly ever go to bed before three or four in the morning."—"Can't you get to sleep before then?" "Yes, I sleep on the sofa in the drawing room. Then, when day begins to break, I wake up and go to bed. It's not so bad as in the dark. . . . Tell me, did you come for any special reason?" "Yes, I need money." "So? Yes, of course. Forgive me for not thinking of it myself." He went to the safe, took out a hundred francs, made a note of it, and gave me the money. "Can you manage with that?" he asked. "I haven't much loose cash at the moment. . . . How are your affairs going? Are you progressing?" "I don't know," I said. "You don't know? Well, I don't understand anything about it. I don't want to talk you into anything. But do you know what I thought? Shouldn't you arrange your life—on a different basis, shall we say? You could help me out, for example. Dopffer would show you everything. You wouldn't need to be here the whole day. I should like to have you here, really." "There's no point in discussing it, Gouffé," I said, "I'm sticking to my decision." "Well, it was only a suggestion!" He slapped me on the back, and although I sat there as calm as a stone, he said: "Don't excite yourself, my dear fellow. I meant it for the best."

But from then on, it became an obsession with him that I should adopt a "profession." He really pestered me about it. At first I didn't understand; but then it gradually dawned on me: he had begun to draw comparisons between his life and mine, and he didn't come out of it well—my life made him feel uncomfortable. If my friend Germaine Chottin hadn't had a minor business problem at this time, I should probably have kept away from him. But as it was, I took her to see him, and I noticed that he was immediately captivated by her gentle charm.

One evening he called on me in my room at the Hôtel des Mines; this had never been a frequent occurrence and during the last few months it had ceased altogether. "Yes," he said with a laugh, "if the mountain won't come to Mahomet. . . . I never see you nowadays! Don't you need money?" "No," I answered curtly, "I don't need anything at the moment." "Aha," he said in some surprise. He walked up and down, then he started again: "Yes, what I wanted to say was—your friend, little Madame Chottin—well, I've bought railway shares for her. By the way, she's really entrancing. Do you know what? You should marry her! Yes, really, that's an idea. Join my firm, become a partner and marry her!" "Stop talking about it," I said from my corner. "You know I shan't marry her." He asked hesitantly: "Then you don't love her?" "Yes, I love her all right. But I shan't marry her. I have something else to do in life." "My God," he cried, "what is there to do in this life?" "Yes," I rejoined, and felt sorry for him, "that is really your problem, Gouffé." "After all," he retorted with more heat than was usual with him, "I have my business, haven't I? I earn my living; in fact I'm kept pretty busy!" "Then why did you say, 'What is there to do in this life?' You contradict yourself."

He looked at me nonplussed. "Oh, well," he said then, "we don't understand one another on this point. Don't forget I'm twenty years older than you. It's quite natural I should take life rather more seriously." "Do you?" "My dear fellow, I'm a businessman. . . . But come, don't let us quarrel! I didn't come for that. Well, what were we talking about just now? Oh, yes, little Madame Chottin. I don't know, I believe that if I were twenty years younger. . . ." He broke off with a laugh and said:

"Dopffer paid me a compliment today. He said, 'You get younger all the time, Monsieur Gouffé, you don't look more than forty.'" He broke off again and asked me with distrust in his voice: "You don't say anything?" I had to smile. "Yes," I said, "Dopffer was quite right, you're looking magnificent—if that's what you want to hear."

A few days later, I also received a visit from Germaine; she often comes here in the afternoon, makes us some Turkish coffee, reads to me or chats with me. She did so that afternoon. She busied herself about the little copper saucepan with the long handle, put it on the spirit cooker, and said: "Do you know that your brother-in-law is really a very nice man? He's so steady, so reliable. I'm genuinely fond of him. He's good-looking too." She looked over at me, but I said nothing. I wanted to hear more. And everything came exactly as I had foreseen. Shouldn't she perhaps marry him? She didn't like being alone. She pouted slightly and said: "I'm really too young to play the eternal wallflower, aren't I? You agree with me, don't you?" The ruses people adopt are so transparent; sometimes it touches my heart. I stared in front of me and thought: I can't give you the answer you would like to hear, sweetheart. Finally I said: "You aren't even considering it, Germaine. Let's talk about something else."

It all made me feel very sad. Once I saw my brother-in-law in the street; it was early evening and horribly windy and wet. As he didn't notice me, I followed him for a while. It was no weather for walking, yet he was just strolling along. Every now and then he stopped in front of a shopwindow, but he didn't look in properly; he just stood there gazing at the rain-splashed panes of glass. Then he stood at the edge of the pavement, the wind tearing at his overcoat, and he stared at the horse-drawn omnibuses; and all of a sudden he looked about him with a groan, like someone who is sick of everything—and as he did so, he spotted me. I noticed that seeing me gave him a shock; he actually gasped with shock like someone caught doing wrong. That was a glimpse into a life, I thought.

But I only smiled and said: "Well, are you out looking for adventure?" We talked together as we walked along the street in the wind and rain. Then he confided: "I don't want to go home—I had a visitor yesterday. Just imagine, I came home around ten o'clock; I opened the door of the apartment more or less lost in thought, lit the lamp, went into the drawing room, and put the lamp on the table. Then I went to the cloakroom and hung up my hat and coat. I came back into the drawing room, but I stopped dead in the doorway: there was somebody sitting in the corner of the sofa! He had one leg crossed over the other, and although there was not a sound to be heard, he was talking and laughing and shaking his head. Do you know who it was? I myself! He was even dressed in the very suit I had on! It was an exceptionally horrible impression—I stared at him and knew I was looking at myself. Then the apparition vanished without a trace. I had a feeling of total emptiness in my head. . . . Well, what crazy experiences we go through! Just think of it: I'm seeing ghosts!" "Yes," I replied, "such things do happen." But inwardly I was shocked: this apparition seemed to me like a threat, and it showed me for the first time in what a bad way Gouffé really was. I thought to myself: sometime I shall have to tell him the truth.

To avoid misunderstanding, however, I should perhaps stress that the change in the relationship between my brother-in-law and myself probably did not strike anyone else. Still less, I imagine, did anyone but myself notice the change that was taking place in his being. In a sense, he continued to be his old self. He was still so calm and sensible. But he radiated a different aura, and anguish was gnawing away inside him.

One evening he came to my room again. "Well, Gouffé," I said, "what do you want?" "Oh God," he said with a laugh, "I hope I'm not bothering you! It really sounds as though I come only when I want something!" I didn't answer. He ran his hand over his forehead and said: "You know, I'm worried. I'm seriously worried, Edmond. Our conversation the other evening stuck in my mind for a long time." "You mean, when we talked about your ghost?" "No, no, I don't mean that. I mean the other evening, when I came to see you. To tell you the truth, I have even talked to Dopffer about it—that will show you how much it has been on my mind. I will tell you frankly that I have come to a decision. Edmond: this life must stop! You must get down to something steady! Don't misunderstand me—you know I'm perfectly willing to help you; indeed, it's a pleasure for me to help you, but . . ."

I interrupted him. "I haven't asked you to help me. I haven't done so for quite a long time. Hasn't that struck you?" "Don't lose your temper!" he shouted. "Listen, I'm older than you, let us talk things over calmly. I only want what is best for you, you know that." Again I interrupted him: "Do you know what is best for you?" I asked him. "Stop dodging the issue," he replied. "It's not me we are talking about!" "Never mind whether it is you or me we are talking about," I rejoined. "Perhaps you're not so certain about that as you think. But I refuse to discuss my life with you." "Why?" he demanded, taken aback. "Why not? Haven't I earned the right to do that?" "No," I said thoughtfully, "although you were always kind to me, you haven't earned the right to do that." "At least you're honest," he said with a perplexed little laugh.

"Yes, I think I'm honest. I don't want to hurt your feelings, Gouffé. I like you. And I'm sorry you can't find your way in life." "What?" he shouted. "I can't find my way in life? What do you mean by that? You're funny!" "No, Gouffé," I said, "there's no point in your picking holes in my life. You'd do better to worry about your own! Have you ever really looked at it? Did you ever spend an hour on that, tell me?"

"Listen, my dear fellow—I'm close on fifty! I'm a grown man!" "I'm asking you, did you ever take a good look at your life?" "My God, what rubbish! What a question! My life? I'm a *huissier*, am I not? I work, I earn my living." "Yes, no doubt . . . but what I want to know is: are you happy, are you contented?" "You seem to forget that a few months ago I lost my wife—the wife I loved!" "No, I haven't forgotten that. On the contrary, let me remind you of something I said at the time: keep an eye on your pain, Gouffé! It has become dangerous." "Isn't it natural for a man to mourn his wife? Tell me that! And why is my pain 'dangerous,' what do you mean by that? How do you know?" "Because you are attacking my life. What do you want with my life? You don't know it, you don't understand it. What is it you're after? Whether you trust my life as you see it, or whether you mistrust it, make no odds. But your distrust won't leave you in peace, it has become an obsession. Do you know what? It is misleading you. It does not concern *my* life at all."

"What? What?" he stuttered. "I don't understand a word." "Yes, you do," I said. "Now you understand me. And you know I'm right. This terrible distrust relates to your life! But you haven't the courage to face the fact, so you attack my life." He wiped his brow with a handkerchief. "You can drive one to distraction with your vagaries!" he said and then added: "Well, why don't you go on? You can't come out with such a statement and then just leave it at that." "So you want to hear more, do you? I've been thinking about you a lot, as a matter of fact. And I came to this conclusion: when you said 'I feel no pain,' and I answered 'Beware of this pain you don't feel,' we were both right. Your happiness was an illusion. Now it is gone and your life is empty. You have nothing to think about, nothing to hold on to. That is why you have created for yourself a new illusion—something to think about. And that was why you came to me, that was what you wanted from me: I was to allow my life to be changed and dominated by you, as my sister Eugénie, while she was alive, was to allow herself to be loved by you. But I'm not Eugénie." "Listen," he said with a gulp, "do you know what you're saying? What you are accusing me of would be an incredibly dirty trick!"

I smiled again and felt very sad on his account. "Oh no, Gouffé," I said, "you're not capable of doing a dirty trick. You're the most decent man in the world. There's nothing evil in it—that's how people generally act and live and love; sometimes they do one another good by it, and sometimes harm, it's pure chance. That's what your life is like." "Your life is different, is it?" he said with a hint of rather uncertain mockery in his voice. "Yes," I answered calmly, "my life is different." "Ah well, you're a poet." He laughed and laid his hand on my shoulder. "I didn't mean to upset you, really not, my dear fellow! You may be quite right. We probably do take ourselves too seriously." "No," I said, "we don't take ourselves seriously enough." "You're too argumentative

for me this evening. I'm tired." He stifled an imaginary yawn. "I'm
going."

I accompanied him to the door. His hand was already on the knob.
"There was something else I wanted to say," he murmured, and stared
down at his feet. "Yes, your little Madame Chottin—tell me, were you
serious when you said you loved her, but you wouldn't marry her?"
"Yes," I answered. "Just fancy," he said, laughing and shaking his head,
"the ideas we get in our loneliness! I have actually been wondering
whether perhaps I shouldn't ask her . . ." He looked questioningly into
my face. "Don't ask her, Gouffé," I replied sadly. He tried to laugh.
"No, no," he said, and dismissed the thought with a wave of the hand.
"It was just an idea. I'm much too old for her anyway."

After this conversation we saw each other more often; it became a
need for him. This was hardly surprising: he met Germaine from time to
time, it's true, but he never put his question to her; he had no friends
besides myself—he had always prided himself on not needing "anyone
but Génie"; his apartment had come to seem sinister to him, and in spite
of all its too homely furniture his office was no home to him. He now
called on me regularly, almost daily; and I too, if shopping or idleness
brought me to the Boule Miche neighborhood, frequently looked in on
him, for I knew that anguish was gnawing away inside him. More and
more often, it seemed to me, he was seized by a sudden revulsion
against the artificial shell he had created for himself in his office.

"Come," he said in his outwardly calm fashion, "let us go somewhere
else—after all, I sit here all day long!" We sat together in bistros and on
café terraces, in dairies and restaurants, and on benches in the public
gardens. I knew that with other people he acted as though everything
was the same as before; he still talked about me to Dopffer, and also to
Germaine, in terms of fatherly concern: what was to become of me,
would I never see "reason"? But to me he never spoke another word
about it. On the contrary, he said: "When I'm gone, you will have no
more worries. You are the only person I care about." Apart from this, we
used to sit there arguing. Again and again he returned to the conversation in which I had told him the truth. "No," he would say with a
laugh, "the ideas you get into your head! You're a visionary, Edmond."
Then we would argue about life.

We were sitting together like this one afternoon toward the end of
May on a bench in the Luxembourg; it was in the garden directly behind the Senate. Children were sailing their boats in the little round
pond, in the center of which the fountain was plashing in the sunshine,
and there was a warm smell of lilacs. "Do you know," I asked, "that you
are living a double life?" "Oh, my God, Edmond!" he replied. "I—a
double life? I'm no longer living at all! Do you call what I lead a life?"
"Perhaps not," I answered. "I was speaking of your inner life. You have

split yourself. You have become two." "What extraordinary things you say! One could almost start to find oneself interesting, after listening to you!" "Do you know the *Song of Gilgamesh?*" "No, I'm not interested in verse." "Oh, you don't read any books; times are too grave for that, eh?" But because my face did not change, he did not understand my irony. "Your situation is that of Gilgamesh; everyone is in the same situation, but they don't know it." "What situation? What are you talking about?" "This Gilgamesh," I said, "was a mighty king in Uruk; he had a friend named Enkidu, whom he loved above everything and who was all in all to him; but suddenly he died."

My brother-in-law looked at me with interest. "What did he do, your Gilgamesh?" "He ran through the world wailing: 'In my bedchamber dwells death, and wherever I flee to, there is death.'" "Well," said my brother-in-law, disappointed, "that's not much." "He had once been a mighty king, but that had lost all importance for him—it didn't help him in his distress. He abandoned everything and set out into the world that lies behind power; there dwell the ancestral spirits, dragons, and demons. He fled thither to find a remedy against death, which threatened to overwhelm him." "Did he find it?" asked my brother-in-law rather indifferently. "Yes, he did," I answered, "but that's not the important thing; the important thing is that he wrapped himself up so completely in his anguish that he cast everything aside and wandered to the end of the world in order to master this anguish."

Now my story gripped him after all. "So," he said attentively and thoughtfully, "and what, for instance, would be my kingdom?" "Your kingdom," I replied, "is your office, with Dopffer as Prime Minister and the clerks as the administrative machinery and your clients as the nation." "What?" he cried in amazement. "Am I to abandon my profession?" "No," I replied, "but accept it for the burdensome necessity it is and do what is real! Your kingdom, Gouffé, is illusion, convention, middle-class respectability. Just take a look for once at what lies behind middle-class respectability."

I still wonder if I did not do as much harm as good, when I tried so hard to help my brother-in-law in his anguish. He really misunderstood me too grossly. Something like a week after this conversation about Gilgamesh he told me the following. (It was here in my hotel, down below in the bistro; we were both drinking pernod, which I am very fond of because of its poisonous sweetness.) Anyhow, my brother-in-law told me the following:

"You know, I really shouldn't take too much notice of your advice. You're too eccentric for me. No, don't get angry. Of course, it's my fault; after all I'm old enough to know better! But just listen to what I have been up to!

"Yesterday evening I was sitting outside the Véron. I was terribly bored. I had already looked through a whole pile of newspapers and magazines; everything bored me. Then I thought to myself: Edmond is right, this conventional, middle-class life is deadly dull; one should forget it for once! I grew thoroughly restless. I was tickled by the idea—though I hadn't an inkling how to set about it—of going in search of adventure.

"I paid, rose, and strolled along the boulevard. I came to Port Royal. The stalls in which they sell fruit, flowers, and cheap jewelry were still open, little carbide lamps were swaying in the breeze, and a young sales-girl, who must have noticed my aimless sauntering, leant over her counter laughing, held up a bunch of prickly leaves with red fruits on them, and cried: 'Monsieur, Monsieur! Voilà des pommes d'amour, ça dure toujours!' Heavens above, I thought, ça dure toujours? Well, I strolled on. Across the road stood the Prison de la Santé, where public executions used to take place (or do they still take place there?); then chance made me run into an acquaintance, a certain—no, his name doesn't matter. I couldn't say I ever liked him particularly, in fact I only knew him slightly; I considered him rather disreputable and also a trifle common, but at this moment I was delighted to see him.

" 'Hello!' I called. 'How are you? What are you doing?'—'Oh,' he answered, 'doing? Just wandering around. What is there to do?' He was obviously in much the same mood as I; I invited him to a drink, and he suggested a game of cards. But I didn't feel like it. 'No,' I said, 'I'm in a sort of mood—I don't know: like when I was a youngster! I'd really like to get up to mischief!' 'Even if there was a sound thrashing to follow?' he asked with a laugh. Then he said: 'God, if one only had money —it would just suit me to go on a really juicy spree again.' 'Man!' I cried. 'That's an idea! I invite you! Let's go on the spree!'

"So we went on our spree. We had a drink at this place and that, listened here to a chansonette and there to a conférencier. And we also went into a brothel, where we were served by horrible women in short chemises who pressed up against us; my acquaintance had a good time with them, pinching them and smacking their backsides—I won't go into detail; you will understand, that wasn't the right thing for me. 'Don't you like the cows?' asked my acquaintance. 'Devil take it, I just adore them!' 'No,' I replied, 'they're not the thing for Père Gouffé.' 'I see,' he commented with a rather nasty grin. 'Shall we cross over to the other bank for a change? That suits me. Just wait—I know a magnificent market! But we shall have to take a cab.'

"It doesn't matter where the place was. It was a gloomy, almost sinister district of back alleys. It took us a long time to get there, and over the door hung a red lamp. First we entered an ordinary taproom; a few people were standing round the bar. But my acquaintance walked straight through this room; he signaled to me with his head, raised a dirty green

curtain of heavy material, and pushed open the door behind it. It led
into a small, very shabby room; the walls were bare, with a few damp
patches, and the light from candles stuck in the necks of bottles made
the shadows of heads, necks, and shoulders flicker to and fro on them; for
there were a great many tables in the room, with customers sitting at
them, their faces lit up by the candles. As we entered they all sat silent.
My acquaintance went to a small table standing rather on its own in the
middle; all the customers followed us with their eyes. I don't know why,
but it smelled of horses; it was nauseating.

"Suddenly a lad minced over to us, wiped away the little puddles of
wine and beer on our table with a filthy cloth, turned from the hips and
asked, smiling with pursed lips and gazing up from beneath raised eyebrows: 'Two bottles, Messieurs?' 'Yes,' answered my acquaintance. The
wine came, two bottles and two glasses; I paid. 'May you enjoy it' piped
the lad and was gone again. So far, apart from our order, not a word had
been spoken in the room. Whether their faces were in darkness or candlelight, they were all staring at our table, calmly and attentively, many of
them openmouthed, which gave them an added look of concentration. As
far as I could see, they were all youngsters, some of them almost boys;
but they were very differently dressed: one group in tilted students' caps
and open blue shirts, the other with ostentatious, tawdry elegance; the
two groups were intermingled as they sat there silently watching.

" 'These young beauties,' said my acquaintance, loudly and unabashed,
as he filled first his own glass, then mine, 'are future reinforcements for
the convict settlements. They cost between two francs fifty and ten francs
apiece, but in the entrance hall it's cheaper.' He drank and licked his
long lips in his beard. The silence all around and the continual staring
were making me ill at ease. I felt suddenly hot. I drank—it was the usual
vin ordinaire.

"After a long time a lad sitting comparatively close to us rose without
warning, but perfectly calmly, and walked unhurriedly to our table,
stopped, and stood there scrutinizing me. He was actually rather a pretty
boy, about seventeen, with light brown hair and light-colored eyes; but a
scar on his upper lip made his face look somehow dangerous and at the
same time vaguely sordid. He was wearing a sailor suit of blue cheviot,
the trousers tight over the thighs and wide over the small shoes, the jacket
double-breasted, and underneath it the pale, white skin. He took one of
the bottles by the neck and said without a smile: 'I suppose you don't
mind.' He raised the bottle to his lips and took a long draught, but he
immediately spat out what he had drunk in a wide arc and cursed in the
direction of the wall: 'What swill is this you've brought, you whore?'
The voice of the lad who had served us squawked in its affected, quick,
repulsive treble from a distant table: 'Fie, friend, don't be so vulgar, you
will frighten our suitors away!' So he was sitting among the customers,

who continued to maintain a total silence; they watched the scene at our table intently, the candle flames reflected in their eyes.

"The youngster at our table didn't even seem to have heard the answer to his oath; he began to scrutinize me again. I felt ghastly. For the sake of something to do, I took hold of my glass; the lad's eyes now rested on my hand and spotted the sapphire and brilliants on my ring. He let out a long whistle of amazement. He sat down, laid one of his forearms on the table and gazed into my face. My acquaintance laughed. 'The scum scents prey,' he said with amusement. The youngster looked at him and then back at me. He gazed unwaveringly into my eyes. 'Are you coming with me?' he asked at length. 'How much is it going to cost, Beautiful?' demanded my acquaintance. 'I didn't ask you, Fish-face,' retorted the youngster, without deigning to glance at him. 'You need a good box on the ears, you rascal!' cried my acquaintance gaily. 'But, Messieurs,' squawked the horrible treble from the encircling silence lit by the flickering candles, 'no rowdiness, please! This is a respectable house!'

"I felt more and more uncomfortable. The youngster pensively rolled himself a cigarette from a little packet of tobacco he had taken from his trouser pocket; he bent down, lit it at the flame of the candle, inhaled deeply, and let the smoke drift past the tip of his nose and up into the air. He rested his head on his hand, so that his face was concealed from my acquaintance, and looked at me again—a long, searching look, as though deep in thought; then suddenly, but perfectly calmly, he showed his tongue, he thrust it in and out between his lips, and winked one eye. I can't tell you how vulgar it looked; although no one besides myself could have seen it, the treble immediately squawked across to us: 'Stop it, Tattoo Tommy! Let the gentlemen choose for themselves!' I gulped and whispered to my acquaintance: 'Let's go.'

"At this moment a second youth rose and came over to our table; he was wearing a light-colored suit whose shabby elegance was reminiscent of the circus, and a yellow tie; he was blond with a potato nose and watery eyes; but the most repulsive thing about him was the fact that he had covered the multitude of oozing pimples on his immature yet debauched face with a thick layer of pink powder. He sat down beside his comrade, sniffed, and said: 'Show the gent how pretty you are from the waist up.' Thereupon he began to unbutton the jacket of our lad, who didn't protest; his naked skin was tattooed all over with obscene symbols, figures, and scenes, in blue and red. As though attracted by the exhibition, or rather spirited over (for I hadn't noticed anybody walking in the flickering semidarkness), there were suddenly two or three more lads standing round us. They were not looking at the tattooed chest, however, but all staring fascinated at my hand with the ring. 'Let's get out of here!' I whispered breathlessly.

"Now there was a scraping of chair legs on the wooden floor, whispering and a low murmur, a hushed sound of movement on all sides—just imagine it: they were shifting their tables and chairs over, crowding around more and more tightly, in a circle that edged closer and closer. We were surrounded by these future reinforcements for the convict settlements, as my acquaintance had called them—thirty, forty, or maybe fifty of them, united in sullen, tense, avid ill-will, a gang of cutthroats, the candlelight flickering in their eyes. The walls were in darkness; all the light was now concentrated in a small area with us in the center. I was scared stiff. I jumped up.

"'I want to get out of here!' I cried. My acquaintance was standing beside me; he laughed wryly and said: 'The riffraff are only playing up. Come along.' I admired his courage. I kept close to him. He was now standing right in front of the inner wall of youths (most of them had already risen to their feet) and said slowly: 'Stand aside, will you?' It took a second, perhaps two, then the youth facing him reluctantly stepped eighteen inches to one side; those behind him, one after the other, also yielded these eighteen inches—a narrow passage in the midst of menace and danger, my dear fellow! I pressed through after my acquaintance. Will they drag me back by my coat-tails, I wondered, and I could feel my heart and temples pounding wildly. When we had passed through the passage, the horrible, false treble squawked once more in sudden excitement: 'No, no, Messieurs! You won't misunderstand a little joke!'

"Immediately, the mass began to move again. We heard muttering, whispering, and running footsteps. We were at the door; the lad who had served us reached it at the same moment. Whether he was going to trip us or lock the door in our faces, I don't know. Everything now happened with lightning rapidity. With an oath, my acquaintance raised his hand, a hand with short, thick, strong fingers, and jabbed the thumb and forefinger with all his force into the lad's eyes; the latter yelled at the top of his voice, streams of red tears poured down over both cheeks; he clapped his hands to his face, staggered back, and fell with an indescribable whimper to the floor. My acquaintance tore the door open; we were in the taproom; the door slammed behind us. The whimpering continued unchecked, sometimes rising to a scream, behind the thick green curtain. There were no more customers in the taproom. The landlord was washing glasses; he raised one to the light and examined it, then put it away on the shelf behind him, clicking his tongue; he seemed to be deaf.

"We hurried through the dark, silent alleys. Gradually I came to myself again. 'Good God!' I said, gasping with exhaustion. 'That was some adventure!' My acquaintance shook his head, ground his teeth, and muttered with a kind of grim humor, almost to himself: 'Sweet little dears. They should have their necks wrung like chickens, one after the other.'

He raised both hands, clenched them into fists, and twisted them round, pressed close together."

This, roughly, was the tale my brother-in-law told me. His story made a disagreeable impression on me, and I reflected on it for some time. "No," said my brother-in-law, "that wasn't good advice you gave me, Edmond. I just am a middle-class man." "I never meant that," I said. "You see, I'm a typical middle-class man!" he started again. "A little escapade, a little adventure every now and then—that's all right. But for the rest—perhaps I really ought to marry again?" "Perhaps so." "You don't think anything of love?" "Oh, yes!" I rejoined, and laughed. "If I were a poet, as you sometimes say, I should sing it. Something like this: Love is a blessing among men, the loved one blocks new vistas to the lover; where the boundless converges into incomprehensibility, there is the beloved head; where we stagnate within ourselves, there is the beloved hand that conjures feeling from skin and nerves; and when we can no longer endure ourselves, there is the beloved womb that conceives and receives us." "You really are a poet!" he cried in astonishment. "Love is an illusion," I retorted drily. "You and your everlasting paradoxes," he said angrily. "I believe you are simply a nihilist! Or what do you want?" "I?" came my answer. "I want to go where the demons are. I want to look into the great jaws. I want danger."

He looked at me completely baffled. "But you," I said, "are not the man for that. I really think you would do best to marry." "So," he rejoined with a certain pensiveness, "I'm not the man for that. . . ." But when we said good-by outside the door of the hotel, he said once more: "I don't know either. . . . But shouldn't I perhaps ask Germaine—shouldn't I ask little Madame Chottin? You wouldn't have any objection?" "Try it," I answered sadly.

Really I have nothing else to tell you. I saw my brother-in-law a few times after that; but we had no more conversations of any particular interest—in fact, it was clear to me that he avoided discussing his inner problems, and especially Germaine, with me. When I saw them both on that Thursday evening, on July 25th, sitting outside the Véron, it crossed my mind that he would probably put the question to her today and hear her no. I thought about this the whole way home.

That was the last time I ever saw him.

Since then I have often asked myself: when I told him he was not cut out for what I called danger (I meant by this, to put it briefly, the truth, the whole truth), did he feel offended, although he had described himself as a "typical middle-class man"? Did he misunderstand me again and misinterpret this danger, as though I had meant something reckless or desperately adventurous by it, an act of abandon, a "leap into the abyss"? But what could he have understood by it? When he looked at me so thoughtfully and said "So I'm not the man for it," had he something particular in mind, a plan, a possibility of convincing me and himself to the contrary? I don't know. What does one man know of another? There is only one thing which I believe I know: he is no longer alive. My poor brother-in-law Gouffé! What have they done to him? Where is he now?

The great silence gives no reply. Shall we find someone who will make it talk for ten thousand francs?

Here is the check. And if any other way in which I can be of service occurs to you, I am always at your disposal.

Yours,

JAQUEMAR

Contrary to his usual opinion—based on much experience—that anything could be proved by psychology and any conclusion drawn from its data, Goron accepted the Jaquemar document as a subtly argued corroboration of what he himself had thought and felt about the Gouffé case. It presented a picture of an individual at the end of his tether. The agonizing void in which the missing man spent his last year, the inner frustration he suffered, and (as Goron added to himself) the particular state of psychological readiness so often found in men at the climacteric age around fifty, this "Now or never!"—everything seemed to indicate that, given the opportunity, Gouffé would indeed have taken his "leap into the abyss"; and Goron shared Jaquemar's conviction that he was no longer alive. It was no longer a question of saving a man in danger, hence there was no urgency; Goron, yielding to a feeling that was perhaps superstitious, therefore left the check for the reward untouched for the time being, devoting himself all the more vigorously to the establishment of his new intelligence service.

Although in little doubt that he would have to carry this enterprise through on his own, he made several attempts, through his emissary Latrille, to enlist the cooperation and financial aid of the Prefecture— in vain, as was to be foreseen. Delattre, as usual, promised "to do his best," at the same time pointing out that the Universal Exhibition was making great demands on the Prefecture, so that the moment was ill chosen and Monsieur Sallier unlikely to transfer any of his meager funds to the Sûreté.

Goron then called Jaumes, Latrille, and (to the annoyance of both) Detective Inspector Soudrais to a conference on ways and means of creating the Sûreté's intelligence service out of its own resources, and proceeded to settle the problem, over the heads of all three, in a way that resulted in further bad feeling.

His intelligence service was established, and without a doubt it worked. After only three days, a local report from Saint-Nazaire, to the effect that a young German named Geissler had offered a ship's captain jewels for a passage overseas, led, through the intervention of the Paris police, to the clearing up of a large-scale diamond robbery that had been under investigation for two years without result—a striking initial success that augured well for the future. The various *départements*, each one concerned about the autonomy of its own local police force and each one turning a deaf ear to the rest, had now acquired a kind of collating and selecting brain cell in the Paris Cité. Who could fail to see the benefit of this to public security—who, that is, except precisely these local police forces, who felt that in the long run it threatened their authority? Such an idea never entered Goron's head. His joy might have been unclouded—insofar as he was capable of unclouded joy—if his new branch had also been successful in the matter for which it had been created; but at the outset this was not so. Day after day passed, nothing that gave any hint of a connection with the Gouffé case came to light, the great silence remained unbroken. Then he made up his mind to cut the Gordian knot.

In the middle of September there appeared in all the Paris dailies and all provincial papers of any importance a second description of Gouffé, almost identical with the first but with an additional statement. Since an accident or crime was to be feared, the missing man's brother-in-law, Monsieur Jaquemar, was offering a reward of ten thousand francs to the person whose information led either to the discovery of the missing man or to the apprehension of the culprits.

The announcement caused an even greater stir than had been foreseen. This was the first time the Paris police had employed the method of publicly offering a reward, and the extent of public excitement was not to be wondered at—indeed, it was part of Goron's purpose. The Gouffé case was once more the talk of Paris, once more every nook and cranny was full of it—the streets, café terraces, and bistros, the Bourse and the *salons*—and now excitement was not limited to the particular circles in which Gouffé moved, the middle classes and the women of the *demimonde*, but extended to the whole population. Very naturally the Press seized popular interest and stimulated it—this, one might say, was its business. Only the way it did so was surprising.

With the shameless demagogy that plays on the public's most mob-like characteristic—its shortness of memory—the papers not only changed their viewpoint but adopted the diametrically opposite one and now indignantly attacked the same "frivolous levity" they had smirkingly advocated a few weeks earlier. From the very beginning, they said, every thinking person had brooded over this gloomy affair with concern, a concern that was all too justified, since the disappearance of a universally respected citizen was no laughing matter and the manifest failure of the responsible security organizations to take any serious steps to clear up the mystery was incomprehensible—such was their inactivity that finally (and probably too late) the family of the missing man had now been forced to call on the public for aid, and, at great sacrifice, virtually to finance their own police force. It was scandalous. . . .

Against such gutter journalism, of what avail were the few voices that tried to get a hearing for truth? They actually did harm by exacerbating Goron's already acrimonious relations with the authorities, who were bound to feel themselves under attack—an attack that was entirely in line with Goron's own complaints. How could they fail to suspect the hand of Goron, when a paper expressed amazement that the appropriation of the Sûreté, the most important guardian of public security, was manifestly inadequate—or why else should a relative of the missing man have been compelled to put up the money for the reward? And what would be the effect of this strange state of affairs in a case where the relations of the victim had no money for such a reward?

It should have struck Goron as sinister that the Prefecture, generally so ready to find fault, wrapped itself in deep silence, a silence out of which there came to Goron's ears only the vague rumor, spread with relish by Latrille and cautiously passed on by Guillaume, that Monsieur Sallier had called on Monsieur Lozé at the Ministry of the Interior "on special business." Goron dismissed the news with a shrug of the shoulders; he really had other things to think about at the moment.

Once again, as a few weeks earlier, visitors thronged outside his door, in Guillaume's room, and in the corridors of the Cité, a picturesque rabble this time, attracted by Jaquemar's ten thousand francs and hoping to derive their murky pleasure and profit from the mystery:

back-street amateur detectives, their imagination debauched by reading cheap shockers; women who told fortunes from coffee grounds; telepaths and spiritualists; in short, charlatans and rogues of every kind, and not least the self-accusers, whose morbid lust reached its climax whenever any outstanding crime came into the news. Most of them made off with their tails between their legs after Goron had held them for a few minutes in the crossfire of his flashing pince-nez and his impatient questioning. His aggressive, staccato voice, the initially impudent then more and more apologetic replies, the stamping and the vicious shouting of the powerful police officer—this aural evidence of the scene of inquisition within, which always followed the same pattern, discouraged many of the riffraff listening outside; open-mouthed and with a gulp, they edged away and made off.

But there were quite enough of them left, and it was amazing and exasperating how clever stupidity thought itself. One man brought along a bottle which he refused to hand over without payment, because it contained the key to the mystery. He had fished it out of the Marne. Goron snatched it unceremoniously from his hand and pulled out the note that was inside it: "I am the murderer of Monsieur Gouffé. Because I prefer death to disgrace, I am taking my own life. M.E." A brief writing test proved that the numbskull had not even felt it necessary to disguise his handwriting. And practically everything Goron had to listen to was on the same level—thus, another man claimed to be a medium possessing second sight and stated that if he were taken to the scene of the crime he would probably be able to provide a description of the culprit: a small advance of a thousand or even five hundred francs would suffice to call the supernatural powers into action.

This vulgar stupidity violated the dignity of the mystery. And stupidity went hand in hand with malice; for the latter, too, was excited, and produced all kinds of oral and written attempts at blackmail and threats to drag the missing man's name through the mire with heaven knows what revelations concerning his most intimate life if silence was not bought at a price. There was also no lack of letters of denunciation, the writers of which promised to drop their anonymity as soon as the police had acted on their information. The name of Dopffer, the head clerk, cropped up again and again, once coupled with an exact statement of where he was hiding his victim's corpse— to wit, bricked up in the coal cellar of his country cottage at Saint-

Germain-en-Laye. Goron had no doubt that this was an act of vengeance, probably on the part of some formerly hard-pressed debtor; but to ignore the accusation was not consonant with the discharge of his official duty, and the sensible Dopffer, thrusting his chin out of his cravat and expanding his chest, commented that it was altogether in his interest that the police themselves should prove the emptiness of "this infamous and idiotic slander." An investigation on the spot naturally brought to light nothing at all.

These attempts to dupe the Sûreté reached their acme in the stratagem of a certain Cathelin, whom some spy must have informed of the facts known to the police; for without knowledge of the scene with Gouffé and Madame Chottin outside the Café Véron, he could not have hatched the plot with which he sought to catch Goron. This Cathelin, a homosexual, a great lover of the fine arts and himself the author of some very mawkish verses full of world-weariness, was known to his friends as "Mayflower" and to the police as the most stony-hearted blackmailer in Paris.

He had himself been denounced by a wooden-legged pedlar named Gilot, who made the following statement: As he stood begging on the evening of July 25 at the corner of the Rue Delambre, a dandified individual (whom he hesitantly identified from the rogues' gallery as Cathelin) had given him three francs to deliver a note to the gentleman at the table across the way; the lady sitting with the gentleman had been just in the act of leaving; the man who gave him the money instructed him to reply to any question on the part of the recipient of the note with the words "Ce sont les jours d'amour—I can say no more!" Gilot carried out his instructions; the gentleman—from his description, evidently Gouffé—had not asked any questions, but, on glancing at the letter, had shown signs of terror, even clutching at his heart.

In view of Cathelin's terrible reputation, there was a certain ring of truth about the story, and it was only thanks to Goron's unerring instinct that it did not fool anyone for long. He had not only Cathelin (who hedged and prevaricated, instead of presenting an unambiguous alibi), but also his accuser, placed in solitary confinement, in darkness and on bread and water. Gilot quickly broke down and revealed the plot; the plan, it goes without saying, was for Cathelin to become more and more deeply embroiled in incriminating contradictions, only to come out with a cast-iron alibi as soon as Gilot had cleared off with the reward thus obtained under false pretenses. The abortive jest gained "Mayflower" the aesthete a round of hearty laughter from Press and public and six months' imprisonment in the notoriously harsh Poissy prison.

With this, the sterile turmoil, the witches' sabbath of charlatanry, perversion, perfidy, and would-be deception that Goron had provoked with the offer of Jaquemar's ten thousand francs, died down. What now? He stood exactly where he had stood ten days, four weeks, or two months ago. A dogged hopelessness took possession of him every time he thought of the Gouffé case, and this happened several times a day, not only in the morning, when Guillaume reported the fruitless researches of the intelligence service, but also during the course of the day and in the midst of other business; and the more he realized his inability to solve the riddle, the more obsessed with it he became, so that he began to ask himself where this affair was going to lead him. Was he dreaming, or was it some kind of vision, when one day he saw Gouffé facing him across his desk? He looked exactly as on the photograph in his office, but he sat there in the posture of Jaquemar, his head hanging, saying in a low voice: "It's a pity about me."

Strong characters turn to advantage even the self-doubts by which others are overwhelmed; the nagging question whether he had omitted some necessary, or even remotely conceivable, step in this affair created in Goron a state of readiness, the force and tenacity of which were proved at the first opportunity. One morning, in the course of his report, Guillaume laid on Goron's desk as "perhaps really not without interest" an issue of the *Quotidien Provençal* in which Sub-Inspector Créneau had placed a cross beside the following item: The body of an unknown man had been found near the village of Millery, taken to the anatomical theater of the School of Medicine, and confiscated by the police, who would give no further information at this juncture in order not to prejudice a line of inquiry which they were following up. The secretary stood beside the chief, leaning attentively forward from the waist; Goron was sitting bolt upright, his bald head, with the hair round the crown stubbornly on end, only slightly bent; he scrutinized the report and, after a minute's silence, without looking up, he said in a tone of voice as though the truth had now revealed itself to him: "Guillaume—that is Gouffé."

With this moment a new chapter opened in the story of the Gouffé case. There was really no "common-sense" reason, apart from the fact that the Millery body had as yet no name, for thinking it was Gouffé; but Goron was unshakably convinced of it, and his efforts were directed not so much toward establishing the unknown man's identity as toward proving his own theory and making further deductions from it. He took so little trouble to conceal his attitude that his colleagues, all of whom (with the exception of Guillaume) were opposed to him, could hardly fail to wax indignant over this typical example of Goron's "unscientific" flights of imagination, or, following Latrille's example, to laugh at it as "Goron's fancy."

There was indeed something fanciful about his refusal to listen to reason, even when—only a few hours later—the Marseilles police replied to his telegraphic inquiry that they hoped to be able to make a definite statement concerning the Millery body that same evening, having already established its identity almost beyond doubt. He pestered them with urgent inquiries, kept reminding them of Gouffé's description, and simultaneously addressed himself to the *Quotidien Provençal's* reporter, to whom he promised the sum of two hundred francs if he would immediately wire him any information he could gather. He quite failed to see that, by so doing, he was introducing a certain personal element and giving the impression of going over the heads of the local police, whose status was equal to that of the Cité, a psychological factor quite extraneous to the case but likely to prejudice its progress.

No, he was deaf to reason; late that afternoon he received—simultaneously with the report from the representative of the *Quotidien Provençal*—the conclusion of the Marseilles police, now couched in much curter terms: the "disputed" body had now been finally identified as that of a lawyer named Herbier, who had been missing for some time; and even Guillaume could not believe his eyes and ears when Goron thrust aside the police report with an irritable exclamation and turned to that from the journalist, which had arrived along with it.

It gave an excellently clear picture, especially of the neighborhood in which the body was found. The village of Millery, some ten miles from

Marseilles, was linked with the city by a road which, just outside
Millery, ran around the brow of a hill, its outer edge protected from
the steep, scrub-grown slope by a chest-high, whitewashed brick wall;
by leaning over the wall, it was possible to distinguish a foaming
mountain torrent; but neither the railway line nor the footpath which,
screened by trees, ran along the riverbank, was visible. This footpath
was used by the Millery peasants as a short cut; for some time they had
noticed a smell of putrefaction that grew continually more penetrating,
until finally they requested the local road mender to investigate and
remove the cause of this unpleasantness. The road mender had to
clear a path up the hillside with a sickle, but it was not long before
he uncovered the source of the nauseating stench: a shapeless great
sack lying in the scrub and undergrowth, above which a vast swarm of
buzzing insects, in the shape of a vacillating cone, was whirling madly
round as though intoxicated with greed.

The road mender fetched the Millery gendarme; together they
hoisted their mephitic burden on to a cart and transported it without
delay to the Marseilles anatomical theater, where it was immediately
examined by the deputy police surgeon, Dr. Levreault. The body was
that of a completely naked man who had been tied up with a very
long, tough cord in the position of a child curled up asleep, and then
stuffed into the coarse jute sack. It was, however, impossible to judge
from the vague statements of the two men, or from Dr. Levreault's
uncivil response that it was not his job to issue information to the
public in advance of the police, how far decomposition had gone or
whether the face was still recognizable.

Goron let the hand holding this report sink down, and meditated;
then he rose resolutely to his feet, growling that he must get down
there "before they commit any more blunders," took his hat from the
hatstand, and hurried to the door. Here he turned around once more
and told Guillaume to let Jaquemar know that Goron wanted him to
go to Marseilles and would fetch him from his hotel at ten-thirty sharp
to catch the night train.

That night, Goron, accompanied by Soudrais, fetched Jaquemar from
the Hôtel des Mines as planned. After giving them all sorts of advice
as they drove to the station in his carriage, Goron saw them off from
the Gare de Lyon for Marseilles.

There, arriving early in the morning at the Security Police station in a pretty, tree-lined square, they met with unforeseen difficulties. The chief's secretary, a man whose shabby indigence was reminiscent of the Paris Sub-Inspector Créneau, but who had more of the weasel about him than the latter, did not invite them in. He spread out their papers on the wooden barrier and studied them, blinking his red-lashed eyelids; and then, humming and hahing dubiously, he knocked softly at a tall double door that led into the next room, through which he disappeared. A few minutes later he returned and explained with every show of officious regret that, although the papers identified the gentlemen as emissaries of Monsieur Goron, they did not carry any weight in Marseilles; for this they would have to be issued by an authority superior to the Marseilles Security Police, not by one on the same level like the Cité; he was extremely sorry. His face dark with rage, Soudrais, the boor, blustered: did they think here that the Paris Sûreté sat up all night for fun? In the name of his official position he demanded to see the body, otherwise he would "show them a thing or two."

The little man withdrew into the next room again with much shrugging of the shoulders. Thereupon a scene of theatrical comedy was enacted. Pushed by the weasel-like clerk, the two leaves of the door flew open. Behind them, leaning on a stick, stood a tall old man, flabbily massive, with flowing gray-black hair and a long prophet's beard. He raised the stick and began to shout, his red-rimmed eyes popping. He was Beaujean, the master in this house, would they please understand—master—and he forbade any more blundering interference; the Millery body had long since been identified, recognized by Herbier père as Herbier fils, without the least resemblance to the Gouffé sought by Paris; would they kindly stop pestering him? "Out of my sight!" yelled Beaujean, pointing his stick at the two flabbergasted visitors. "Out of my sight!" And the little clerk closed the door in front of the angry old man.

Inwardly amused by this dramatic slap in the face for his chief, Soudrais agreed with an indifferent "As you wish" to Jaquemar's request that they should try the deputy police surgeon (the regular police surgeon, Dr. Lacassagne, was on leave). After keeping them waiting half an hour in his completely empty surgery, Dr. Levreault, a man of thirty at the most and already a picture of firmly rooted self-importance, with a massive red face, bushy, ash-blond eyebrows, and deep furrows around his hard mouth, received them with authoritative reserve. As a pathologist he could assure them that, medically speaking, there was no doubt about the identity of the dead man of Millery: firstly and secondly, the corpse had neither a scar on the left ankle nor Gouffé's short brown hair, but long black hair like Herbier; but thirdly, and in particular, examination of the contents of the stomach carried out by himself showed remnants of the same meal as Herbier had eaten on the day of his disappearance.

Dr. Levreault concluded, squeezing a slight smile from his dignified gravity, that he could understand the gentlemen wanting to claim the beautiful corpse, but Marseilles could not part with it—they needed it for themselves. To this Soudrais, slipping easily into the coarsely jesting tone, remarked: fair enough, but the body wasn't "a virgin" after all, and it could do no harm for them to have a look at it. There was no objection to that, as far as he knew, replied the doctor in some surprise; the anatomical theater, as the State morgue, was open to anyone, and if Siller, the doorkeeper, did make any difficulties, they should refer to him, Dr. Levreault.

It was not quite so easy to view the corpse in the School of Medicine as this statement had led them to expect. Not that the doorkeeper Siller raised any obstacles; on the contrary, he listened to Soudrais's and Jaquemar's request without surprise and, in fact, without answering. He was a bright-eyed old soldier with a gray waxed moustache and wearing a tall, stiff round cap with a horizontal patent-leather peak. His lean, intelligent face seemed to be lit by some unspoken knowledge that afforded him secret amusement as, muttering under his breath, he turned away from the visitors and made ready to conduct them into the basement; he lifted a large bunch of keys from a hook on the wall and lit a sort of stable lantern—taking his time over everything as though alone. Then he signed to them with his head to follow him and, still muttering to himself in his odd way, led them down the stone staircase; finally, after an unexpectedly long descent on steps that grew narrower and narrower, he walked ahead of them through the underground corridors.

A few steps further took them up into a somewhat more solidly built, perhaps later, section of the subterranean vaults. Here Siller halted before a low arch, beyond which a heavy iron door, rather like that of an enormous safe, was set into the wall. Jaquemar and Soudrais were standing close behind their guide who, after turning various keys, opened the door and led the way in, holding his lantern level with his head. They followed in his footsteps, Jaquemar reluctantly and pressing a handkerchief to mouth and nose on account of the noisome stench in the icy air, Soudrais with a disgusted "Brrr"; but Siller appeared quite undisturbed, although the deodorant caustic solutions that stood about the flagged floor in shallow vessels intensified rather than dulled the nauseating reek.

Enormous pillars, like gigantic tropical flowers, opened out near the base into slightly ribbed, leaflike vaulting that formed the ceiling of this sepulchral chamber only a trifle higher than a man. Here and there, on low stone slabs similar to those used as tombstones in ancient American burial grounds, lay human corpses with pointed noses and hands crossed over their chests like figures on sarcophagi, faces obstinately averted or heads bent over backward, but all of them stretched out naked in their everlasting muteness. The only exception was the corpse Siller now approached; it lay on its side with knees bent, curled up like an embryo, its head sunk deep between its shoulders and looking down at itself as though bashful. The thick black cord with which it had been bound both crossways and lengthways looked almost like a net, as though the corpse had been fished out of life, an unwilling catch entangled in these meshes, and landed in this icy darkness filled with silence and unimaginable desolation.

Siller turned to his companions. The light of the lantern glittered vivaciously and almost craftily in the damp, hard brightness of his eyes beneath the patent-leather peak; Soudrais took Jaquemar by the elbow and pushed him closer. With his bewildered squint, but more intently than usual, indeed hungrily, he looked over the top of his handkerchief at the desecrated body, at the nakedness of the inanimate mass of flesh and the ghostly, disintegrating face; he closed his eyes and whispered into his handkerchief something like "No, it isn't Gouffé." Naturally he could not have recognized either his vanished brother-in-law or anybody else in this face; for putrefaction and the greed of maggots had done their work on it and a violent blow or kick, as though from an elephant's foot, had crushed it, so that the one remaining eye protruded, goggling, and a smashed tooth gleamed in the matted beard as if the dead man were trying to spit it out.

Jaquemar turned away; with his rather too dainty step he hurried to the door and waited there, his handkerchief still pressed to his mouth and nose and his head hanging as if frozen in an attitude of mourning or tearless weeping. Soudrais, after taking a final look at the Millery corpse and shaking his head, came over to him, followed by Siller, and asked: "Well, is it him or isn't it?"

"How should I know?" responded Jaquemar, lowering his handkerchief and looking at the boor as though in amazement.

Next morning at the Cité Goron utterly refused to entertain the idea that the Millery body was not that of the missing *huissier*. He was convinced neither by the outcome of the police investigations, nor by the medical examination, nor by Jaquemar's "No, it isn't Gouffé." Soudrais had been sent to Marseilles to confirm that the dead man was Gouffé and he had made a "pitiful mess" of his mission, because he had been "unbelieving" and willing to let himself be talked into accepting the "superficial judgment" of the local authorities. What had he done to get at the truth, what investigations of his own had he undertaken, to whom had he addressed himself outside the narrowest circle directly under the influence of the local police?

Naturally, Soudrais also lost his temper, and shouted with boorish spite: Let the chief curse him if he wanted to, he was only a simple detective sergeant, but he knew what he knew! The man wasn't Gouffé, that was certain; but it was also certain that there was something fishy about the fine Monsieur Jaquemar! Why else did he change completely from one minute to the next after the first horrified look at the corpse, "as though he'd been kicked in the teeth," and why did he sit there on the way home as white as a sheet, with clenched teeth, and without getting a moment's rest or sleep? He, Soudrais, had pretended to be asleep and had watched him closely, he had had "plenty of bad hats in his custody" and he could only say that if this fellow didn't have a guilty secret. . . . "Stop!" shouted Goron. "Don't plague me with your foolish fancies! I forbid you ever to mention this ghastly nonsense again!" "Forbid me if you want!" bawled Soudrais. "But I know what I know!"

Jaquemar, he said, had given the show away with his contradictions and his shilly-shallying to gain time, first "no, no," then again "yes" and "perhaps" and he "hoped not." "What was that—what are you talking about?" interrupted Goron, pricking up his ears, suddenly quite matter-of-fact. "What contradictions?" Well, before he retired to his hotel "feeling ill," Jaquemar had instructed him to tell Goron he "hoped" the dead man of Millery was not his brother-in-law. He "hoped"? So he wasn't sure? He was in doubt? "And you only come out with it now, after all that futile blather?" barked Goron, jumping to his feet, snatching his hat from the hatstand, and making off.

And so it was. Jaquemar, who was lying on his bed behind the screen, fully dressed, looking indeed very pale and wearing a strange, almost malicious and certainly reserved expression, declared to the insistent Goron that he could not recognize the dead man in the "catacombs of Marseilles" as his brother-in-law; nor could he see how Herbier père could possibly have recognized him as his son, since what lay there in the vault was merely the "crushed and desecrated relic of what had once been a life," but not a man with a human face. Jaquemar, watched by Goron through his pince-nez, stared at his hands that were resting on his stomach; he made his silent munching movement of the lips and added that he feared it would eventually be identified as the body of Gouffé.

Where did Goron stand now? He felt strengthened, took Jaquemar's doubt as certainty in corroboration of his own view, looked impatiently around for a chance to produce the final proof—and remained totally unaware that in the meantime an extremely dangerous rumor had been set afoot against him, a whispering campaign launched in his own backyard that was all too likely to spread beyond it and do irreparable harm to his reputation. Soudrais, furious with injured pride, told first Latrille, then anyone willing to listen (and they were all willing to listen), that the chief had refused to hear the truth about "that fine Monsieur Jaquemar" and had stamped his foot and forbidden him to say another word about it. Latrille, after glancing around cautiously, whispered a remark that set Soudrais's imagination working overtime: "Perhaps Goron has an *interest* in keeping Jaquemar out of trouble?" Jaquemar, he pointed out, had put up the ten thousand francs, Jaquemar was a *grand seigneur*, a man of strikingly generous disposition; Latrille wasn't saying anything, but "we all have our weaknesses, haven't we?" The stupid boor listened to this round-eyed, his hairy paw over his mouth, and stared after the rumormonger, who, with a brisk movement of the right hand and shoulder in farewell, made off.

Meanwhile, Goron redoubled the urgency and frequency of his requests to Créneau and Guillaume to search the Provençal papers for some news item that would provide if not a reason, at least a pretext for the Sûreté to intervene (encroach would be a better word) in Beaujean's territory. Since no such item presented itself, his restlessness grew and harassed both himself and his subordinates. The door of his empty room was forever open; he could not stick to any task and yet interfered in them all; he turned up everywhere, badgering everyone, carping and criticizing and leaving behind ill-feeling among his colleagues; and here and there, on the desks, he left one of his black cigars to smoulder away and burn ugly holes in the wood—this really amounted to a vice with him.

Late one afternoon—the Cité was already emptying itself of police officers—he stood there gazing gloomily out of the window, exhausted by another day like this; he glanced toward his desk, hesitated, and walked over to it and dropped into his chair. He took the Gouffé papers from the drawer and from among them the envelope marked "Not to be opened till after my death"; he examined it from all sides, felt it—and slit it open.

Apart from a second envelope of soft, thick paper, the outer cover contained only one single document, written neatly and tidily but in a rather shaky hand on a sheet of grained, handmade paper with a rough edge that bore at the top, encircled by a wealth of flourishes, the heading "Statement of My Last Will" and at the bottom Gouffé's signature; to the right and left of this were two seals in red sealing wax, one of them bearing the writer's initials A.G. in a wreath of flowers, the other the Jaquemar coat of arms: on a waved field a fist driving a spear, like a flash of lightning, into the snarling, gaping jaws of a rampant dragon, with the usual heraldic decoration of helm and feathers at the top. Beyond this half-romantic, half-official looking embellishment, the document held nothing new for Goron. It confirmed that Gouffé's will, lodged in the bank safe, was valid *in toto* and that Jaquemar was the sole heir, with the one exception of a so-called "Eugénie Jaquemar Gouffé Foundation," which was to be administered as heretofore by Dopffer and the interest from which was to be paid annually to the Au Sacré Coeur de Jésus Girls' Home at Angoulême, "an institution which, it seems, owes its existence to the charitable endeavors of the Jaquemar family and to which, in any case, my late beloved wife gave active support."

The significance of the document lay in the fact that it was dated

July 24, 1889, the day before Gouffé's disappearance, and that something must have prompted him to draw it up. The rest of its message, as has been said, was well known to Goron from his study of the other documents in the Gouffé case—but only to him, for out of official discretion he had not mentioned it even to Jaquemar, while for his part Jaquemar had never let slip any reference to the inheritance in his hearing. The second thick envelope, however, was addressed to Jaquemar personally; and once more it bore a heading that sounded loftily romantic or queerly tragic, but the lettering of which, unlike that of the other document, was jumbled together and moreover, probably through the use of poor blotting paper, smudged and drawn down below the line in elongated smears of ink: "Monsieur E. Jaquemar. To you, Edmond, friend and brother-in-law, for—when it is over."

Goron, the cigar between his canine teeth, and his right eye closed to keep out the smoke, sat irresolutely in front of it; but ten minutes later he was on his way to Jaquemar.

He did not find him alone. Lebigot, the gaunt medical student, and Jaquemar were sitting facing one another on two kitchen chairs of the same rough type at a short table, with Madame Chottin occupying a pouffe at Jaquemar's feet. While the two others looked toward the visitor and Jaquemar, on recognizing Goron, rose, Lebigot kept his birdlike gaze fixed on the chessboard, still deep in the interrupted game. Nor did he utter a word of greeting, but merely laid his hand on the marble foot of the paraffin lamp on the table, a lamp whose fashionable elegance, with its red silk shade richly ruched at the corners and borders, seemed out of place in the shabby emptiness of the hotel room. Clasped by Lebigot's great hand, its light, while remaining just as soft, seemed to grow increasingly intense as the rapidly advancing dusk condensed into night.

Goron, having been bowed to the only armchair and now sitting on the edge as though ready to jump up, handed over the letter, remarking that it had "really been confiscated by the police." Jaquemar, moving his chair across, took it without visible emotion except, perhaps, a certain reluctance and with the unfriendly expression he had worn ever since his visit to the Marseilles mortuary.

They now formed two groups: Lebigot at the table glued to the chessboard and occasionally rubbing his chin absent-mindedly with his left hand (which produced a rasping sound), and a little away from the table the other three: Goron on his armchair, Jaquemar on the kitchen chair facing him, and Madame Chottin on a footstool beside him.

Jaquemar, with the same unfriendly expression, turned the letter around in his hands, then opened it with his little finger and drew out several sheets of soft, thin paper. Something heavy slipped from the paper into his lap, and he lifted it up and held it for a minute thoughtfully in his right hand. It was a long, very fine gold chain with a pendant that was also of gleaming, leaf-thin gold, the size of a fingernail and heart-shaped, with foreign characters engraved in the center—an amulet, as Madame Chottin remarked with a low exclamation that sounded pleased. Jaquemar, without response, handed it to her, unfolded the thin, rustling pages, and began to read what was written on them, mumbling half to himself but nevertheless so that everyone could hear. This surprised Goron, who had expected Jaquemar to study the contents and then pass the pages to him to look at. The following was the text:

EDMOND, MY DEAREST LAD,

How strange is the human heart, and its ways are as intricate as the ways of Destiny. Is that not so? Do you know, the hat is still lying beside me on the desk—the hat I had already put on to go to the notary and—disinherit you. You, the only person to whom my heart clings! And yet I wanted to disinherit you—yes, I suddenly hated you, can you understand that? When you were here just now and wouldn't take any money from me again, this hate shot into my heart; it seemed despicable of you.

Forgive my stupidity, my dear fellow—but that's how it was. Tomorrow I shall see Germaine. I had been looking forward to it all day, but after you had been with me, my joy was gone, and I said to myself: "I shan't get her after all—because of him! He doesn't want her, but he holds her! If he doesn't want her, he could give her to me!" And then I hated you even more. You know, it didn't occur to me that a human being is not an animal or a thing and that no one can make a gift of him, he must make a gift of himself (and perhaps he can't even do that, anyhow you once said something of the sort). It only occurred to me that you manifestly get everything you want and even what you don't want, while I get nothing at all. And do you know that it was an even more malicious idea that held me back, so that I put my hat down on the desk and said to myself, "Stop, think it over carefully." I suddenly thought: Suppose that is no punishment for him; how can one tell with him whether he cares about money? Perhaps I should be punishing him much more by

giving him the money than by withholding it from him? Then I took a
bottle of cognac from the cupboard, and a glass, and sat in the armchair
by the window (I'm in my office); from time to time I drank, and while
I did so I thought over everything.

Do you know, my friend, that you once gave me a terrible shock?
Shortly before Génie's death you had a conversation with her, and she
asked you whether life was good. You replied: "Yes, life is marvelously
beautiful." I was half out of my mind at the time through anxiety about
Génie, but this remark struck me at once, and I thought angrily: What
childish nonsense he's talking, and at a moment like this! But later I
kept thinking of it again and again, and every time this remark came
back to me it gave me a shock! What, I thought, he, who appears to
everyone so quiet and shut-in and melancholy, he finds life "marvelously
beautiful"—not merely beautiful, but "marvelously beautiful"; and I—
how is it with me? Everyone thinks me balanced and calm and even
gay, and yet I torment myself so and don't find it beautiful at all. Is it
true, then, that he loves life and I do not love it?

Was it silly to be so tormented by this question? Or don't you think
so? It was as though I had been cheated out of my life, and every time
I came to this conclusion I recalled an incident from my youth. When I
was twenty I had a Jewish girl friend; she was a pretty girl, very intelligent, but also very warmhearted and, in spite of her so-called "Jewish
head," extraordinarily naive. We were as good as engaged. She lived
with a married older sister, very wealthy people; she herself was from a
small town, where her parents were still living—she came here to see life.
One evening there was a small party at her home; we had all drunk a bit
and danced; we were all young people.

Apart from her, I had danced particularly with a young woman who
appealed to me a lot; she was blonde, cuddlesome, childlike—some friend
of Marcelle's (that was my fiancée's name) who had come without her
husband. The party broke up around midnight. Now, the house had a
long entrance hall like a passage. I walked along in front of the rest of
the gathering with Marcelle on one arm and her friend on the other—
we were in a very gay mood, and as my relations with Marcelle were
known to everyone, I kissed her goodbye. "Children!" cried the young
woman, laughing. "I can't bear to watch you. It makes me envious!"
Whereupon she tore the front door open to run out; as bad luck would
have it, however, Marcelle was standing in such a way that the heavy
door struck her hard on the temple—so that she was flung back against
the wall and struck the back of her head. Of course, we all crowded
around her immediately, especially the guilty friend; Marcelle was very
pale, the tears were streaming down her cheeks; but she was soon smiling
again and everything seemed to be all right.

On the way home, the other guests gradually dropped off, and finally there was nobody left but myself and this young woman. I was probably a bit drunk, and I was so young and happy; I pressed the young woman's arm against my body and cried: "Ah, love, love—I should like to love!"—"Why don't we do it, then?" she answered softly. We looked around—well, you know what I mean, it happened, in a dark corner in a park. In fact, it was very beautiful. I took her home, and we knew that we should never utter a word about what happened to anyone else. But as I approached the house where I lived I received a terrible shock, for while still some way off I saw that the servant girl from Marcelle's house was standing there arguing excitedly with my landlady.

Then, without stopping to think, I did something of which I have often felt ashamed since (curiously, I have never felt ashamed of my act of infidelity): I ran softly and as quickly as I could around the next corner, came to the back garden of my house, climbed the railings, raced through the garden, and slipped silently in at the back door. I crept swiftly upstairs to my room, opened the door, tore off my collar, tie, jacket, and waistcoat, and then went downstairs again. "What's going on?" I cried, and stepped out of the darkness toward the door. "There you are!" cried my landlady. "But I knocked at your door." Well, to make a long story short—Marcelle had started to feel ill, she had vomited, and her sister had sent the maid to fetch me. I was to calm her down; she was in a very excited state. So we set out. I went just as I was, without jacket or tie, and we hurried to Marcelle's house.

I was taken straight in to her. She was sitting on her bed; her cheeks were burning and her eyes gleamed feverishly. "Oh, dearest!" she cried, and stretched out both arms to me. "How good that you are here—I was longing for you so much! Come, give me a kiss! Oh my—my Alphonse!" And she pressed her lips to mine. They left us alone. The doctor had already been there, she had to have cold compresses, and I was supposed to calm her. I placed the wet cloth on her forehead; she lay back quietly and happily. I held her hand, which was very hot. It was quite clear that she harbored not the slightest suspicion against me, but my bad conscience forced me to ask her a question; and eventually I inquired: "I came quickly, Marcelle, didn't I?" "Oh, yes," she cried, sitting up again, so that the compress fell on the blanket. "Oh yes, my darling, thank you, I'm so grateful to you. I'm happy, Alphonse, when shall we marry? Oh, I'm so happy!" And all at once she unbuttoned her nightdress and with both hands behind her head undid a chain with a small gold heart on it. "This is my *Shadai* heart!" she exclaimed in her blissful exaltation. "As a baby in my Moses basket I wore it on my breast. The letters stand for *Shadai*, that is 'The Eternal,' and it is an amulet. I have never parted from it, but now you must wear it, for I love you more than my life."

But the next morning she was dead; she had died instantaneously from a cerebral hemorrhage. I wore this amulet up to my marriage with Génie, then I put it away; but when Génie went from me I put it on again. It hasn't really brought me much luck, and now I intend to take it off again. But I shall leave it to you, Edmond, my friend, after my death, so that you shall think from time to time of those who are being cheated of life.

Yes, I didn't really mean to write all this, but something quite different—what it was I can't remember now—I must have drunk too much cognac (I drank a few more glasses while I was writing), and now I don't feel like writing any more. Edmond, forgive me for having hated you for an instant, forgive me in fact that it has happened often—ah, my God, I must really be drunk, what "undying" words I am calling out to you, as though from the grave! I'm still alive—indeed, you once told me I lived a double life! Oh, you Gilgamesh-Edmond, good luck to you on your path to the demons! I and my double life—I should like to be happy again for once! I would throw away your whole inheritance for that, my dear fellow! Would you then pull a long face and complain about me—among your demons? Forgive me, my friend—I don't want to offend you, but all of a sudden I am badly drunk; it happened in the fraction of a second, everything is spinning. Ugh, it's horrible!

Always your ALPHONSE (huissier)

Paris, July 24, 1889

P.S. Suppose Germaine said "yes" after all?

"Hurray!" said Lebigot at his table, sticking out his neck with an impassive face and moving a man on the chessboard. "If you carry on like that, my dear sir, you will have lost your queen in another five moves." The queer fellow's remark had a releasing effect, falling in the midst of the rather awkward silence that had followed the reading, while Jaquemar thoughtfully folded up the rustling pages. Disregarding young Madame Chottin's comment, made with a shake of the head, that Gouffé, "poor man," must have been in a terribly confused state, Goron and Jaquemar engaged in a brief, curiously acrimonious dialogue.

"Monsieur Jaquemar," asked Goron, sitting forward in the chair, gripping one arm with his pudgy fist, his pince-nez awry, "did you know you were Gouffé's heir?"

Jaquemar made his silent munching movement of the lips and replied after a few seconds' pause: "I entered upon this inheritance at Marseilles."

"Will you give me a clear, straightforward answer: did you know you were Gouffé's heir?"

"I might have known."

"Where did you get the ten thousand francs for the reward?"

"I borrowed them from Madame Chottin."

"On the security of this inheritance?"

"There was no need for security. I said 'Give'; she answered 'Take.' "

"But you yourself? What security did you envisage in your own mind?"

"No security was necessary there either."

"Did you not think to yourself: I shall pay it back out of the inheritance?"

"If I had thought about it, I should have thought that."

"How could you have been so sure?"

"Whom else could he have made his heir? He only had me."

"And Madame Chottin?"

"That's just it, he didn't have her."

"And so long as he didn't have her—that's to say, hadn't married her—you were the natural heir, so to speak. Is that how it was?"

"Exactly like that. I told you in my letter that he said: 'When I am gone, you will have no more worries.' He was very wrong, my poor brother-in-law Gouffé."

"In other words . . ."

"In other words, I was the only one who had an interest in his death—if that's what you want to hear."

"But, Monsieur! You're insulting Monsieur Jaquemar!" objected Madame Chottin, looking charmingly bold as she did so. "You've no right to talk to him like that."

"Why does he answer the clown?" said Lebigot from his table. "Is this a police station?"

"What about you?" Goron flared. "Where were you on the night of July 25 to 26, if I may ask?"

Lebigot turned around leisurely on his kitchen chair, looked at him with his hard bird's eyes, and retorted: "The hell you may. You can go to the devil."

"What have you got your knife into *him* for?" asked Jaquemar calmly, looking Lebigot in the face with his squinting gaze. "He's only doing his duty."

"No offense, then—if you're only doing your duty," remarked Lebigot unmoved, and turned back to his table.

"You really do misunderstand me," said Goron, nervously tugging at his collar. "You too, Madame."

And in a tone that gradually became more matter-of-fact he explained that, under the circumstances, a more or less natural suspicion fell on Jaquemar, a suspicion that he did not share in the slightest—that, on the contrary, he considered utterly preposterous—but that, nevertheless, might meet with secret and perhaps even with public support, especially when the ambivalent feelings that were evident from Gouffé's letter, and also from Jaquemar's own description of his relations with the missing man, became known.

On the very next day after Goron's acrimonious conversation with Jaquemar, however, the development of the Gouffé case took a turn for the better. It was as if the circumstances that had hitherto stood obstinately in the way of any progress now melted into thin air, throwing the path wide open to a further advance. First thing in the morning, as Goron, bad-tempered as usual, was about to hurry through his antechamber, Guillaume rose behind his desk and brought him to a stop with the remark that there was an exceedingly interesting item, printed under the heading "Local News" in both the *Quotidien Provençal* and the *Petit Marseillais*.

Leaning over the desk beside his secretary, Goron read the following newspaper announcement, which was circled with red pencil and further singled out by an exclamation mark in the margin: "The lawyer Herbier, Jr., who had been missing for several weeks and was erroneously identified with the mysterious corpse found at Millery, has returned home safe and sound from a trip to Monte Carlo, of which he had omitted to notify his family." "There you are!" snorted Goron, grinding his teeth. "I knew it. The dunderheads. Telegraph for details immediately." He straightened up and hurried into his room, shaking his head. But the telegram was no sooner on its way than Guillaume's name rang out from Goron's room, repeated several times in the greatest impatience. As Guillaume entered he was met with the statement that, come what may, a pretext must be found for Goron to go to Marseilles, and: "Read this." The sheet of notepaper held out to him was a personal dispatch from the reporter on the *Quotidien Provençal*: Fragments of an old trunk had been found near Millery and seized by the police; it was not clear why, but probably in connection with the body found there earlier, and on account of which the Cité had first approached him, the reporter—for which reason he considered it appropriate to inform them "as before."

A second, more urgent telegram was dispatched to Beaujean at Marseilles. Latrille was sent for, and the three of them—Guillaume and Latrille, led by Goron—ran along the corridors and burst into the "intelligence service," to find the little room heaped with newspapers but without Créneau. The latter had just gone out to find Goron and proudly inform him that he had discovered "something important as required." Finding the chief's room empty, and disappointed at not being able to present his discovery personally, he came back in his shabby jacket and to his amazement saw the three men rummaging through his newspapers and was promptly sworn at by Goron. Asked where on earth he had got to, he pointed in some confusion to a copy of the *Bouche du Rhône*, at which all three, Guillaume and Latrille peering over Goron's left and right shoulders, now read. "That will have to do!" said Goron, and hurried out of the room without a further word.

It was late in the afternoon, and Goron was back in his room, so that he was unable to ring his office when Beaujean's answering telegram arrived from Marseilles. The Millery corpse, erroneously identified by Herbier *père* as Herbier *fils*, was the center of a case that was well on the way to being solved but about which they could not, at the moment, enter into correspondence, since it was not the practice of the Marseilles police to discuss their secret investigations with outside authorities.

As to the remains of the trunk found in bushes three miles from Millery, they must disappoint the Cité if the latter imagined it had anything to do with "their" Gouffé case: one of the pieces had a relatively well-preserved luggage label pasted on it on which even the observer least skilled in detection could read that this trunk was sent from Paris to Marseilles on July 26, 1888, i.e. approximately one whole year before the *huissier* disappeared. Insensitive to the point of being thick-skinned in personal matters, Goron did not allow himself to be irritated by the maliciously sneering tone of this communication; factually, however, it almost thrilled him and intensified into a certainty his conjecture that Gouffé's body had been transported from Paris to Marseilles in this trunk.

Guillaume's always respectful but repeated objection that the year was wrong and that "the gentlemen would surely be able to distinguish an eight from a nine," he dismissed with a wave of the hand; that, he said, was of no importance. Guillaume should note, rather, that the route was correct, the date of July 26 was correct, and the only thing wrong was the 1888—which therefore they must have misread, it must be 1889! With this and with a "This evening at the Gare de Lyon, then!" he left. Soudrais shook his boorish head behind him with a contemptuous laugh; Latrille ran the tip of his left ring finger to and fro over his lips and remarked: "Pity he is such a fool, he knows his job." And when Guillaume replied to this: "He is a great man, Latrille," he looked at him and answered thoughtfully, with a smile in the corners of his eyes: "But all the same he'll break his neck."

The following morning they arrived in Marseilles—Goron, Latrille, and Soudrais—and the leader pushed his way through the milling crowd at the station, beckoned and whistled to a cab outside, and with a brief sign to his companions clambered up to the seat beside the astonished coachman. This was how he made his entry into the city which only a few months later, as a result of his activities, was to become the scene of the most staggering episode in French police history: perched high up on the coach box, his arms crossed over his fat chest and his black top hat pulled down almost to his pince-nez. They drove uphill, then along a street that gave glimpses of the glittering harbor, from which the odor of stale fish and spicy tar common to all harbors drifted over to them in the cool sunshine of the autumn morning, and through the Rue Cannebière to the tree-lined square that terminated it. Here, in front of the extensive but antiquated headquarters of the Security Police (the left and rear wings of which housed the Prefecture itself), two brightly colored sentry boxes flanked the huge, seemingly low archway—a delightful picture to which Goron, of course, paid no heed.

His visit was what his visits usually were: an invasion. Followed by his two aides, he marched purposefully down the stone corridors, came to Beaujean's antechamber, and went straight through the little gate in the wooden barrier. The clerk, whom Soudrais recognized from his previous visit, threw himself in the way, jumping up at Goron's chest like a leaping fish; but he was pulled away by Latrille's muscular arm with the question, "What do you know about the card-sharps on the Paris-Marseilles express?" Goron reached the high double door, knocked briefly with the knuckles of his right hand, and opened it.

Beaujean stood leaning on his stick by the window. He turned his head with its flowing locks and prophet's beard incredulously, raised his stick, and began to shout: "Don't you know you have to wait till you've been announced, you ill-mannered stranger?" The stocky little intruder was now in front of him. "Goron, Sûreté, Paris," he introduced himself. "And I," answered Beaujean gulping and throwing his head back, "I am Beaujean!" "Delighted," said Goron, holding out his hand, which the other took at first hesitantly, but then clung to, pressed, and actually massaged. His colleague, his great colleague Goron, they were honored, enchanted, overwhelmed. Goron freed himself and with the flat of his hand spread out the warrant signed by Carnot on top of the letters that were lying on the imposing diplomat's desk so that there would be no misunderstanding. He was there in connection with the Millery body, the time had come for clarity in this matter.

Beaujean, with a spiteful glance at the warrant, muttered something about "unnecessary solicitude" and limped past, dragging his right leg. Yes, indeed, the dead man of Millery—who should understand Goron's concern better than he who, in spite of his infirmities, had for months spared neither trouble, vigilance, nor labor—"but clarity?" His eyes in his pain-racked face closed, he clutched with his large hand at the void and finally exclaimed: "Where is clarity?" He let his hand fall back nerveless against his flabby, massive body. "We down here, insignificant people that we are, humble people, are content to hope. Whoever the dead man is . . ." "He is Gouffé," said Goron. Again Beaujean closed his eyes and nodded bitterly, but gradually he stopped nodding and began to shake his head. "No, my esteemed colleague, much as we admire you, truth must be respected; we know little enough about the unfortunate man of Millery, but if there is one thing we do know it is that he is not Gouffé; for death, like life, has its language and he who lay there in the brushwood let the living know he was there and mutely cried "Seek my name, do justice to my memory!" But when did all this start? In the first half of July, when Gouffé was still enjoying life and love in the sight of all, the odor of death had already commenced to plague and admonish the peasants of Millery, the good, reliable tillers of the soil.

Goron, in a moment's irritation, threw back his head and exclaimed: "They are mistaken, it was after July 27." Beaujean tore at his beard, stopped to think, and mastered his feelings. "Very well," he said, and banged on the floor with the rubber tip of his stick; he turned his big eyes toward the door, one leaf of which immediately opened a little way to reveal the torso and weasel's face of the little clerk. "Bring the witness Lafarge, the man under arrest, for our honored visitor to see!"

Goron sat down with a bump in the armchair behind the huge desk and gazed expectantly through his pince-nez at the door, while Beaujean, after a venomous glance at this disrespectful guest, hobbled back to the window and stood there muttering at the pane. They remained like this, without exchanging a word, for several minutes, until the door opened again and a man entered wearing a coachman's cape, which the clerk held between thumb and forefinger. The new arrival stood there awkwardly twisting his battered hat in his two hands and looking like a bear in girth and weight by comparison with his dwarfish custodian.

He had a straggling beard and strands of hair fell from his half-bald head over his low brow; his nose had large pores and was as red as an overripe strawberry, and his small eyes glittered craftily. He cast a quick glance at Goron, took no notice of Latrille or Soudrais, who had followed close on the couple's heels, and shyly obeyed the sign made to him by Beaujean who, only momentarily put out by the two new intruders, pointed with his stick to the floor in front of him. "Here, witness Lafarge, 'witness' remember. In return for such important testimony as yours, previous misdemeanors may be overlooked. Here, poor fellow." As he spoke, Beaujean made a sign of dismissal with his beruffled left hand to the clerk, who silently disappeared.

The witness, Richard Lafarge, born so and so at such and such, a cabdriver by trade, but at the moment *mis à pied*—that is to say, deprived of his license—on account of drunkenness and other irregularities, spurred on by leading questions, meaning looks, and encouraging gestures from the Marseilles police chief, made the following statement: On the night of July 5 to 6, while slightly under the influence of alcohol and hence in an obliging frame of mind, he took "three male persons" with a heavy trunk from Marseilles station to Millery; having been asked to stop and wait after rounding a sharp bend in the road, he saw the three men disappear around the corner with the trunk and thought he heard a heavy object fall to the ground and slither along. As the three men did not reappear, he lost patience and turned back, without setting eyes on his mysterious fares again until—"Until when, witness Lafarge?" interrupted Beaujean, gesturing with his hands like a conductor drawing his orchestra to a crescendo.

"Until you showed them to me here and had me put in clink."

"For," cried Beaujean, raising his right hand, "they are fortunately in our custody, three worthless, shady characters without papers, unable to say where they had come from or where they were going, pedlars, vagabonds, antisocial from head to toe, so entangled in incriminating circumstances and their bad consciences that they could not declare: 'We were at such and such a place seen by such and such a person on the night in question!'—the night, great colleague Goron, of July 5 to 6, three weeks before the disappearance of your poor Gouffé."

"You old wag!" said Latrille, winking one eye and nudging the gigantic cabby, who squinted down at him half-furtively, half-amused. "Who do you think you're kidding? We're not from Marseilles." This enormity (which was later widely reported in the Press) set Beaujean gasping for breath, but he had no chance to retort because the same moment Goron was standing in front of him asking: "Where are the remains of the trunk? Will you please show them to my two officers?" "They are in the cellar," replied Beaujean uncomprehendingly. "My subordinates will be pleased—" "No, you, if you wouldn't mind, you personally!" And Goron, since Beaujean stretched out both hands defensively and opened his mouth in his beard as though to cry out, turned his gaze maliciously to the desk and the warrant that lay upon it. Beaujean, his face contorted with rage, nodded. "Follow me, then!" he cried, banging the floor once with his stick, and limped out of the room ahead of Latrille and Soudrais.

They had scarcely closed the door behind them when Goron's vicious, staccato voice rang out inside, growing louder and louder;

then there was a thud, like a heavy sack falling. Latrille scratched the corner of his mouth with a smile, while Beaujean listened to these sounds with an expression of horrified incredulity before limping on along the corridor, his big hand over his shocked face.

When they returned ten minutes later there was silence in the police chief's room. Beaujean entered and stood rooted to the spot, while Latrille and Soudrais peered around him from either side at the scene within. Goron was standing with his back to the window, his arms folded on his chest; in front of him on the floor kneeled Lafarge, his tearstained drunkard's face and clasped hands were raised in entreaty, and his hat lay a few yards from both of them, where it had rolled. "That's settled," said Goron. "Stand up!" He went to Beaujean: it was all rubbish, the fellow had never carried the three men, had never seen them before the confrontation in this building. "What," whispered Beaujean, rolling his eyes toward the witness, who rose painfully to his feet, supporting himself with his right hand, "what, you have recanted again, slapped truth in the face again?" Lafarge sniffed, wiped his nose with the back of his hand, and made a deprecatory gesture: "It's no good going on about it, Monsieur, you told me they were such bad hats, they were bound to go to New Caledonia for life, so I thought: Well then, why shouldn't I tell him what he wants to hear—so long as he gives me back my cab license!" "Lafarge!" yelled Beaujean, "Lafarge, you drove them, you shan't do violence to the truth, you drove them!" "I hadn't even got a cab at that time," said Lafarge in a small voice. "My license was taken away from me on July 2."

Meanwhile, the three Parisians were bending over a piece of trunk that Latrille had brought up with him from the cellar. "Get out!" screamed Beaujean, hobbling along on his stick after the coachman, who was tiptoeing to the door as fast as he could go, making little gestures of entreaty with his folded hands. "Get out!" Goron looked the enraged police chief in the face unmoved. "Where is the Millery body?" "The Millery body?" Beaujean recovered his senses. "Where is the Millery body?" He swayed his head as though intoning a psalm: "Ah, where indeed, where we all come to in the end," and he nodded his head gravely, "in the cool black earth." "He must be exhumed, there must be a fresh post-mortem." H'm, yes, Beaujean quite understood—but how was he to be exhumed? Did not time have its rights

—it had its power, in any case, and all at once a note of triumphant scorn rang in his unctuous speech: "The unfortunate man is at rest, yes, he is at rest, he rests with others in the mass grave at La Guillotière, forever 'unknown'!" "That's impossible," barked Goron, "impossible." "It is so," replied Beaujean, nodding his heavily furrowed brow.

Goron hissed through clenched teeth: "This is an act of unparalleled irresponsibility." "Irresponsibility?" Beaujean blinked. "Irresponsibility?" He put his hand to his ear as though to hear something he would not admit having heard; his face turned scarlet and he began to yell, with his yellowish teeth flashing in his beard, louder than Goron had ever yelled: "Away with you, out of this house, go back where you came from, malaperts who cannot distinguish between mine and thine! The dead man of Millery was found in territory under the jurisdiction of Marseilles, he belongs to Marseilles, and Marseilles can do with him what Marseilles pleases! He was released by the Prosecutor General's Office as unknown, and unknown he has gone to his last resting place, and, gentlemen from Paris, let me tell you this: he has gone unknown into the great anonymity to which all flesh falls victim, even that of the great head of the Paris Sûreté when it pleases Heaven to call him; and who am I, Beaujean, insignificant person that I am, to interfere with the course of the world, since the earth eats up everything and everyone?" He gesticulated with his stick, saliva flew out of his cursing mouth, and Goron, suddenly quiet, stood at the desk, his two fists resting on it, and listened uncomprehendingly, his head slightly to one side, so stubbornly silent that before his silence the enraged Beaujean's wrath and eloquence dried up and he stood there speechless, his chest heaving.

"I hope," said Goron as soon as Beaujean had stopped, "that this piece of thoughtlessness can be made good. I shall get in touch with you tomorrow and report. Thank you."

On their continued journey, which led first to the station, it was Soudrais who sat on the coach box and Goron who sat beside Latrille in the back of the cab. He wrinkled his nose this way and that over the fragment of trunk, as though sniffing at it, peering at it with eyes that looked sore and blind because he had taken off his pince-nez; while Latrille, who held the fragment in his hand, looked down at it with a vertical fold in the forehead of his pock-marked smuggler's face, fascinated by it. Goron took the fragment himself and turned it in all directions: it was about eighteen inches long and five inches wide, made—as could be seen from the jagged edges—of wood, and lined on the underside with blue paper covered in white or silver stars, only thin scraps of which remained, and on the upper surface with a coarsely woven fabric of a brownish color. The luggage label, which was pasted on this side, had been cockled, pulped, and flaked by the alternation of wet and dry; nevertheless the black border was almost undamaged and the words and figures inside it fairly distinct:

PARIS/MARSEILLES

Train 3

No. 1326

26 July 88

There could really be no doubt that the numbers and date had been read correctly—although the figures were not printed but stamped, and so smudged and washed out as to be almost illegible; on top of this, the mass of paper and gum toward the lower edge was balled up and twisted, so that it was possible to attribute the appearance of the figures to chance distortion. This was what Goron pinned his hopes on when he thrust the fragment back into Latrille's lap with a categorical "Must be 89." Latrille raised his right eyebrow and shrugged his shoulder. "You'll see," commented Goron, pressing his pince-nez back on his nose.

But at the station they had no luck. The consignment notes were sent every month to be checked by the head offices of the railway company in Paris, so it was impossible for the Marseilles office to look them up on the spur of the moment. Should they write for them? No, answered Goron, and turned back into the milling crowd in the booking hall without a word of thanks, his two aides behind him. They drove back uphill into the town, with Soudrais on the box, toward the middle-class residential district in which Dr. Levreault had his practice.

The maid, surprised to see a group of men at the door and intimidated by Goron's gruff "Security Police, Paris—is the doctor in?" as he pushed his way in, ran half behind, half in front of him into the waiting room, saying she would at once tell *monsieur le docteur* they were there. Without removing his hat, Goron, who for some reason felt thirsty, went straight over to a small table standing in the corner between two plush-trimmed windows, overtopped by an indoor palm, took a carafe and a glass, poured himself water and drank. He was still holding the carafe by the neck in his right hand and the quarter-full glass in his left a few minutes later, when footsteps approached from the next room, the door opened, and the massive Dr. Levreault appeared in it, stern-faced and wearing a white surgical gown, the doorknob in his hand. "Monsieur Goron, will you come this way please?" "Come on," said Goron, with a movement of the head to his companions, and walked past the doctor into the consulting room, which smelled of ether. "Their conversation will be brief—brief and unpleasant," remarked Latrille behind him, in an undertone but loud enough to be heard by Levreault, who raised his eyebrows.

The conversation did indeed seem to be taking an unpleasant turn; for Goron, after inconsiderately putting down the carafe and the glass on the doctor's desk, did not even give him time to invite them to take a seat. He had had the dead man of Millery buried, said Goron. He had done nothing of the kind, retorted Dr. Levreault angrily, he had performed the autopsy, that was all. He performed it as deputy for Dr. Lacassagne, the police surgeon? How many autopsies had he performed before? About a hundred, probably, "let me remind you I am a pathologist." But how many as a police surgeon? It made no difference whether a dissection was performed as a pathologist or as a police surgeon. How many autopsies had he carried out before as a police surgeon? None. Very good, now what about the findings—on what grounds had he come to the conclusion that the man was not Gouffé? On the simple grounds that the corpse did not exhibit a single one of Gouffé's characteristics: he had no scar on his ankle, had different hair, and had a different height, 5 feet 11 inches instead of 5 feet 10 inches.

Latrille and even the stupid Soudrais pricked up their ears. After a moment's irritation, Goron remarked that this must be a mistake. A mistake indeed! came the retort. Could Levreault offer any explanation for this difference in height? Of course, that the man wasn't Gouffé. "It is Gouffé," said Goron, the discrepancies would be cleared up; the man was also supposed to have had Herbier's food in his stomach, and then Herbier "cheerfully" came home. Dr. Levreault's big red face with the white eyebrow tufts turned purple. It pleased Goron to examine and rebuke him like a student, but the fact was that the result of the analysis of the contents of the stomach, though it might have been a coincidence, was medically irrefutable and in any case only one link in the chain of deduction, which was conclusive, regardless of whether it was to the liking of the Paris or Marseilles police, in whose peculiar conflicts over questions of jurisdiction he, as a man of science, took no interest. Thanks to some warning instinct, however, he had preserved one piece of evidence, and he invited the gentlemen to see for themselves.

Thereupon he pulled open one of the drawers of his desk, a grim expression on his face, and took out a thin white paper parcel. With his thick, well-washed pink fingers he unfolded it on the blotting pad and, while the other three stood grouped around him, he drew forth a few long, greasy black locks of hair, like those of a gypsy orchestra leader. Was this Gouffé's hair, light brown and short according to the police description? No, said Soudrais, shaking his head with a laugh. Meanwhile, Goron stared at the piece of evidence malevolently through his crooked pince-nez, as though by so doing he could persuade it to turn short and light brown; all of a sudden he seized one of the locks with his thumb and index finger and dipped it in the glass from which he had previously drunk. He swished it clumsily this way and that in what was left of the water, which quickly turned a reddish color, then earthy brown, and finally took on the appearance of cloudy black ink. At the sight of this, the protruding eyebrow tufts of the stern Dr. Levreault drew closer and closer to the bridge of his nose until they almost met.

The hair, when it had been withdrawn dripping from the glass, placed on the blotting pad, and dried by vigorously pressing a piece of blotting paper on it, bore no resemblance to the gypsy locks lying beside it; in particular, the hairs adhering to the blotting paper were short and brown, dark rather than light brown—but, as Latrille cheerfully remarked, it would probably turn light brown if washed in warm water to remove the grease from the scalp as well as the earth, filth, and blood that had already been cleaned off. Correct, said Goron, brushing the cleaned hair onto the paper containing the other locks with his cupped hand and slipping the whole package into his waistcoat pocket. Gouffé's hair, no doubt of it; would Levreault please inform Dr. Lacassagne that a second autopsy must be carried out the following morning, the earlier the better, and what was the name of the doorkeeper at the School of Medicine? Siller, stammered Levreault, his air of authority somewhat shaken—and he was grateful for the lesson. Goron, who had already turned away, came to a halt.

"*Monsieur le docteur* Levreault," he said with spinsterish precision, "it is impossible to work without hypotheses. The healthy brain possesses an innate imagination, which it can bring to bear even on those facts it cannot prove. You can rely on that. It is intellectual arrogance to try to dispense with it. *Adieu*."

Out in the open again and after a moment or two of hesitation, he ordered Latrille and Soudrais to proceed to Millery. They were to look into Beaujean's assertion that the smell of putrefaction had been noticed by the local peasants as early as the first half of July, "which is impossible, don't let anyone talk you into believing it." With this he left them standing; he slumped into the rear seat of the waiting cab and drove to the School of Medicine.

Here, in the plain building with its low-pitched roof and the tricolor hanging from the short mast, the good fortune that had begun in Levreault's consulting room continued as though working independently to smooth the path of Goron's investigations. Anyhow, Beaujean was deceiving himself in imagining that he had checkmated Goron by the premature burial of the disputed corpse; his well-aimed blow was nullified by the prudence of the doorkeeper, Siller. With his lively ice-blue eyes beneath the horizontal patent-leather brim of his cap fixed attentively on his visitor, he listened to Goron's inquiry and answered in a brisk voice accustomed to giving commands that, since the examination of the dead man of Millery had perhaps been carried out by the "youthful" Dr. Levreault with insufficient thoroughness from a police point of view, since the body had been inspected so fleetingly by the gentlemen from Paris and then so hurriedly buried, he had taken the precaution of placing an old hat on the dead man's head and marking the coffin with a white cross— there would be no difficulty at all about identifying it in the mass grave at La Guillotière.

Goron, in something approaching an outburst of warmth and affection, patted the erect old soldier's skinny back with his pudgy hand, telling him that he was the only conscientious official he had met in this city and that his efficiency would not go unrequited (in fact, he later received five hundred francs from Jaquemar's reward). For a start, would he make a point of being present at the now urgently necessary exhumation, "to prevent any further irregularities."

Cheered and, if possible, more determined than ever, Goron drove back to the Rue Cannebière and alighted at the Hôtel Keiler, where the master detective, of whose arrival they had been notified from Paris, was greeted with diffidence. At the stroke of two, he was called to the telephone. He gave various instructions to Guillaume and concluded by telling him to ring back at four o'clock for a provisional report. Sure enough, it was a few minutes to four when Latrille and Soudrais returned from their mission to Millery, which had met with the greatest possible success: their methodical inquiries had elicited nothing whatsoever to confirm Beaujean's assertions, but had revealed the almost unbelievable fact that since the discovery of the body, not one single officer of the Marseilles police had appeared to inquire into the thorny question of the date on the spot. The road mender and the gendarme, admitting frankly that they had no sense of time, refused to commit themselves to a date, but referred the Parisians to the innkeeper, whose attractive premises, consisting of the house and a leafy garden, were the first to be encountered on approaching the village from the Marseilles highroad and not far removed from the point at which the corpse was found.

The innkeeper stated with certainty that the penetrating odor did not become evident until the beginning of the second week in August, so that business was as active as ever in July but declined visibly from the said date, until the garden and guest rooms were finally completely deserted—a statement that was convincingly borne out by the entries in the register of guests. They could find absolutely no one in the whole of Millery who was prepared to back up Beaujean's view regarding the date; and the source of this date would have remained a mystery, had not Latrille, before they set out, taken a look at the records of the Security Police and in particular the report drawn up at the time of the reception of the body at the School of Medicine. This stated that an (unnamed) individual who had accompanied the melancholy transport had, "after exhaustive

questioning," quoted the first half of July as the date in question. Latrille succeeded in tracking the man down in Millery; he was a work-
shy zany who at first stuck obstinately to his original statement, then
began to beat about the bush, and finally admitted sullenly that the
actual date had been more or less put into his mouth, that he had
suffered from the noisome stench "for a long time," but whether it
had started in the middle of July he couldn't say—perhaps it had been
the beginning of August!

In short, Beaujean's assertion was founded on sand; Goron's delight,
mingled with indignation, at this discovery was at its height when
Guillaume's second telephone call from Paris added to it still further.
The Chief's instructions had been carried out. The engine driver of
the afternoon express due at Marseilles at midnight had been given
all the things requested—a dentist's description of Gouffé's teeth,
samples of hair from Gouffé's brush and comb, and Gouffé's army
pass which, contrary to his other papers, did in fact give his height
as 5 feet 11 inches, instead of 5 feet 10 inches. As regards the consignment note for baggage No. 1326, however, the head office of the railway company stated that no such number was issued in July, 1888;
the items dispatched in that period ran to only some seven hundred;
and not until this year, 1889, the year of the Universal Exhibition, was
the number in question reached and even exceeded; it must therefore
date from July, 1889, and according to the consignment note at the
Paris office package No. 1326, a trunk weighing 230 pounds, was
brought by a man who paid an excess-weight charge of 18 francs, on
the evening of July 26, to be carried on train No. 3 from Paris to
Marseilles, where it was collected the next morning without being
first stored at the station.

This information was so conclusive that Goron had every justification for waving aside Soudrais's pigheaded objection: "But it says
88 on the luggage label." He was quite happy to let "the Lab" (the
criminological laboratory of the Paris Prefecture of Police) rack their
brains over this problem; so far as he was concerned, there was no
doubt that this was the trunk in which Gouffé was transported from
the scene of the murder in Paris to Marseilles and Millery and with
which "the gang" had laid a fatal trap for themselves; for even if one
man had handed in the trunk, there must have been more than one
person involved—probably two, a man and a woman, the latter

serving as a decoy—and it would be odd if they could not lay hands on the Paris cabdriver who, in all likelihood, had carried the murderer and the cumbersome piece of luggage to the Gare de Lyon. In this hope, however, Goron was disappointed.

Punctually at midnight Goron was standing, with both hands in his overcoat pockets and his hat pulled down toward his pince-nez, on the station platform. The huge engine of the Paris express came puffing almost gently into the station, its two eyes sending out twin beams of light; Goron, before it had come fully to a stop, clambered up the iron ladder amidst a cloud of hissing steam and took possession of Guillaume's package.

So great was his impatience that he ordered his cab to turn around shortly before it reached the Hôtel Keiler and drive straight to the address of Dr. Levreault, who, thanks to their instructive encounter that morning, was willing and even eager to make a microscopic examination of Gouffé's hair immediately, despite the lateness of the hour. In his dressing gown, his wiry eyebrows bent over the brass tube and his thick pink fingers operating the focusing screw, he sat at the desk while Goron stood beside him. Then he raised his head and forced from his authoritative gravity a weak smile and an even weaker joke: no doubt about it, Monsieur Goron had taken truth by the forelock; the sample from Paris corresponded "to a hair" with the hair that had been washed there that morning—it was Gouffé's hair, he should look for himself. Now Goron sat over the microscope. "I thank you," he said, and stood up. As they were parting, the doctor commented with a hint of embarrassment that he hoped the delay in getting at the truth, for which he was partly to blame, would have no injurious consequences. Goron replied without acrimony, though curt as always: "Don't worry, truth doesn't turn rancid like butter."

Under these circumstances, the autopsy next morning was little more than a formality. Dr. Lacassagne, the police surgeon who performed it, a small, unfriendly man with a bloodless sheep's face, a zigzag parting in his dry, graying blond hair, grizzled blond beard, and narrow spectacles, was a man of great experience in his own field; he was able to demonstrate that the bared anklebone of the "Millery corpse" showed a slight roughness due to abrasion and also that there was a difference between the weight of the right and left leg—both of which observations pointed to an earlier injury and, in conjunction with the examination of the teeth, left no doubt about the identity of the body.

This was what Dr. Lacassagne, in Goron's presence, reported half an hour later in his nasal voice to the police chief Beaujean; and what the latter was forced to listen to, as he stood behind his desk leaning on his stick with averted face like an offended monarch being forced to abdicate by a delegation of representatives of the people: "Monsieur Beaujean, the Millery corpse has a name. I have come to report to you that Monsieur Gouffé's estate is open to his heirs. I beg you to announce this to the Prosecution Department in Paris. The dead man of Millery is Alphonse Gouffé."

"And as regards the remains of the trunk," added Goron maliciously, "I have taken the liberty of ordering these to be forwarded to the Paris Sûreté. Will you kindly see to it that this order is punctually executed."

Beaujean limped away from his table to the farthest corner of the room; he turned around with eyes ablaze and threw his right hand into the air. "Take it away!" he shouted and turned his face and body to the wall.

For the third time the Gouffé case became a sensation. The disclosure that the shamefully desecrated Millery body was that of the much-discussed "huissier galant," and that there was every prospect of uncovering an exceptionally brutal capital crime, evoked unexampled excitement among Press and public—in those relatively calm days, when the misdeeds of individual malefactors still played the role assumed in our own time by the crimes of States. Everyone forgot that what was now sensational truth had been regarded a few weeks earlier as "Goron's fancy"—just as Goron himself, after so much scorn and criticism, was suddenly once more "our tried and trusted, and always unerring M. Goron," the master among European police officers. This time it was really the case itself that became a sensation and held all strata of the population in the grip of a morbid fascination, a kind of lust for horror. That this should have been the general reaction was inevitable, for the perception of unvarnished truth is beyond the power of the multitude.

This caused Goron no distress; he needed public interest and had to accept it as it was—provided it was strong and kept to the point!

He made sure that this would be so; he took charge of the sensational-
ism and succeeded in nipping in the bud the many undesirable trends
that showed signs of developing.

The Cité issued its information with economy and method. After
the initial announcement of the identity of the Millery body, more
detailed statements were successively put out concerning the round-
about and difficult course the investigation had been forced to take
in order to arrive at this result.

In short, it was a well-planned Press campaign devised and carried
out by Goron to achieve certain clearly defined psychological ends:
first, the importance and horror of the Gouffé case were to be rammed
home, then public interest was to be concentrated on the one
object that might be expected to cast some light on the mystery.
Police inquiries at all the trunk manufacturers in Paris and the rest
of the country elicited nothing beyond the fact that the trunk in
question was manifestly not of French manufacture, but was perhaps made in Germany or England, and in any event abroad. Goron
had all the more reason to congratulate himself that his Press campaign would gradually and inescapably draw into its vortex the Paris
representatives of the great foreign newspapers, rendering the Gouffé
case a cause célèbre outside as well as inside France. Moreover, he was
relieved to note that the superior authorities, especially the General
Prefecture of Police and the Ministry of the Interior, as a rule so
concerned that the police should avoid the limelight, paid no attention to his spectacular activities—that is to say, they did not allow
themselves to be drawn into open disapproval; indeed they maintained
a total silence. So long as he was given his head, it mattered not at all
to Goron why this was so, and it never for one moment occurred to
him that the fish-eyed old man in the Ministry, Chief Public Prosecutor Lozé, and the sybaritic Sallier were secretly saying to themselves: "This is Goron's hour, but ours will not be long in coming."

Was it really his hour? One day he received a visit (which had
become very rare lately) from Jaquemar of the bewildered eyes. Mumbling almost unintelligibly that he should look at it, he handed
Goron a photograph mounted on not very thick cardboard, and
watched Goron place it on the desk and study it. "What's this?"
he asked.

It was the likeness, about the size of a hand, of a young and beau-

tiful woman, a half-length portrait but printed lengthways, because
she had been photographed lying on an ottoman or sofa with her
head slightly raised, and resting on one shoulder, possibly naked, but
wrapped to a point just above the nipples in a black-and-white checked
silk shawl that somehow seemed to be distressing her, almost as
though she were tied up in it and unable to move her arms. The
expression of the face—with its tigerish little nose, the eyelids three-
quarters closed in lascivious anguish, and above them the eyebrows
slightly raised toward the middle, over the bridge of the nose, which
made them look simultaneously agonized and a trifle clownish—
was in charming concord with this appearance of being bound. The
young person whose shapely, plump, and naked body was partially
revealed, the snowy skin contrasting with the lacquer-black hair and
the lacquered look of the painted lips, must have been an actress,
a chansonette, or something of that sort, who had herself photographed
in this thoroughly artificial pose for professional reasons; for it was
easy to see that she was beautiful without all this paraphernalia and
that the rather mawkish setting did not really suit her.

"Who is this woman?" asked Goron, the fat on his hamster cheeks
trembling. "Do you know her?" Jaquemar inquired back, looking
at him with an expectant expression in his squinting eyes, as Goron
planted the pince-nez on his nose again and glanced up. "Was she
one of those you questioned at the beginning?" "No," replied Goron,
looking back at the photograph, "I've never seen her." Jaquemar
lowered his head with deep furrows in his brow. Not long before
his brother-in-law's disappearance he had lent Gouffé a book of which
he was very fond and which he had always wanted Gouffé to read;
for this reason, he had not pressed for its return, but only looked for
it in Gouffé's bookcase after the latter had vanished; when he found
it and took possession of it, he had come across the photograph
between the pages, where it had perhaps served as a bookmark. The
strange thing was that he had often browsed through the book since
recovering it, and had also got Madame Chottin to read aloud to him
from it, without either of them noticing the photograph; on the other
hand, there were all sorts of markers between the pages indicating
his favorite passages, while the picture was at the point of the center
stitching and hence firmly wedged in and not very noticeable. He
had lighted upon it the previous evening quite by chance while

turning the pages at random as he yawned sleepily—but the sight of it had frightened him.

"A strange story," growled Goron, resting his head in his hand in such a way that he was supporting it and at the same time scratching the crown of his unruly hair with his fingers. "Does anyone know her?" Jaquemar shrugged his shoulders. No—and yes; he had the definite *feeling* of having seen her, and in some connection with his brother-in-law—perhaps at one of the formerly quite-frequent soirées at the Rue des Ecoles, perhaps on a café terrace where Gouffé had greeted her, or perhaps in the office in the Boule Miche. The last hypothesis seemed the most probable from the fact that Dopffer, the head clerk, was likewise convinced, when asked, that he recalled the face—the face, but not the circumstances in which he had seen it; perhaps she had once visited Gouffé privately at the office and Dopffer had caught a fleeting glimpse of her as she came or went; it was certainly a face that, once seen, would not be forgotten, and for this reason Dopffer felt quite certain the woman was not one of the *huissier's* regular clients.

"I don't know whether this thing is of any value," grumbled Goron, nervously shifting his shoulders in his jacket. "Nor I," responded Jaquemar, silently munching with his lips with his customary expression of resignation. But she was a hitherto unknown figure from the circle of Gouffé's acquaintances, a—well, fascinating apparition, and, he added: "To whom does a woman give a photograph like that? Surely only to someone with whom she has, or hopes to have, an intimate relationship." The melancholy and frail young man said this in a faltering voice and seemed to pay no heed to Goron's acid comment that women shrink from nothing in their self-love and needed no conditions before indulging their exhibitionism. "Taking off their clothes is their business." "The sight of her frightened me," reiterated Jaquemar.

Goron's skepticism toward Jaquemar's new clue did not go very deep and, in any case, did not prevent his making quite extensive inquiries, chiefly among Gouffé's clients. These did not, however, bring to light either the name of the mysterious beauty or any other definite information about her—beyond the fact that several people, mostly men, felt she was "somehow" familiar, in the way that we so often have a forgotten name "on the tip of our tongue" but unfortunately cannot get it any further than that. Soudrais, to whom these investigations were entrusted, looked at the photograph, his lips thick and moist beneath his moustache. "Hot stuff," he commented, nodding his head appreciatively. "I can't believe that nobody knows her." Which perhaps makes her all the more interesting, thought Goron, saying: "Give it to me. That's done with. Now for the exhibition of the trunk."

This exhibition of the trunk was the ultimate goal up to which Goron's Press campaign had been leading. In the meantime, the fragments of the Millery trunk had been carefully fitted together to form a reconstruction of the original container, while subsequently experts and skilled craftsmen had carefully built, in the same material, an exact copy of this sinister piece of luggage as it had been in its undamaged state. In the middle of November there began an intensive, week-long publicity campaign for the strange exhibition to be held in the shadow of Notre-Dame, in the Paris mortuary, the Morgue, to which the general public were pressingly invited—so pressingly that this exhibition became the talk of the town even before it was opened, and was also the subject of sensational reports by foreign newspaper correspondents, was in fact written and talked about throughout Europe and in America, like an epoch-making art exhibition.

The crowds at the opening were tremendous, and as is usual with any such mass gathering, the true purpose of the assembly was forgotten and this grim occasion turned into an opportunity for popular merrymaking. No uninstructed person, seeing the throng outside the Morgue, could have guessed that it was crime, death, and one man's fanatical pursuit of the truth that had drawn the rollicking multitude to this sad spot. It was a radiant day in early winter, and cheery snowball fights were going on, the gay shouts of those hit by snowballs mingled with the cries of the newsboys and the street pedlars hawking sweetmeats or shellfish, and roast chestnuts heated on portable stoves. There was plenty of time, for no one could push his way straight into the mournful building, entrance to which was controlled by the police; people had to be patient, and they were patient because the fascination of evil (since time immemorial more powerful than that of good) hung in the cheerfully echoing snowy air and gave those who were waiting a secret thrill between the shoulders and in the pit of the stomach, the only stimulation that equals, and perhaps surpasses, the delicious throb of lust.

Inside, of course, under the martially disciplined surveillance of the gruff Soudrais, silence reigned, the silence of the tomb, into which a trill of merriment occasionally penetrated from without and to which the muted scraping of the visitors' feet as they filed past lent a note of gloomy solemnity, even of fear, as though a loud noise might wake the evil spirit that had created this occasion.

Through the frosted glass ceiling of the little room fell the pallid light of a snowy day. On entering through the open door, the visitor saw the only two objects on show in this strange exhibition. They rested on two low platforms in the far corner: to the right the remnants of the trunk, and to the left, with its lid raised, the replica, both of them protected from the public by a thick red velvet cord suspended between brass uprights. A framed notice in black letters behind glass, at the foot of the platform, explained in great detail the material of which the receptacle was made and the use to which it had been put in the Gouffé case. On the white wall behind Soudrais, who was on guard between the two platforms, hung another framed notice promising a thousand francs' reward for any information leading to the identification and arrest of the man who had brought this trunk and its macabre contents, weighing 230 pounds, to the Gare de Lyon on the evening of July 26, and there dispatched it on its journey to Marseilles—any information to be addressed either to the Security Officer permanently on duty in the office of the Morgue, or to the Head of the Sûreté, Goron, personally.

Meanwhile, the visitors—among them children, holding their mothers' hands, who stared with their fingers in their mouths at the apparently insignificant exhibits, which were yet so full of meaning—the visitors, with a few exceptions, took no interest in the police offer; they had not come for advantage or profit, let alone for the sake of truth, but to savor the stubbornly mute power of suggestion that the spacious trunk-coffin, in its original shattered state and in the smart reconstruction, seemed to exercise on them as though radiating some sluggish force.

The exceptions, of which there were twenty-eight on the first day, were all of them cabdrivers. After rubbing their noses thoughtfully with the backs of their hands, they whispered awkwardly to Soudrais, who showed them the way to the office where, one after the other, they retailed the same cooked-up story to the sly Latrille: a man whom they could barely distinguish as he stood on the dark street corner with the heavy trunk beside him—and of whom, therefore, they could give neither a description nor an address—had called them that evening to help lift the trunk into the cab and drive with it to the Gare de Lyon, which services he had rewarded with a generous tip. Many of them came in waterproofed boots and heavy, many-tiered coachman's capes. A hundred of them came in the first three days, but the one for whom Goron confidently hoped did not come.

His calculation was wrong—and yet in due course it hit the mark. Interest in the exhibition was already ebbing, and, because the material covering the trunk was apparently of British manufacture, Goron was thinking of going to London and asking Scotland Yard to make inquiries at textile factories and obtain a list of customers from any factory that might possibly be concerned—when a happy coincidence saved him the trouble. On the seventh day he found in his morning post an express letter containing a sample of blue paper dotted with silvery stars and a communication from the firm of Malcolm Grattan, Piccadilly Circus, London, W.1. In this letter Mr. Grattan conjectured that the much-discussed trunk might be one of his manufacture, provided that the inner lining corresponded to the enclosed sample of paper, which, so far as he knew, was a special product used exclusively in Grattan trunks, and provided also that not only the main material (poplar wood), but also the subsidiary materials, webbing, partitions, and locks were the same, which could only be ascertained by examination on the spot and not from descriptions. He concluded that he would be happy to supply further information, "Yours faithfully. . . ."

Goron lost no time. Formalities for the trip were completed, tickets for train and ship bought, the trunks—both the original and the replica—fitted with covers, packed in boxes, and sealed by the Public Prosecutor's Office; the necessary documents appointing him to deputize in his chief's absence conveyed to the obsequious Chief Inspector Jaumes; and the same evening, under the star of success, Goron set out on his excursion to England.

But this trip did not benefit his physical well-being. The land journey, from the Gare Saint-Lazare to Dieppe, he naturally passed in refreshing slumber, snoring under his newspaper, which he had opened up and spread over his head even before the train started. But on the cross-Channel steamer he found the stuffy cabin unbearable and climbed, black cigar in mouth, up creaking stairs and steep iron ladders with banisters sticky with rust to the topmost deck, buffeted forward or sideways or pushed and dragged backward as though by invisible ghostly fists, for a heavy sea was running. The night was full of wetness, of prickly moisture and limy scraps of salty foam, filled too with howling, whistling, and an elemental din; and the trembling ship rose as light as a breath on the surge of the mountainous waves, shook itself as it took blows on bow and sides from thundering breakers that splashed over it in slapping sheets of spray, and afterward dipped first hesitantly and then precipitately, blindly, as though there was nothing left but to plunge its head into this roaring and raging flood, with water pouring off it in all directions. The propeller rose out of the waves high into the air, rattled in the void, and shook the boat as though with a furious ague.

Goron himself was soon seized with fever. At first, he had felt at ease as he leaned pensively over the rail high above the ship, his hat pulled down over his forehead, his coat collar turned up, and his cigar between his canine teeth lashed by the wind until it looked like a blazing paintbrush, from which the sparks every now and then flew out in a spray of burning dust over his small oval pince-nez; but then icy tremors took him between the shoulder blades, his lips grew stiff. Shivering, he grasped his coat collar and burrowed down into it, but without gaining any feeling of comfort, with chattering teeth, he was forced to go down below again to his groaning cabin, where, under the hanging lamps that swayed violently this way and that, he sent for cognac which burned but did not warm him.

Leaving Newhaven, once more by train, he huddled freezing in his upholstered corner, peering out with bleary eyes from which he had removed the pince-nez into the rimy landscape and the misty dawn. This morning glimmer was deathly still, and instead of making way for daylight it actually grew denser, darker, and more like night the closer they came to their destination, so that when the train steamed into Victoria Station an hour and a half before midday, night really seemed to reign beneath the sooty glass roof, inhospitably lit by the pale, diffused light from the lamps on the platform struts. Faces were ashen and fatigued, and in this ghostly turmoil Goron, with his overpedantic English, had great difficulties with the customs officers, who did not want to let the sealed trunks through for fear they might contain tea; but they were satisfied when he suggested that one of the officers should go with the trunks to Scotland Yard and hand them over to the Metropolitan Police just as they were, with unbroken seals.

What prevailed outside, however, was not night; it was a "peasouper," a dense, brownish-yellow fog such as occurs in large industrial areas, in which the gaslamps glimmered rather than shone, encircled by soft haloes. It was freezing cold and damp. And yet there was a certain eerie cosiness about this atmosphere; the windows of the shops, enveloped in a soft light like that of a living room, invited people to enter and browse; a trickle of pedestrians passed by without haste, the traffic plodded on in the roadways, and no one seemed aware of the apocalyptic gloom which the mute and dripping winter's morning had cast about the largest city in the world.

Outside the station, the hansom cabs stood waiting in long rows, charming vehicles in which the coachman sat above and behind his fares, with the reins passing over the roof. The shivering Goron took a seat in one of these with his modest little suitcase and, peering into the cosy, end-of-the-world gloom outside, was driven toward Piccadilly Circus. The further he drove, the more savagely he was plagued by an itching and pricking in his right eye, which he therefore kept perpetually closing, so that anyone catching sight of this face at the cab window would have wondered whether it was twitching and blinking so queerly under the compulsion of a tic or whether the man was intentionally winking at some unidentifiable person in the fog.

Mr. Malcolm Grattan, in his elegant trunk and fancy-goods shop in Piccadilly Circus, was a man of that greyhound type which is not rare in the British Isles and whose representatives create the impression of looking younger than they really are, narrow-skulled, smart, and sophisticated—a man of bright, quick, and slightly artful mind and bearing, possessing a kind of wiry effeminacy, speaking fast and from well forward in his mouth. He reacted with a "Delighted, Sir," when Goron introduced himself, knowing at once who he was and

inviting him with the words "Step right in, won't you?" into his
private office, where there were flowers and books and the scent of
Virginia tobacco, a deliciously spicy smell like a mixture of dung and
honey.

As to the trunk—without prejudice, of course, to the necessary examination of the actual object—there was already "little doubt" that
it was one of his; the only doubt there might originally have been
related to an insignificant difference in the size, which was, however,
explained by the fact that he had taken his measurements not from
the trunk itself, but from the space in which the last example sold
had stood; meanwhile, new specimens had arrived and showed exactly the measurements quoted by the Sûreté. "Would you care to
take a look at them?" he asked and led Goron back into the shop, to
a point where, beneath a varnished notice saying TRUNKS, there stood
piles of brand-new trunks of all sizes and among them two—one closed
and one with its lid open—which, after being placed on a small platform, looked exactly like the Millery trunk. "Definitely," said Goron
with finality, blinking his eye, "that's it." "I think so," replied Grattan.

On the way back to the private office Goron asked, Could he remember the purchaser? Grattan turned and answered no, unfortunately not, he saw too many people; he stood still to let his visitor
enter first before adding: including foreigners and especially French
people, who were sent to him by business friends in the hotel trade.
Did he know this person? Goron inquired and, without sitting down,
handed him the photograph given to him by Jaquemar—he was so
tense with expectation that he forgot the blinking of his eye. "Dear
me, yes," said Grattan, bending down with the photograph under the
green-tinted glass shade of his desk lamp. "Of course, I remember
now."

He recalled the whole scene. The young lady had been accompanied by an elderly man who spoke good English but "who didn't
seem a very pleasant person, by the way," rather popeyed, with strikingly thick lips in his beard, and hairy hands; he chose the trunk,
while the young woman stood by with beaming eyes, but uninterested.
Not addressing anyone, and in little more than a murmur, she said
something which he, Grattan, would in any case have had difficulty
in understanding, because of his "poor French," but which sounded
like: She wanted a trunk, not a coffin—whereupon the man looked

at her with a gulp, while she shrugged one shoulder "the least bit."
Incidentally, the photograph didn't give a very clear picture of the
person, who really looked totally untheatrical, and at the same time
"if I may say so" more innocent than in the snapshot and more
dangerous, as though with retracted claws, and fascinating above all
by virtue of the extraordinarily powerful radiance of the dark eyes in
the delicate white face. He was very surprised that he hadn't remembered this really unforgettable figure of his own accord.

"Excuse me a second, will you," he said, and hurried out, to return
after a moment with a thick account book, which he opened under
the light from the desk lamp. "It was in July or earlier, wasn't it? . . .
There we are!" The trunk, a Hermes C model, had been sold on July
3 to Miss Gabrielle Bompard and delivered the same day to her
address, the Chévron Private Hotel, Hallam Street, W.1. Grattan
looked down at Goron, Goron looked at Grattan, literally with one
dry and one wet eye, because the tormenting irritation in his right eye
had caused it to stream with tears. "Having trouble with your eye,
Sir?" asked Grattan with amiable concern, disregarding his interest in
the matter of the trunk. "You should see a doctor." "No doubt,"
replied Goron with a nod. "Chévron then, and what was it, Hallam
Street? Many thanks, see you tomorrow morning at Scotland Yard."

The Chévron Private Hotel was an old-fashioned building of three
floors, with no sign. When Goron entered, he found himself in a hall
with thick carpets that clearly retained the character of a private house,
although it opened to the right, without a door, into a small waiting
room with a cosily flickering open fire. To the left a narrow staircase
with a thick pile stair carpet led upward, and at the far end of the
hall, facing the entrance and built under the stairs, was a small office
with pigeonholes for mail and keys, a desk, and a cheerful lamp, behind which a man of foxy appearance with a goatee beard stood waiting to greet the new arrival with the modest suitcase.

This was Monsieur Chévron in person, a very elegant figure with
fair hair streaked with gray. As he bowed with deliberation from behind the desk to greet the celebrated guest, he closed his eyelids beneath his foxy eyebrows, which seemed to deepen the cunning little
folds at the corners of his eyes; a gleam suggesting the bitterness of
experience cheerfully overcome glittered from his greenish eyes when
he reopened them and gave the lips of his well-spoken mouth an ex-

pression of intelligent circumspection, a mature charm, that went perfectly with his foxy appearance.

He recognized the photograph handed to him by Goron at the first glance—"Who could forget such a lovely girl, Monsieur Goron?" he said, licking his lips appreciatively—and he also remembered the trunk quite clearly. He had himself led the man who delivered the massive object on his back up to Mademoiselle Bompard's room, and the young lady had entered into a conversation about it; she stood silently in the doorway for a while and then suddenly asked him, in the quiet way that characterized both her demeanor and her voice, how he liked the trunk. "*Très bien*," he replied, adding for the sake of honesty that he supposed its rather cumbersome size was due to the clothes which Mademoiselle was purchasing here in London in the company of her uncle. She was not going to fill it in London, she answered, looking at the trunk with a dreamy smile, but in Paris.

As to this—well, uncle, who had come to visit her a few days earlier, he was an unattractive character, bull-necked, with dangling fists and oily hair combed over his bald pate, vulgarly servile but given to malicious side glances; in short, quite repulsive, so that even Madame Chévron—an Englishwoman to whom objectionable gossip was traditionally abhorrent—wondered how such an entrancing young girl could go with such an unappetizingly decrepit, elderly man; for it was impossible to believe that the relationship between them was a family one, especially as the first thing the man did when he arrived was to inquire at the desk, after looking around shyly: "Has Mademoiselle had any visitors since she has been here, gentlemen visitors?" —an inquiry which "naturally" met with a rebuff. Mademoiselle Bompard stayed in the house from June 24 to July 5, the so-called uncle, Monsieur Michel Bompard, from July 1 to 15. He left the day after receiving a telegram which he, Chévron, had chanced to see while showing the room to a new tenant in the absence of his guest. It lay open on the table, a strikingly senseless telegram, unsigned, and containing the terse message: MUST LOVE BE BEAUTIFUL—"which it really doesn't seem necessary to communicate by telegram," said Monsieur Chévron, raising both hands and nodding his foxy face with a close-lipped smile.

Goron asked whether the room Mademoiselle Bompard had occupied was free; saying that it was, Chévron stepped out from behind the desk with a neat, unhurried movement of the body and led him up to it. Tall and slim in his well-cut suit, with pearl-gray striped trousers and a frock coat that revealed its silk lining at every movement, he joined Goron and mounted the stairs close to him, but slightly ahead. They had only to ascend to the second floor and walk along the narrow corridor, on a runner that deadened their footsteps, past a few doors, before they reached the one they were after. With a word of apology, the master of the house entered in front of his guest.

The room was brooding in a blackish-gray twilight that seeped in through two windows hung with draped curtains (the twilight outside must have darkened again) and made a curiously desolate, in fact gloomily hostile, impression, as though no visitor was wanted here. The flame from Chévron's match slashed a rent in the darkness, and the objects in the room seemed to jump up indignantly and lurch about; immediately afterward everything was bathed in a rosy glow, friendly and safe, for the soft light of the table lamp under the red shade with a fringe of glass drops, from which Chévron straightened up, spread cosiness and something resembling warmth, even though Goron shivered.

There was austerity in the snugness and a hint of antiquity, a humbly old-fashioned look in the midst of the comfort; the ceiling was low, the wallpaper patterned with small flowers, and the fireplace narrow; beside the hearth utensils with brass handles leaned, as though tied in a bundle, in a wrought-iron stand, and in front of it, on the flowered carpet, stood two simple bent-legged armchairs. Only the bed, which was broad and deep, with Gobelin tapestry on the head and footboards and bearing an eiderdown and an openwork embroidered pillow, seemed out of place in the virginal restraint of this quiet room. The impression of quietude arose, above all, from the thickness of the beautifully draped curtains which, even in the rosy glow of the lamplight, seemed to radiate a hint of pallor and totally obscured the view outside.

In this room Goron passed his time until the following morning. True, he went out once, on Chévron's recommendation, to Berkeley's famous barnlike Roast Beef Restaurant, but he looked with distrust in his blinking, prickling eye at the little nickel carriage heated with a spirit flame and the huge chunk of bloody meat, from which a generous portion was hacked off and put on his plate along with Yorkshire pudding; he ate almost none of it and, after buying quinine and a bottle of Scotch whisky, fled back to Hallam Street.

For he was a sick man as he lay on the sumptuous bed that a few months earlier had served her whom he had set out to hunt down—on it, we say, because the showy piece of furniture was deceptive and did not by any means offer the luxurious comfort it promised; the mattress was as hard as a board, and the tubby Goron, around whose head, hot with fever and alcohol and with one weeping eye, the corners of the big pillow kept irritatingly closing, lay uncomfortably on his bier. It was a martyr's rack, and despite its width, Goron, in his restless state, was in perpetual danger of falling off. He huddled up as though wrapped in his own feverish shivering, sank back on to the showy pillow—and slept, heavily and deeply, fathoms deep below all consciousness.

When he awoke, the gleam of the light morning mist was entering, friendly but cold and shadowless, through the curtains. His fever had worn off, but his eye was hurting unbearably; and he gazed in anguish at the photograph of Gabrielle Bompard which he had propped against the candlestick, in the copper of which the burned-out candle had left a cone of dull-white wax. A feeling of astonishment crept over him to see how marmoreal she now looked, with her closed lids, and as the foolish thought crossed his mind that after all it had been pleasant to sleep with the depraved creature, he noticed that an overpowering prostration was taking possession of him, which grew greater and greater and which he could not shake off by the act of will involved in getting up. On the contrary, the wretched weakness left behind by the fever, which made every movement, every action, an effort, intensified this festering lethargy. Even the nauseatingly bitter taste in his mouth seemed to spring from it, and in a black mood he left the room and, as though drained of blood, staggered downstairs, giving at the knees and supporting himself on the banisters.

Fortunately, Goron enjoyed the meager compensation with which habit and nature requite the self-sacrifice of men with a great sense of duty: he was harshly insensitive toward his own moods, and an hour later, at the Scotland Yard police court, no one could have noticed any sign of exhaustion or depression. Yet he cannot have found the ceremonious hearing particularly gripping. The centenarian Sir James Ingham presided: above a gorgeous robe and under a stiff wig a skull with almost black lips and despairing eyes in which the glimmering blue of the irises seemed unable to hold together and here and there to have run out into the reddish-yellow of the eyeball. Holding a copy of the Bible in his uplifted right hand, Goron repeated after him the solemn oath: "I swear that the evidence I shall give shall be the truth, the whole truth, and nothing but the truth. So help me God." Pressing his handkerchief to his sore eye, he listened to the glib Mr. Grattan and the *soigné* M. Chévron swearing the same oath, and beyond this confined himself to keeping a watchful and distrusting eye on the accurate recording of the statements, which, if not entirely conclusive, were nevertheless so incriminating as to place Mademoiselle Bompard under a truly horrifying suspicion.

"Write that down exactly, word for word," he said, interrupting without formality and making a pecking movement with his forefinger in the direction of the clerk. "It's important." The only new fact to emerge, however, was fresh proof of the already well-established identity of the Millery trunk: it occurred to Grattan that he had noticed a defective place on the lock of the trunk he sold to "that fascinating young woman (of course, nothing to speak of)" and had painted it over with ink, and as luck would have it this particular piece and a trace of the repair had been preserved. "Would you believe it?" he exclaimed. "There it is!"

Nevertheless, Goron was able to take all this back with him in black and white, embellished with attested signatures and monumental official seals, an authority for action which, in these hands, was extremely dangerous to Mademoiselle Bompard. He reached Paris late the following evening, weakened and in greater pain than ever, after an oculist whom he had visited in Oxford Circus shortly before leaving had done something to his eye with a pointed instrument and then smeared it all over with a slimy ointment—pretty run down, that is to say, but with a kind of grim pleasure mingled with his ill-humor. The city was extraordinarily wintry, incomparably icier than London had been; a whistling wind drove dust and crusty hailstones in whirling vortices above the partially frozen tarmac of the side streets and the deserted boulevards, along which the homecomer with the modest suitcase, a crepe bandage at a slant around his head, rode in his cab toward the Rue de la Glacière; for Jaquemar, though now well-to-do and perhaps wealthy, had not abandoned his poor neighborhood and still lived in the Hôtel des Mines. He was going to see Jaquemar because it was too late for the Cité.

In Jaquemar's room a ghostly light reigned: the lamp was burning on the table with the wick turned down, bathing the large, almost empty room in a nocturnal dusk; at the same time, there was a frosty glimmer in the uncurtained windows whose panes were covered with ice ferns, a reflection of the howling wintriness outside, the pale, stormy sky and the snow-filled crevices in the walls and roofs of the houses; and this pallid, benumbed light created a vaguely hopeless, icily resigned effect, especially as the wind wailing outside blew sharply in through cracks in the window and suffused the rather warm air inside with arctic drafts. Perhaps this was why young Madame Chottin, who was keeping Jaquemar company, sat on her stool beside the wing chair in overcoat and fur hat and with her hands in a muff, as though ready to go out, while Jaquemar himself, dressed as usual and probably interrupted while striding to and fro, stood in the middle of the room, squinting across at the door through which Goron entered.

Not until after they had greeted one another and Madame Chottin's solicitous inquiry about the bandage had been answered by Goron with the terse comment, "Eye trouble, nothing important, only troublesome"—not until then did a nasty dry cough betray the presence of another person, Lebigot, the medico, who was sulking in a corner by the glowing iron stove with his back to the others and swathed like a mummy in several rugs. He neither uttered any greeting nor showed the slightest interest in Goron's report, to which the young woman listened with a kind of incredulous interest, while Jaquemar, who was standing at the window, responded by remarking, as though to himself: "Gabrielle Bompard, no, I've never heard the name—but there are certain things people keep to themselves."

Indignantly, but not without a hint of malevolent joy, Goron came to speak of Gabrielle Bompard's remark that they were supposed to be buying a trunk, not a coffin. Jaquemar answered somberly: "I told you the sight of her frightened me." To this Madame Chottin replied with a touch of reproof: "I think you should see her, Edmond, before you hate her." Jaquemar turned slowly around and gave her a significant look which, however, seemed to express neither agreement nor disagreement; it might have meant, Who is talking about hate? or, hate is not enough—in any case it was a significant look, the meaning of which, however, escaped Goron. He could have spared himself this visit; for if he had secretly promised himself (and why else had he come?) that Jaquemar might meanwhile have remembered the young woman in the photograph more distinctly, he was disappointed. Jaquemar shook his head with a rather obstinate expression and repeated: he had the *feeling* he had seen her somewhere, and somehow in connection with his brother-in-law Gouffé, and yet he had had no inkling of her existence. When Goron commented that this was a contradiction, he merely nodded, without making any attempt to explain further.

At the Cité, and aided especially by Guillaume and Latrille, Goron set in motion a manhunt such as the history of international crime had never known before. The portrait of Gabrielle Bompard became as familiar to the public of the day as that of any film star to the public of our own time; it appeared, spectacularly displayed, in all the newspapers and illustrated periodicals of the European continent, Great Britain, and America; it appeared again and again, always with fresh, skillfully presented details concerning the crime against Gouffé, the ghastly way in which the face had been stamped out of recognition, his journey in the trunk to Marseilles, the few mysteriously perfidious remarks known to have been uttered by the suspect whose picture appeared above—and in the feelings of the public, horror became mingled with enchantment at her loveliness. No statesman, actor, or artist could have boasted of being so impressively and repeatedly publicized and pictured as the young woman Goron was pursuing with his hatred. Her face, with the closed eyelids, blazed forth from the poster pillars of the big cities, it hung behind black wire guards in advertisement boxes and on the walls of every police station in Europe, Russia, and even the Far East; sailors who went ashore on leave in Singapore, Capetown, or Valparaiso saw it in the customs shed, farmers in the American Middle West and cowboys in Texas and New Mexico found it nailed to a wooden board in the general store—everyone knew, and the police of the whole world were looking for Gabrielle Bompard.

Goron, untiring in his dogged perseverance, was beginning to wonder how he could add fresh fuel to the flames of interest he had whipped up, so that they should not die down prematurely—for weeks

and months had passed, it was already February, and so far his call to
the world had received no answer beyond the echo of empty excitement—when Latrille, the normally superior and ironic Latrille, stormed
into his room one morning dragging after him a man in uniform looking totally flabbergasted. This, he said, was probably the most stupid,
imbecilic official anywhere in the world, and certainly the only one in
Paris who had never heard of Gabrielle Bompard! What had happened
was this: The previous evening, while Goron was still sitting at his
desk, a veiled young lady had appeared in the Cité and asked to speak
to the head of the Sûreté. The official inquired whether she had an
interview pass. When she replied with a smile that she had not, he
tried to hand her one, with a request that she should fill it in, including her address, and await a written acceptance or rejection of her
application at home. The lady refused to take the form, but thanked
him with an embarrassed little laugh and turned to go. Then she
turned back for a moment, and, standing where she was, asked whether
he would do her a favor. Would he please give his chief the following
message: "Mademoiselle Bompard regrets that under the circumstances she must forego calling upon Monsieur. She detests formalities."

2

THE TRIAL

Goron had every reason to fear that a person who had evaded
the hungry clutches of the police as skilfully and obstinately as
Gabrielle Bompard, having reported of her own free will and been
turned away, would now vanish into thin air again; and although he
must have realized that the incident made his department look
ridiculous, he had no hesitation about immediately revealing it to the
Press. What did it matter if this woman who already enjoyed a
secret popularity on account of her beauty and her shocking reputation, now had laughter on her side as well? What did it matter if
police stations of the arrondissements, who were immediately placed
on an emergency footing and instructed to carry out what was virtually a street-by-street, house-by-house search, laughed up their sleeves
at their superior authority's hysteria and failure at the crucial moment? What did any of this matter so long as she, who had become
an obsession with him and had been embittering his life for months,
did not escape again? In fact, nothing of the sort happened; on the
contrary, she walked straight into the trap, and for a reason that
would never have crossed the minds of the men at the Cité.

She appeared at Jaquemar's—and appeared is the right word. Lebigot had just gone out and carelessly left the door open, causing
Jaquemar to look up from his armchair as a cold draft cut across the
stove-warmed room. It was the day after her visit to the Cité, about

which he had not yet heard, and the afternoon dusk was just beginning to fall; outside the window it was snowing, and everything was so quiet, outside and right through the house, that even the softest footsteps should have been audible.

He had not heard anything, however, he merely saw; he saw with eyes that grew wider and wider as he looked, while his gray face turned a shade paler, till his whole expression was one of utter dismay. She was standing near the doorpost, not leaning against it but nonchalantly erect, and since she was being looked at, she brushed the veil suspended from her hat to one side and back. She looked at him with dark eyes verging on black, which shone so brightly in the delicately white face that, seen in conjunction with the brows that rose and almost met above her nose, they made her look as if she were smiling; this impression was intensified by the blue-black hair that stood up in artistic confusion all around her little hat, like the rays that surround the faces of the sun on the pendulums of baroque clocks. She did not utter a sound; nor did the young man whose eyes were gripped by hers; she simply stood there, with a kind of trusting awkwardness that might have sprung rather from his unexpected silence than from any innate shyness. She evidently found nothing odd in her presence there, and it came so naturally to her to walk soundlessly that it never occurred to her she might have taken him by surprise.

Jaquemar would have found it impossible to say later how long they remained staring at one another—it was one of those moments outside time, during which lives change, but which, in fact, last only a moment—before he said to her through frozen lips: "What do you want?" Then, startled by the sound of his own voice in the great silence around them, he lowered his eyes and stood up. She came closer, without dropping her eyes, shutting the door behind her with a groping hand as she moved forward. She stood there with her sham smile, perhaps waiting for Jaquemar to invite her to sit down, which he did with a brusque gesture. But she did not sit down. Jaquemar, now with a rising sensation of rage and hate in his heart, repeated his question more distinctly: "What do you want?" This time it produced some result, but not the one expected: although she was standing perfectly still, she gave the impression of struggling; she seemed to find such insurmountable difficulty in expressing her wishes. To the accompaniment of a barely audible sigh through the nose, and a faint growling sound, as if her throat did not want to let her voice pass, she gave vent to disconnected noises resembling words but utterly incomprehensible, and then fell silent with a despondent shrug of one shoulder, after which she stared down at the threadbare carpet.

Jaquemar looked at her once more, against his will, because he was undecided what to do next; and a complex feeling, an indefinably sweet horror, crept over him. The overwhelming thing was not that she was so much more beautiful than in the theatrical portrait; nor that anguish and lust conjured up in the living face an even more enigmatic smile, something sphinxlike, a pale Mona Lisa smile that really expressed no inner emotion but owed its existence solely to the play of bodily elements—no, it was not this that sent a melting sensation of lascivious weakness right up to his flaccid arm muscles: her beauty aroused in him an irrepressible, nameless thirst, which, if it was sexual, seemed to endow sexuality with a new role in the world. The little wild-beast's nose with the shell-shaped nostrils that laid bare part of the septum, an enchanting pink with a few black hairs in it, the groove under the nose, and the lips—full, fresh, and alive with naive promise—the little vein on the bridge of the nose beside the inner corner of the eye, a tiny blood bladder of a somehow indiscreet brownish-blue color, and the half-gay, half-anguished brows in which a few hairs stood on end—everything was so finely and accurately formed, so delicate and yet so bold, like the beauty of a Siamese cat, which, on a larger scale would look rapacious, pantherlike, and terrifying.

This was how she looked, and he felt that what threatened to emasculate his hate was something he had never had to reckon with until it surged irresistibly and uncontrollably into his heart during these few seconds. There was an innocence about this person whom he knew without a shadow of doubt to be guilty of Gouffé's death, knew with a knowledge that had no more need of proof than breathing requires an act of will.

But this moment of weakness also passed. Jaquemar's squinting eyes filled with hatred and were lowered. "What do you want of me?" he asked in a tone of almost disgusted animosity.

Without warning, but without haste, she took the little hat from

her head; and Jaquemar, who did not look up, heard again the low sighing, growling sounds that suddenly gave him the idea that perhaps
she could not speak French, that she was a foreigner and came from
far away, where people spoke heaven knows what language; and yet
he realized at this same moment that the difficulty she had in expressing herself was embarrassment, embarrassment or some other inner
inhibition; isolated words emerged from her mumbling—spoken in a
tone that was half-offended, half-inquiring or even jesting—the general
sense of which was: "You were looking for me, weren't you?" He was
indignant to think she might possibly be joking, and he said brutally
and grimly: "It's the police who are looking for you." Then she answered distinctly: "I've come about the reward."

Her voice, so long as she was mumbling, had been deep, warm, and
soft; but this statement rang out high and clear in the silent room,
though it was joyful rather than impudent, just as her dark eyes (of
which the irises were so large they left almost no room for the whites)
shone triumphantly, without being impertinent.

With a face drained of expression, Jaquemar indicated the armchair;
she sat down, not in the armchair, however, but on the uncomfortable
wooden chair standing at right angles to it. She sat there with her little
hat in her lap, gave her head a shake so that the coiffure of spiky curls
was loosened, beamed at the young man, and watched as he, left with
no other choice, sat down on the edge of the armchair.

So she knew Gouffé's murderer . . . and as she nodded agreement
to this remark, he suddenly yelled in uncontrollable rage: "Why didn't
you come sooner?" She wasn't welcome even now, she murmured
with an astounded and melancholy shrug of the shoulders. Less for the
sake of an answer than as a means of recovering his self-control, he
asked: "And why have you come now?" She raised both hands, and
Jaquemar, squinting out from under lowered lids, saw that they were
yellow and thin and that the fingers were, so to speak, bowlegged and
knock-kneed, that is to say they were bent in various directions; under
other circumstances this would have struck him as funny, but now it
gave him a feeling of disgust—or was it the story she was telling, to
the best of her ability, but barely intelligibly, that gave him this sensation of nausea?

She had come from America, where she had been living with her
friend Carapin in a suite of rooms at the Waldorf-Astoria Hotel. One

morning at breakfast Carapin had opened the paper and seen her picture in it, together with a compromising report linking her with the "Gouffé business." Carapin, a highly respectable middle-class man, though easily convinced of her innocence, was not to be pacified until she offered to go with him to Paris so that the matter could be finally cleared up. She was angry that he should have made this proposal without any thought for the unpleasantness to which he was thereby exposing her, and they had quarreled over this during the voyage and after their arrival in Paris. Then Carapin had left her, so that the whole point of her journey was gone; and she did not know what she might have decided to do had it not been for the fact that, in his ill-humor, Carapin had forgotten to give her any money. She was therefore dependent on the reward offered by Jaquemar, and that was why she was here.

The careless frankness of this account set the blood pounding in the young man's temples, so that, grinding his teeth with rage and scorn, he spat out: "Why should you get a reward—since it's you they're looking for?"

"I?" she retorted with an artless smile. "They're making a mistake. I was just a bystander."

"You were just a bystander," repeated Jaquemar with closed eyes.

"It was Michi," she went on, looking at the carpet. "He did it and now he will have to pay for it. I will tell you where to find him."

"Me?" answered Jaquemar, and felt that for some reason he was gasping for breath. "I'm not the police!"

"But it's your money," she said in surprise.

"Money, money!" he cried angrily. "Are you really concerned about that, even now, when your neck is in danger?"

"But that's what I'm here for," she replied, with a little nod that was both polite and obstinate.

"You will go with me to the police," said Jaquemar, softly and pensively, and thought to himself—disregarding some deeper idea—that he would have to call on Lebigot to help him transport her to the place that she would undoubtedly fight tooth and nail to keep away from.

She did indeed relapse into her resistant muttering, and Jaquemar remarked, more ironically than he really felt, that the idea didn't seem to appeal to her. They weren't interested in her there, she finally managed to say, they wouldn't see her. He contradicted grimly: "On the contrary, they're indeed very interested in you. They certainly *will* see you."

"Without an interview pass?" she asked, clearly and distinctly.

He looked up, surprised and indignant at this apparent joke, but as soon as he saw her eyes he forgot to think about it any more; he compressed his lips and stared down at the floor again. It was already very dark in the room, and the snow outside the windows was falling in soundless, blackish-gray beads. He shifted his eyes and gazed almost blindly at her feet in high white button boots that fitted closely round the strong ankles and reached to the beginning of the calf, emphasizing the lines of the vigorous, finely shaped leg. Vaudeville, he thought, full of hate, and heard himself ask: "Who is Michi?"

"Eyraudt," she answered. "I'll tell you where you can find him, and they will lay his head at his feet."

"What about you?" interrupted Jaquemar. "Who are you? You seem familiar. Have I ever seen you before?"

"I have seen you," she said. "It was in Gouffé's office. Gouffé was making difficulties for Michi, and I was supposed to put things right. But we talked about something else. As I was leaving, you came in. But you had no eyes for me, you looked at my feet, as you are doing now."

"What 'difficulties' was Gouffé making for him?"

"He was trying to take money away from him."

"Idiotic," burst out Jaquemar, and went on staring at her white boots.

"Michi was rather unhappy about it," she said.

"Idiotic—as if Gouffé would take money away from anyone!"

"But he did so," she retorted, with gentle persuasion, "and he paid dearly for it. But that was later, and there was jealousy in it too. It's always like that, money for women and women for money, and they stamp one another's faces in for it. Michi was very keen to sell me, he was very keen to have the money; but he hated him for it, and when he came into my room and I was in my dressing gown, his eyes popped out of his head and grew bloodshot, and then it happened. But afterward he was so agitated that I had to give him a glass of cognac, and he drank it out of the same glass from which Gouffé had been drinking just before—"

"Stop!" screamed Jaquemar.

"But you want me to tell you about it," she said politely, and fell silent.

For a while they sat mute, Jaquemar breathing rapidly; meantime it had grown completely dark in the room, and only the falling snow outside the windows evoked a dull, flickering glimmer in the gloom.

"It's cold here," she remarked shyly. "We shall catch cold."

"I'm going to call Lebigot," he said. "We shall take you to the police—make your confession there!"

"Certainly," she said, now speaking as though darkness made it easy for her, almost without hesitation, in her warm, soft voice. "I will show you the little room and explain where the dressing gown cord was, with which we were unfortunately playing until Michi came in. Also where the trunk stood, before and afterwards. Then Gouffé lay inside it sewn up in a bag, and I was alone with him again. Then I thought to myself: If I bring someone in from the corner by the café for an hour of love, let him undress and get into the bed in which he wants to enjoy himself with me, and then open the trunk so that he can have company, because I have to go out again—he will get a fright."

Jaquemar felt as though his scalp was growing tight, and he whispered with a gulp: "You are the most depraved creature I have ever met—poor Gouffé!"

"That," she rejoined, "is our bargain. You can't forgo the truth, because you are paying so much money for it, and I can't forgo the money, because I can't stay here. I want to go back to America."

"Really!" he cried, with a wry laugh.

"Yes," she answered simply. "That is my plan."

"You will never leave this country again," he said somberly.

"Don't you think so?"

"I can promise you that."

"When Michi came back in the early hours of the morning," she continued without any transition, "he had not collected any swag at all; it had all been in vain, and if his wife had not had all kinds of jewelry, he would have been in the same position then that he is in now, since I shall tell you where you can put the handcuffs on him. With the proceeds from the jewelry we went to Marseilles, and next morning, when the porter and the page boy lifted the trunk containing Gouffé, there were red spots on the floor. Michi turned pale, but he gained control of himself and shouted at me: 'Now the bottle with your damned dye has really broken!' Then the men carried the trunk out, and we went with it into the mountains in a coach which he drove himself, because he didn't want to have any stranger with us.

"And with the next ship we sailed to America. He wanted to start a liquor distillery, and Carapin was going to put up the money; but because he was always in a bad temper and behaved coarsely and beat me and Carapin was a kind man, I went off with Carapin. And to revenge himself for that, he will run to the end of the earth and will not be able to stop on the brink of the abyss and will jump in and will clutch out in all directions trying to drag me down with him."

"He'll succeed," ground out Jaquemar, staring into space and squeezing his interlocked fingers together so hard that the joints cracked.

"No," she rejoined, with the hint of an embarrassed laugh. "He won't succeed. But he might get me a bad reputation, and for that reason too it's important that you should know the truth."

"I, I!" yelled Jaquemar, flaring up again. "You shameless beast! I'm not your cavalier!"

"But you are after the truth," she said sharply.

Intending to bring this intolerable conversation to an end by at last calling Lebigot, he jumped up, hurried with his mincing walk to the door, wrenched it open, and ran into Goron, who had just raised his hand to the knocker. The two men, the elder with the crooked pince-nez and the flat turndown collar and the young one with the squinting eyes, were barely able to recognize each other, since Jaquemar's room was dark save for the shadowy glimmer from the falling snow outside the windows, while the corridor was lit only by a miserable little oil lamp standing on a half-moon-shaped wall bracket on the landing and burning with a yellow, flickering flame in its prettily curved glass chimney. But Jaquemar did recognize his visitor in the nocturnal twilight; he grasped his coat with both hands and ejaculated: "Thank God you've come!" And he himself was struck by the inexpressible feeling of relief Goron's arrival brought him, for all at once he felt he could breathe again, that he was under powerful protection, that he was saved, that he had become all of a sudden a different person, once more with sharp, precise thoughts and a vigor that flooded his veins with the shock of a beneficent and quick-acting drug. "You're going to get a surprise!" he whispered, as though to himself, with an irrepressible giggle, and went back into the room; he struck a match and busied himself at the paraffin lamp standing on the table between the two windows, which, with its marble base, seemed out of place amidst the poverty of its surroundings.

Meanwhile, Goron stepped into the room before the wick had caught and stumbled over the edge of the threadbare carpet; the floor and the furniture shook under his weight, and this trifling incident caused Jaquemar a senseless feeling of disappointment out of all proportion to its significance, so that, with gloom in his face, he looked up again from the lamp that now poured its strong light into the room.

Since the young lady sitting on the wooden chair with the little hat in her lap kept her face turned to Jaquemar, Goron introduced himself with an awkward bow and doffed his bowler hat. Thereupon she looked at him with her dark, shining eyes, and, like Jaquemar before him, he turned a shade paler. He snatched the pince-nez from his nose, thrust his face forward, and then replaced his pince-nez; the hat fell from his hand and rolled a little way across the carpet. His bewilderment was comical; the young person on the chair laughed, or at least seemed to, although not a sound was audible; anyhow she tilted her head merrily to one side, her shining eyes directed not at him, however, but into space. Perhaps she was only amused because Jaquemar commented sardonically from his table: "I said you were going to get a surprise." But he stood there with the same somber expression on his face while Goron sat down in the armchair, without taking his eyes off this woman he had so long sought, hated, and avidly desired.

Jaquemar fetched a chair like the one Gabrielle Bompard was sitting on and set it down next to Goron's armchair; he sat down on it, staring gloomily down at the floor as before and making the usual silent munching movements with his lips. Then Gabrielle Bompard stopped gazing into space, looked at the two figures sitting in front of her, and finally made a slight inclination of the head that might have been a greeting or an invitation to speak or both combined.

"So there you are at last!" snorted Goron. "You—you . . ." and his words were lost in a gulp of mingled fury and triumph.

Was she struggling again? Jaquemar looked up. To the accompaniment of all kinds of almost inaudible little sighs, she uttered a confused jumble of words that meant approximately that she had been turned away from the Cité. But all the time her unusually lovely black eyes shone undimmed, nor did the slight smile vanish from her face —no doubt both the beaming eyes and the smile expressed nothing and had no meaning, they were merely a quality of the flesh, a play of physical forms, with which nature had endowed this vicious creature, an endowment so fascinating that the lack of meaning was of no account, or rather compelled increased admiration, because the senselessness of nature is beyond man's comprehension and hence seems to point to something superhuman. Jaquemar could not take his eyes off her, and recognition of her beauty combined with his hatred set his brain reeling and filled him with vertigo. "You were turned away, were you?" he heard Goron say. "That won't happen again! Stop that stuttering! What are you trying to tell us?" She looked into Jaquemar's face and, with many little groans, in broken phrases and interrupted by painful hesitations (with which her beaming eyes formed a curious contrast), she said something that could be interpreted as, "I want the reward."

"Is that so," said Goron, pressing his flat collar to his breastbone. "The reward! Your claws smeared with blood, you come and ask for the reward! That would just suit you!"

She continued to look at Jaquemar, gave her customary little polite and stubborn nod, and said clearly: "I'm not asking for a gift. It's my due."

"So you're not asking for a gift, eh?" scoffed Goron. "Don't worry; nobody is going to make you any gifts!"

She started her groaning and sighing again, and difficult as it was to understand her way of talking, the general sense was clear and to the point. She could not help being a witness to the bloody deed committed late in the evening of July 25 last year, a Thursday, in the annex of the Villa des Fleurs pension in the Rue d'Assas, opposite the Maternité and only a few steps from the Café des Lilas; the culprit, to her misfortune before and at the time, but no longer, her lover, had forced her to flee with him by threatening to denounce her and also to "wring my neck" (this was the expression she used), a thing he was entirely capable of doing—as she had just seen with her own eyes; for with his short, thick hands he had strangled Gouffé "like a chicken" out of jealousy and greed for money and then, to render him unrecognizable, trodden his face in with the heel of his boot; "upon my honor" no deed was too foul for him; she had to go with him and, since he was always hanging around and spying on her, she had until recently no chance to denounce him. Now, however, she was here of her own free will and wished to report: "The murderer is called Michel Eyraudt and lives, because of the many French-speaking people who had settled there, in a small town in the state of Massachusetts."

In his disgust, it crossed Jaquemar's mind, with ever-increasing surprise, how different the whole story sounded now, as she forced it out with the greatest difficulty, beaming at him all the time, from the way it had appeared before, when she was speaking to him alone. The difference lay not only in the style of the narrative (so far as one could speak of style in connection with her groaning and stammering) but the events themselves appeared in a different light. Although they did not contradict factually what she had said before, a change in timbre and a shift of emphasis put a different complexion on everything. What she had told him sounded like an intimate, secret murmur in the night; what she was now saying, taken all in all, like a police report. She wouldn't last an hour; she would entangle herself in her own wriggling and lying, and finally, caught and immobilized as in a net, she would be flung down into the abyss where she belonged.

"You will have no difficulty in wringing her neck, since Eyraudt unfortunately didn't do it," said Jaquemar to Goron, brushing the back of his hand across his lips and without taking his eyes off her.

"You have a completely mistaken idea about me," she replied, without taking offence, putting her little hat on her head and pulling the veil down over her hair and her face; the veil was close and black like a mourner's and left nothing uncovered but the delightfully carnal, smiling mouth and the chin, and it gave her whole face the appearance of a carnival mask.

"I never doubted that to know you would be terrible," whispered Jaquemar, breathlessly and with a changed expression on his face; for a fresh astonishment had taken possession of him, even greater than he had felt before. Her imperturbability and the readiness she had shown, by putting on her hat, to follow Goron to her destruction seemed incomprehensible and, taken in conjunction with the abominable story she had told in this room, only to be explained as proof of her innocence. He asked himself with a horrified gulp, Am I afraid for her? and heard the smiling mouth in front of him (which now looked larger because the lips stood out more bloodily red in the chalky whiteness of the face) speak and say: "I have done no wrong, no wrong will be done to me."

"Enough!" cried Goron, lumbering to his feet, whereupon Jaquemar also rose as though waking up, but not Gabrielle Bompard. "Enough chatter! On your feet, get moving! You're coming with me. My coach is waiting outside."

"Another coach journey?" she said indifferently, looking at Jaquemar, who stepped to one side and bent down with a completely blank face to pick up Goron's hat from the floor. "Where shall I sleep?"

"Don't worry! We are equipped for such cases. You will be welcome."

"Thank you," she answered politely. "My plan was to stay here."

"Here?!" cried Jaquemar, slowly turning his face toward her.

She nodded to him, also slowly, and the soft, blood-red mouth below the short black veil was smiling.

"Mademoiselle!" rejoined Goron, thrusting his head forward, and his eyes seemed to protrude slightly as he looked at her from behind his quivering pince-nez. "He would no doubt consider it an honor! But I cannot forgo the pleasure: you are my guest!"

She straightened her skirt over her knees and started her groaning murmur again, from which it was possible to make out that she needed a room, because her old room had been free for only the last two nights.

"Your old room . . ." whispered Jaquemar (and Goron stood in openmouthed horror). "You slept—there?"

Well, she was a stranger in the city, she gave them to understand, she was known there.

"In the same room!" shouted Jaquemar. "Where you allowed that accursed deed to be done! Where your beast of a paramour stamped on his face—if you didn't do it yourself!"

"No," she said, tugging at her skirt. "I didn't do it."

"No," he yelled, and took a step nearer, pressing Goron's hat to his chest. "You were 'just a bystander!' And you thought: If I bring in someone from the street and show him the murdered man in the trunk, he will get a fright!"

"But he would have got a fright," she said.

"For pity's sake," gasped Jaquemar, choking, and grasped Goron's forearm. "Get that woman out of my sight!"

"March!" ordered Goron. "Come on, get going! With me, to the Cité!"

She lifted her veiled face with its naked mouth toward Jaquemar and said: "I don't want to. I just want to *visit* him."

The two men burst out at the same moment into the same derisive laughter, and this, curiously enough, calmed their fury. Goron took his hat from Jaquemar's hands and thrust it on his head like a helmet, holding the brim on both sides. "Gabrielle Bompard!" he said in a cold, imperious voice. "I hereby declare you under arrest."

Jaquemar bent down a little and looked at her intently with his squinting eyes. Was she taking it as a joke? She tilted her head in the way that made her look amused—perhaps she was staring through her black veil into space as she had before—and she answered with a kind of childish gaiety: "You can't arrest me."

"I am arresting you on the strong suspicion of being an accessory in the murder of Alphonse Gouffé."

"But that's silly," she retorted coaxingly, with a brief nod.

"Follow me!"

She rose obediently and, turning her face to Jaquemar again, shrugged her right shoulder.

"Why do you keep pretending there's some understanding between us?" Jaquemar flared. "Am I your accomplice?"

"Come along, please!" called Goron, and took hold of her hand.

Then she turned around to Goron at last and said slowly: "You are heaping up trouble for yourself."

With a half-repressed snort Goron set off and dragged her along behind him; there was something bull-like in the way he bent forward, and she tripped along on her strong feet in the white boots, turning around to Jaquemar once more with a slight shrug of the shoulders.

But Jaquemar did not notice. He was staring down at the floor and holding the back of the chair on which she had been sitting so tightly that the knuckles stood out white under the skin of his hand. He remained in this position for several minutes; then he looked up, hurried with his rather too dainty step to the door, which was open, and peered out, leaning with his left hand on the doorpost. At this moment Lebigot came toward him past the dim oil lamp on the landing, his eyelids lowered like a parrot's, and Jaquemar grasped the catch and quietly closed the door. He leaned with his shoulders against the door,

squinted blindly down at his feet, and passed the back of his hand
slowly across his lips.

"Gabrielle Bompard, strongly suspected of being an accessory in the
murder of the *huissier* Alphonse Gouffé, was arrested today at 6:45
P.M. in a room at the Hôtel des Mines." In this one succinct sentence
Goron announced her arrest to the public, in whose reactions he now
had no further interest. He made the announcement as soon as he
reached the Cité with the prisoner and before he had begun his first
interrogation, at almost the same moment as the newspapers, distributed by scurrying newsboys to the accompaniment of excited
shouts, were giving the news: "Gabrielle Bompard calls at the Cité
and is turned away!" At a moment, too, when a message had already
been written to Goron by the Prefecture, in which Sallier, whom the
information had reached surprisingly quickly, expressed his "extreme
displeasure" at this untoward incident.

The late-night papers, however, reacted to this new announcement
by making up their front pages afresh; and only a few hours later the
headline "Gabrielle Bompard arrested!" burst upon the eye in kiosks
and on placards, alongside the earlier sensation. This new turn of
events did not cause the first report to be forgotten, but the two incidents together cast fresh light on both the notorious beauty and "our
trusty Goron"; for the Press (unlike the Prefecture) found it perfectly understandable that such a large organization as the Sûreté
should contain one blissfully ignorant doorkeeper, since "to err is
human," whereas the rapidity with which this venial slip was made
good showed remarkable resourcefulness at the critical moment on the
part of the head of that same institution. Thus the two antagonists,
the lovely and audacious criminal and the fanatical master detective,
gave the papers two favorites to celebrate at the same time—enough
to make any true journalist rub his hands with glee.

Goron might have felt flattered, especially as the writers did not
overlook the fine touch provided by the total omission of his name
from the official announcement, although the arrest was exclusively due
to his personal intervention. Everybody knew this—but how?

Since the newspapermen no doubt remembered that the Hôtel des
Mines was the residence of Gouffé's brother-in-law and heir, Jaquemar,
it was understandable that they should have guessed that the arrest

took place in his room—although they treated this not as conjecture but as fact. But how did they know that Gabrielle Bompard had been to Jaquemar ostensibly for the reward—"ostensibly," that is to say, according to the statement made by Bompard or Jaquemar, the *truth* of which the papers "confidently" left to the police to test? No matter how they came to know all this, they retailed it to the accompaniment of flattering hints that Goron doubtless had his own good reasons for keeping certain facts, as well as his own name, out of the picture at this juncture. Nor did he contradict these innuendoes; he omitted to contradict them, because he had neither the wish nor the leisure to read the newspapers and pay heed to their groundless speculation about a matter on which he was at present working. He irritatedly dismissed a cautious reference to this curious kind of publicity which the intelligent and loyal Guillaume alone felt obliged to make; similarly, he had the Prefecture's expression of displeasure filed away unanswered—in any case, due to red tape, it had not been delivered until the afternoon of the following day, by which time the grandiloquently official malice of its tone sounded merely silly.

While the oval-skulled Delattre was laughing up his sleeve at having prompted his chief, Sallier, to send this note, the men at the Cité had long since embarked on a difficult task. They were all there, Delattre's friend and instigator Latrille, Jaumes, Soudrais, Guillaume, and—in addition to the two principal antagonists, Goron and Bompard —Montardon, the wardress of the cellar corridor that housed the female remand prisoners, an inhumanly fat woman in a black pinafore dress with black lachrymal sacs under her night-gray eyes. Most of the time she was present in body only, for after the first hour her multiple chin sank on her breast and she slipped into peaceful snoring, which occasionally rose to such an alarming, sawlike pitch that the laughing Latrielle had to bring her to her senses with a few vigorous digs in the ribs, always with short-lived success and soon to his growing annoyance, since he himself found it more and more difficult to keep his eyes open and he attributed this to the contagious effect of her boundless mania for slumber. Gradually they all found themselves contending with this craving to sleep, even Goron. He listened with concentration to a statement by the woman under interrogation and at the same moment threw his mouth wide open in an uncontrollable yawn, so that his pince-nez nearly flew off his nose; Gabrielle Bompard alone, tilting her head as though in amusement at this occurrence, showed no sign of fatigue. Goron went doggedly on with his interrogation, with a perpetual tickling sensation in his jaws, no longer backed up by anyone and in a voice that was degenerating into a hoarse bellow.

The hours passed; the gas streamed out of the three-domed wall bracket into the flames with a soporific whistling sound; Montardon was now snoring undisturbed; the men were slumped forward, every now and then nodding off and then coming to with a start, their faces pale and exhausted; the whole scene appeared other-worldly, outside time, emptied of life; but she smiled and beamed exactly as she had at the beginning of this sitting, which ought to have brought her mentally to her knees and yet ended with a defeat for her tormentor that was welcomed with universal relief. At any rate, Goron felt it to be a defeat when, at 4:00 A.M., incapable of continuing, he was forced to wake up Montardon and hand over to her this "hardened criminal" from whom he had failed to squeeze anything remotely approaching a confession.

In reality there could be no question of a defeat. Of this Goron was convinced (or tried to convince himself, and half succeeded) when he nosed his way through the deposition with sore-eyed avidity later in the morning. Guillaume had taken it down with his usual accuracy and had already made a fair copy; and even if he had repeatedly been compelled to write "unintelligible" after Bompard's name, instead of the desired answer, so that some vague and some blank areas remained in the picture—all in all it was clear and eloquent enough. True, at no point had she admitted being an accomplice in the crime, or even an accessory before the fact.

At one juncture Latrille, and even the otherwise mute Jaumes, had intervened and cajoled, almost implored her to admit her guilt, because a confession would "mitigate her very serious position." To this she murmured, as bright-eyed as ever, indeed smiling, and yet with an offended pout: "You want me to lie—just because you gentlemen are tired." And whether out of cunning or from some other motive, she insisted with rare obduracy that they had no right to "imprison" her and that there was no sense in it either. Her last comment, when finally Soudrais, at a command from Goron, shook the snoring Montardon awake, was: "I don't want to go into the cellar with the fat woman again." Yet she allowed the wardress to lead her by the elbow without much resistance, merely shrugging her shoulders indifferently as she moved off, her white boots shining out joyfully and, as it were, eagerly from beneath her costume—a long, full skirt with a leg-of-mutton-sleeved jacket on top—as she walked unhurriedly away. Notwithstanding her grumbling and growling, it was as though she had swept out with a rustle of silk.

Perhaps the most cunning thing about the "method" Goron thought he could detect as he rummaged through her deposition, was this: While admitting the most compromising details, which she was not even compelled to admit and which therefore threw her veracity into all the more striking relief, she not only affirmed her innocence with a naive obstinacy, but kept harping on it in a way that made her appear the aggrieved, rather than the guilty party. They had no right to deprive her of her liberty, they had no right to withhold the reward from her, they were taking advantage of her trust; she was "delivering the murderer up to them," and it "wasn't fair" that their only thanks was to treat her roughly and try to plant the murder on her. "Should I be here if I was guilty?" This, she repeated again and again with something like a shy smile at such lack of common sense, was her main argument; and it must be admitted that this argument had some cogency, a cogency she had bought with unparalleled courage in voluntarily reporting to the police. In truth, would she have come, if she had been held back by the fear that springs from a guilty conscience?

Goron knew very well that the high stakes gave her dangerous gamble a strangely incalculable chance of success; he knew too that, notwithstanding her pseudochildish demeanor, pleasure in the gamble, a passion for gambling, might also be at work in her fundamentally depraved and criminal nature—or was it, he asked himself, simply stupidity? An inhuman stupidity of fatal proportions that deprived her of all insight into the workings of the world, all conception of how much she might be credited with—in a word—weakmindedness? But whether the one or the other motive was at work, or both at the same time, it was in any case her personality—this perverse sweetness accompanied by the shameless way her eyes never stopped beaming (and probably could not stop beaming) even while she was making the most ghastly admissions, that gave her fundamental denial its puzzling, discouraging forcefulness. It discouraged him because it threatened to make him give vent to an outburst of uncontrolled exasperation at quite the wrong moment, when she would shrug her shoulders, as though in astonishment at this evidence of hateful animosity directed against her innocence.

Meanwhile, Goron thrust his despondency aside. What had he expected from a first interrogation? Circumstances, which, in his own mind, he called "nasty"—and it struck him that she had used this expression: "Michi behaved very roughly then, he trampled on his face, and it was nasty to look at"—circumstances would convict her. At the moment she was in the cellar, being looked after by Montardon. Latrille, who had gone to visit her on his own initiative, naturally without getting anything out of her, although, apparently because she felt flattered by his visit, she had treated him with great friendliness—Latrille reported that she was as undejected as during the night, but that down there in the little stone cell, under the blue butterfly-flame burning in the unshaded wall bracket, she looked as pale as death, and it could only have been innate feminine hypocrisy that enabled her to maintain her attitude of unshaken confidence. "We'll soon knock that out of her!" said Goron.

To prevent her hypocritical show of artless candor from creating a misleading impression, Goron resolved to maintain complete silence toward the public until he could make some conclusive announcement. Proof that he had been right to wait came later that very same day. Toward the end of the afternoon he received, along with the abortive expression of displeasure from the Prefecture, another letter bearing a large number of foreign stamps and the postmark "Chicopee, Mass.," although the sender's address was written on the back as "Michel Eyraudt, Poste Restante, Quebec, Canada," which aroused in Goron's breast an almost jubilant feeling of being close to victory. In a faraway corner of the earth a man had been compelled by an ungovernable impulse to disregard his guilty conscience and to talk. It would not be long now before, instead of inquiring into the crime, they would lay their hands on the criminals and would be able to watch them, deprived of their senses by the age-old mutual hatred of accomplices, thrusting one another toward the guillotine. Goron tore open the envelope and read:

Quebec, Canada
January 21, 1890

MESSIEURS,

Because everyone knows what I have had to put up with from this filthy bitch of a woman, American friends have informed me that Mlle. Gabrielle Bompard, alias Geneviève Labodère, has recently sailed for France with her new lover, M. Carapin. It's always the same! She can never get enough and she throws all scruple to the winds in her lechery! It's all the same to me, thank God; for I parted from her when I realized she was an even dirtier trollop than I thought. But she is a danger to the public, no one is safe as long as she is at large, and though God Almighty knows that I wouldn't harm anyone, not even this poisonous insect, and that it goes against the heart of gold hidden behind my rough exterior to act the informer, I regard it as my civic duty to give you the above information.

Arrest her, Monsieur, as quickly as possible! Before it is too late and she has done fresh mischief on the soil of France that is so dear to all of us! For wherever she goes, there is a wave of debauchery and wantonness, scandal, crime, and slander. I tell you frankly that's another reason why I am making this denunciation, from which you can see that I have nothing more to do with the lady, whom I wouldn't touch with a pair of tongs, and that I am innocent, because naturally I should keep quiet and lie low if I had anything to do with her dirty secrets.

A few more hints to help you with your good work. She probably calls herself Geneviève Labodère, and I believe it is even possible that she may stay at the Villa des Fleurs in the Rue d'Assas if she comes to Paris. She ought to shun a place where she has spattered herself with blood, but this hussy has no finer feelings whatever and is capable of anything. And just as she is ready to jump into bed with any fellow who comes along, so her lewd mind is always full of filthy schemes; you can never tell what she is up to—except that it is always something beastly, that's as sure as eggs are eggs! It's quite in the cards that in her scurvy ingratitude she is even plotting against me, and yet I say: Arrest her! Even if the deceitful Jezebel bears false witness against me! I shall soon be able to clear myself, I'm not frightened of that. If my informants are not mistaken, the happy couple took the Transportations Maritimes ship *Marie-Suzanne* from Baltimore and will land at Saint-Nazaire in the middle of February —good hunting, then!

I don't want to pick holes in anyone who has clean hands: Monsieur Carapin is a friend of mine. I wanted to make cognac, and he was interested in the project, only Gabrielle vamped him, because of course she had to do it with him too. She can't see a pair of trousers without getting an itch, and although in my grief I punched her in the eye, so that it turned black and she had to tell him she slipped on a piece of soap in the bath, she still managed to lure him away. He has nothing to do with the matter. He doesn't even know what kind of slut he has hung around his neck. People see the juicy piglet, but not the fleas with which it is covered from head to toe; she cajoles everyone with her mumbling and miaowing and the indescribably filthy things she does in bed, which would leave even the most hardened Don Juan gasping—I can tell you plenty about that!

Not that I consider Gabrielle capable of committing murder—she never does her own dirty work, she's much too cowardly for that and much too crafty. No, she's not a murderer, to that I must bear witness in her favor. But she knows everything—the beast knows everything, and uses her knowledge when it suits her and when she can do the most abominable harm with it.

Now she will deny everything, and I am making this denunciation out of the pure love of God, that right may triumph, come what may, unless she manages to slip her head out of the noose. She will try to! Don't believe her, Monsieur, no word of truth ever crossed those villainous lips. How often has she served me up her stinking lies, when I had caught her at her tricks once again. The innocent heart! She beams as though she had just come from Holy Mass, when she has just been wallowing in a cesspool of lechery! Well, I accepted all that with fatherly composure, but now my honor is at stake.

I must think of my poor family, of my wife and my unhappy little daughter, whose reputation is in danger of being spattered by the filth of slander. The truth must out: arrest her, then, and when you have done so I will come voluntarily to Paris, on my word of honor! I promise you that—on one condition: that I am not handcuffed! For all my rough exterior, I'm a sensitive man; I couldn't bear to be in chains—horrible thought: in chains like a murderer. But Gabrielle is as cunning as a serpent, she will try to pin it on me; I can just hear her, I can just picture with my eyes and ears how she will twist and turn and slither out of it with her damned lies! "Why?" she will ask. Simply because I hauled her over the coals a few times and she wants to get her revenge! Once or twice, exasperated by her vile behavior and the filthy way she carried on with men, I let myself be carried away and gave her a sound thrashing. God forgive me my brutality, which isn't like me at all, but I did it out of a sense of honor, and I can produce friends who will prove this.

She's always spitting in the face of truth, the pig! There's no sense in deluding myself; she will say, "It was Eyraudt!" Because she will protect the man who was really in it with her, so that she can go on sucking the strength from him, until she spits away the empty skin with only the bones inside it. She's a vampire, she sucks out her victim like a spider in its web. But she will hand me over to the police, the accursed, loathsome creature! But I had nothing to do with this affair, I swear it. M. Gouffé was my friend, we used to go out together arm in arm and have our harmless amusements together. Why should I have murdered my friend? Out of jealousy? Then I ought to have murdered dozens of men, I should have been kept pretty busy! For money? He never carried enough money on him to make it worthwhile, the skinflint!

Or am I supposed to have murdered this old friend for the few bits of jewelry he wore? My wife had jewelry that brought in twenty times as much at the pawnbroker's! It's all dirty lies! And appearances are in her favor! That's the worst of it—she always wangles it like that, and I have wept my eyes blind already thinking about my poor family. Oh, this trollop is a curse! Perhaps you will doubt the plain truth I am telling you and ask yourself, How could she have done it? Yes, if only it was so simple to get to the bottom of her damn wiles! But I shall explain everything to you, step by step, even if my honorable name is mercilessly dragged through the gutter in the process! Only arrest her first, that is your duty; I shan't fail in mine: I shall come voluntarily to Paris and explain everything.

For the moment I will just say this: everything that seems to testify against me is a snare and a delusion. It's true I was with her, I can't deny that. About a year ago she came to see me in my office asking for a job as store manageress, but she couldn't put up the necessary surety. Nevertheless, she seduced me the same night, and I will spare your chaste ears a description of the filthy way she got me—I who was otherwise a faithful husband and not given to amorous peccadilloes. Then she had me in her net, and no matter how I struggled I couldn't escape. Once she has got a man in her clutches it's all up with him—oh, I don't advise anyone in his senses to get mixed up with her, for it means certain ruin.

Now, as bad luck would have it, in my childlike trust I introduced her to my friend, M. Gouffé, and although I flogged her black and blue to make her behave herself, the slut ran off with M. Gouffé! And to think of everything I had invested in her—clothes, perfumes, gorgeous shoes, and enormously expensive erotic appliances of a highly private nature—she needed more and more, and ruined me with her brainless mania for squandering and enjoyment, and that was precisely why she had finished with me, she made no secret of it and said with her shameless frankness: "Darling, I must really see that I get something into my little bag!" That's the kind of shameless hussy she is. Yet M. Gouffé was my friend and a man of honor; I should have had to be out of my mind to blame him, I knew how she cajoled and coaxed him, the beast, and I knew, too, that no one can get out of her clutches: anyone she sets her cap for is a lost man.

But because of that I went to London and said to her: "My dear child, to clear the air, tell everybody we have parted; I don't want the good name of my family besmirched and made a laughing stock by your scandalous whoring." I can quite imagine that she will try to make a rope for my neck out of this proposal for peace and justice. But as there is a God in Heaven who sees into the heart of every poor sinner, I had no other motive, no matter what lies she may now try to saddle me with in her loathsome twisting and shuffling, to ridicule me and to place me under false suspicions. She said: "My little crosspatch, buy me a nice big trunk, then I will do what you ask." That's why I bought the trunk! And may Satan fry the beast alive if she tells you something different! By all that is holy to me, I had no idea what she wanted the trunk for! Who can ever know what she wants? Anyhow, I wanted only peace and oblivion. Nor had I any idea what she wanted when she called me back to Paris.

It's no good using kid gloves with that worm-riddled beauty, you should sit her with her bare arse on a red-hot stove so that she opens her mouth without telling lies for a change! For she will lie about this business too. She will say: "It was Eyraudt." Poor Eyraudt! How can I tell what she's cooking up? It's true I came over after it had happened. I was overcome with grief and horror when I saw my poor friend M. Gouffé lying in the trunk. But what could I do then? I had come too late to prevent a disaster. Besides, she had me completely in her power. No one will believe me, but it's true: she actually forced me to make love to her in this situation, and while I was straightening my clothes in all innocence, she already presented the bill and said: "You see, of course, that we must get this evidence out of the way, because it would speak against you!" The bitch twists the words in your mouth.

In reality, as I have said, M. Gouffé was my friend. But she said: "Everybody knows you are on the verge of bankruptcy, and they'll say 'He did it for the money!'" Oh, what despair I was in! For it was true that I had fallen into the hands of the Jews, they had stripped me of everything! And now this on top of all the rest! Was I to let my honorable name be dragged into this sordid affair? To make an enemy of Gabrielle, who stops at nothing? Or to deliver her to the executioner, when in spite of everything (I curse myself for it) I *loved* her? And as I have always been inclined to believe and trust in God, I also thought to myself: Gabrielle is still young, perhaps she will *improve*! And the thought of her head being cut off brought tears to my eyes.

Of course, I curse my soft heart—what misfortune it has brought on me! For that carrion! The most artful hypocrite that ever appeared on the earth, that fishy harlot with her smiling, hard diamond of a heart that has never been moved by anyone's distress! She also said: "The man who did this has a *secret* reason for wanting Gouffé out of the way, nobody can prove it; but of you I can say: 'Not only was he in financial straits and in need of money, but also he was mad with jealousy! He saw

red! He threw himself on Gouffé and wrung his neck like a chicken's.' "
That woman was not ashamed to use expressions like this, even at such a
sad moment, although she was terribly proud of her good upbringing—
ugh!

The truth is that she is utterly without shame in every respect, and
hence it is my humble opinion that, although she didn't murder M.
Gouffé herself, she was hand in glove with the murderer. Perhaps she
will creep off to him, now that she is in Paris, the dirty bitch, to enjoy
herself with him—follow her stealthily, then you may kill both birds with
one stone! For he was certainly her paramour, that's the way she does
things! But who it probably was I shall keep to myself, until you have
arrested her and I come to Paris.

For these reasons I agreed to send the body by express train to Marseilles. And she persuaded me to empty out my poor friend Gouffé, whom
I have always considered a man of honor, over the road wall at Millery
like a bucketful of garbage. I could go crazy when I think that it was I
who had to do that, I who have never harmed a fly, and that I let this
white-bellied poisonous toad stay alive, instead of handing her over to
justice so that her perverse little head could be sliced off—plop, into the
sack with it! If only I had done so! I should be feeling better now. But
Christian pity held me back, and the thought that she was such a young
thing and might perhaps improve.

I don't want to make any suggestions now, I shall keep everything till
we meet in Paris. But just one more hint: It is very likely that the Jews
are at the back of it all, because they are afraid I may sue them for their
cutthroat tricks and swindles. This race has it fingers in every dirty business and probably in this one too, and everyone knows they wouldn't
shrink from murder, since they make a regular practice of killing Christian children and baking them in their holy bread. These submen are
capable of anything! They're as lecherous as goats and in this they're just
right for Gabrielle, who has undoubtedly had it with them too—she would
travel all the way around the earth if she thought there was a nation
living somewhere she had never tried it with! So you should also make
inquiries in this direction; I shouldn't be surprised if there's some plot
here.

Evil-minded people might misinterpret my fatherly interest and think
it suspicious that I went with Gabrielle to America. But it was like it
always is—in for a penny, in for a pound—and after I had once slipped
into the morass—I mean, after the perverse hussy had seduced me into
fornicating in the room where the murder was committed and so co-
erced me into helping to get rid of the body, I had no alternative but to
see she kept her mouth shut and didn't compromise me seriously—quite
apart from the fact that I had taken it into my head to influence the
slut for good, cost what it might.

This may seem like childish optimism on my part. I didn't believe she had committed the murder herself, I don't believe so today, I don't want to believe so—although I ought to tell myself that there is really no crime of which she is not capable, for she is immoral to the depths of her lewd soul. But I hadn't realized it then, and in my naivety I fell for it hook, line, and sinker when she started whining and whimpering her innocence; I went out of my senses as soon as the soft lips and the long-nailed fingers started playing on me the tricks no one can escape from.

I wish I could describe to you the way the cat purred around me and rubbed herself against my legs so that I shouldn't give her away; although I had fallen into this cesspool, I was in despair to the depths of my poor Christian soul to think that I might be absent for a long time from my unhappy family and have to deprive them of my fatherly care, on account of the false suspicion of being involved in an affair I knew nothing whatever about—all because of this whore who is every man's chamber pot! And I'm not just making this up on the spur of the moment; it was because of this despair of mine that she always called me her "Crosspatch" or "Old Crosspatch," and I can produce friends to prove it. So if she wants to sling mud at me (of which I have no doubt) and asserts that I had quite different reasons for going with her, that's all a snare and a delusion, as you can see for yourself, and she wouldn't dare try it on if Old Crosspatch was there to bring her to reason! That will happen, and then you will see how the snake dodges and hisses. She has no taste for the whip—this as a hint to you, Monsieur, if she has the impertinence to serve up her lies to you too! Anyhow, the whole business went on until she ran off with M. Carapin, out of lechery, leaving me utterly desolate; I had given up everything for this criminal trollop, and now she inflicted this humiliation on me.

And she must be squeezing him like a lemon, the poor fellow! She would do the same with the devil: she has never had enough, she's utterly without scruple or restraint; a man has to have the constitution of a bull to live with that woman. Insatiability is her guiding principle, she makes her admirers helpless and docile with it, and you're always completely in a daze with that pathological glutton of a mistress. I wasn't born yesterday, but I've never experienced anything like it before, and the longer you experience it, the more impossible it is to break free from it. I don't give a fig now, pain past is pleasure, but out of love for my fellow men I implore you, who are paid to protect the safety of your fellow citizens: she must be cleared off the face of the earth before she has sucked the strength from God knows how many men and brought them to disaster or their graves. We owe this to mankind, and that is why I am denouncing her, not for selfish reasons. As heaven is my witness I want nothing more from her, she can copulate with whoever she likes as far as I am concerned! The best of luck to you! I'm glad I got off so lightly!

Monsieur, I shake myself like a poodle as I clamber out of the sea of this slimy mermaid and hang my lyre in the temple of Venus—an end to it! I want nothing more to do with the whole thing. One more incident as it occurs to me, just to give you an idea of Gabrielle's underhand character. In Marseilles, Gouffé bled freely (I don't know how he was murdered), and when the men came to fetch the trunk there was blood on the parquet; she laughed her innocent little-girl laugh and said to me: "But Michi, how often have I told you not to carry that dye around in your luggage! Now the bottle has really broken—my lovely clothes!" Just imagine it! That shows you how the woman can lie! Without batting an eyelid! Without any shame! As I told you, I don't think she is guilty of the murder, but she must be rendered harmless by sending her head hopping into the sack—away with pests! God above knows it goes against the grain with me to say a thing like that; but I must say it, and I can promise you I should watch without shedding any tears for her young life! This hussy is a demon, she is beyond redemption, she is too depraved.

I repeat: I shall come *voluntarily* to Paris, once you have arrested her, my word of honor! Only no handcuffs, not that; think of my poor, disgraced family, whom I, led astray by Gabrielle, have already caused so much grief! But God will forgive me, for the flesh is weak.

Once more then: Happy hunting! And à *bientôt!*

Yours sincerely, MICHEL EYRAUDT

It did not require Goron's criminological experience to see through this letter: in its coarse humor and savage vengefulness, it barely left breath for the few threadbare protestations of innocence and promises of disclosures, and amounted to a confession of guilt—the writer was Gouffé's murderer, the letter itself an outpouring of uncontrollable hate, lust, rage, and above all jealousy, that sought only to hurl the faithless accomplice and lover to perdition, caring little if she dragged him to perdition with her in expiation of his mortal passion. She certainly would drag to destruction this man, basically not uneducated, but totally brutalized and devoid of all self-control, who was making a wretched attempt to conceal the truth from others by an attempt at cunning prevarication and from himself by disguising it behind a mask of vengeful rage. The truth was a criminal and suicidal love that proclaimed: "I would rather go with you to the grave than remain alive without you."

The man's fate was sealed, and Goron took steps to see that it should not be long delayed. With his shorthand notebook on his knees, Guillaume sat by Goron and took down telegrams to the French Em-

bassy in Washington, to the Consulates in New York and Boston, to
the Consulate at Springfield, Massachusetts; the American press in
general and the New England press in particular were asked to help
and supplied with the fullest possible information, especially concerning Eyraudt's appearance and peculiarities, a description of which
Latrille had obtained from Bompard in the cellar (including the most
intimate details, which she had revealed to the accompaniment of
radiant smiles). The competent American authorities, the District
Attorney, and the Department of Justice were to be informed and
requested to arrest the dangerous lone wolf and take steps for his
immediate extradition.

Goron had learned from the experience of past collaboration with
them the vigor with which the apparently lackadaisical Americans
snapped into action at the appropriate moment, the scale and the
thoroughness with which they organized their manhunts like a sport
in which everyone took part. An instinct told him that the prey,
blinded by hate and love, was unaware of his immediate danger, so
that in all likelihood he had not yet changed his hunting ground, but
was still using New England and probably Chicopee, the little industrial town in Massachusetts, as his headquarters. If he should suddenly become aware of the danger, he would feel himself caught
like a rat in a trap and, instead of patiently lying low, would take
some sort of action; and whatever action he took would betray him,
in whichever direction he moved he would run into the arms of the
hunters.

Goron knew that the case was drawing to its close. But the case itself, and people's behavior over it, had given him so much trouble
that he wanted to have it sewn up absolutely tight, as absolutely fault-
less as an artist seeks to render his works: no eleventh-hour surprises
were to deprive him of the fruits of his efforts! The personality of
Gabrielle Bompard remained the only imponderable element; she
must be methodically ground down. The fact that, to his annoyance,
he could not think of her in any way other than with a hatred that
clouded his mind reinforced his determination to act with caution
and dogged perseverance.

This woman, like most women, was incapable of being alone: her
strength lay in her effect on other people. An on-the-spot investigation at the Villa des Fleurs was unavoidable; but beyond that, he was

resolved to give her no opportunity to occupy the center of the stage and act a part. He determined to keep her imprisoned in semidarkness, where no sound reached her but the desolate dripping of water from a tap and the low hiss of gas, except when she was brought up for nighttime interrogations which grew increasingly exhausting and in the course of which she was, so to speak, suspended in the smoke of his poisonous black cigars that had already worried her during the first interrogation (turning her face away and wrinkling her charming little wild-beast's nose, she waved the cloud away with her hand).

He was trying to break down her resistance until no price seemed to her too high in order to escape from this forgotten existence underground, and she was ripe for the confrontation with her fellow culprit, which would then do the rest. The Prosecution Department and the Prosecutor General's Office were to be presented, however belatedly, with a clear-cut case, a case in which there was nothing left to unravel and in which nothing could go wrong—and until this point was reached, he would brook no interference from outside!

But did he seriously believe that the public would leave him in peace, after he had so systematically whipped up their interest? The Cité was besieged by the Press, who were not deterred by having to wait hour after hour to catch a glimpse of the beautiful hellcat; and in spite of doorkeepers and interview passes, reporters found their way into the heart of the building and up to the second floor and into the police chief's antechamber and mobbed Guillaume, who, while manfully preserving an appearance of amiability, was increasingly helpless in the face of this throng of inquirers which his boss had conjured up and now had no intention of satisfying. When Goron himself, impelled by the feeling that it might be advisable to report personally on the situation to Examining Magistrate Carnot, emerged from his room, hat on head, he found himself surrounded and brought to a stop by a horde of people shouting, asking questions, and all talking at once (and as a result—unfortunately—he forgot his original intention). He realized that he would not get off cheaply and, almost fighting his way back to his room, he promised that in about an hour's time he would supply the gentlemen with copy worth waiting for.

He told himself that interest must be effectively diverted from Bompard and centered on the other partner in the criminal duet; on Eyraudt, who had an equal claim to this interest and would hold it once he ceased to be the shadowy figure he was now and emerged clearly as the dissolute, cynical, and mendacious character he had half-concealed and half-revealed in his letter. Goron felt that he must make this letter public. He ordered a number of copies to be made and distributed to the Press; and Guillaume, waving the pages to and fro in his upraised hand, made his way through the laughing reporters and up to the writing and copying room that was situated under the roof. Silence fell on the antechamber. Goron turned down his collar with a feeling of discomfort; he had been reluctant to release this letter to the public, he had done it against his will, under compulsion, as when we throw a meaty bone to a pack of snapping dogs to keep them off—and it would have been better if he had not done so at all.

Naturally, the big, reputable newspapers suppressed the most typical, that is to say the most salacious, passages in Eyraudt's effusion; but the numerous scandal sheets felt no call to withhold such matter from their readers, and they sold like hot cakes. Gabrielle Bompard's popularity rose to a rather obscene kind of fame; she was the talk of all the men in Paris, and expressions like "I must really see that I get something into my little bag!" became familiar doubles entendres, employed as an adjunct both to business transactions on the boulevards and to more gallant commerce in chambres séparées and the rosy light of boudoirs. Had he not acted in a moment of confusion when taken by surprise, Goron could have foreseen that, picturesque as Gouffé's murderer was in himself, what made him a sensation for Parisians was his relationship with Bompard as disclosed in this letter, the barely concealed anguish of his jealousy and how highly—unadmitted but unmistakably—he rated the value of the pleasure she could give him. In his frenzy, he was jeopardizing his life rather than know her in the arms of another, thereby throwing an entrancing light on her secret qualities (though he decried them), all of which heated and inflamed the imagination of everyone, whether versed or unversed in the arts of love.

What more powerful sympathy can a woman gain in this world than that engendered in the wish-dreams of each individual, since at this point the most intimate feelings mingle with public imagery and thus a legend is born. Yes, it was true; an aura of legend wove itself around this young woman, after whose flesh everyone secretly lusted in his own way, disregarding or enjoying with a delicious thrill the fact that her embrace spelled perdition, like that of the praying mantis who devours her mate in the intoxication of love, for love and death have been intermingled and united since time immemorial. No wonder, then, that the Press reporters, after all kinds of lewd smirks or high-minded protestations (according to the standard of the paper), began to ask themselves and their readers when the Cité would "at last" raise the iron curtain and permit access to the much-discussed prisoner, so that firsthand reports and the woman's own utterances could complete the picture the public mind had formed of her.

But if this reaction was the opposite of the one Goron had striven for, it was perhaps inherent in the situation and bound to have developed somehow, sooner or later, whereas certain speculative deductions that followed upon this newspaper talk might have been avoided. True, journalists exercised restraint, they named no names, but didn't everyone know where, and in whose room, Bompard had been arrested, and didn't this accord peculiarly well with Eyraudt's hint as to whom she would probably "creep off to" in Paris? Heavens above, nobody in his right mind would think of suspecting the "personage in question" of a crime of which the informer had inculpated himself by his transparent denial; but was there perhaps another, more convincing explanation of that strange visit than the one officially advanced?

Why had Bompard gone to the personage in question? Why had she gone to the Cité? How could anyone distinguish between truth and falsehood in Eyraudt's farrago of brutal accusation, innuendo, and unintentional confession? And since the letter contained so much overt or covert truth, why should this hint not also be accepted as true? In short, was there a hitherto-concealed link between visitor and visited? This was how the fertile minds of the journalists ran, and they infected the always susceptible brains of the masses (if for lack of a more accurate term, we may use the word *brain* in this context).

Jaquemar, around whose person all the speculations were circling like a swarm of voracious gadflies, would have had reason for disquiet; and when, shortly after they began to be aired, he appeared in Goron's antechamber. The latter happened to be engaged, and Guillaume felt it appropriate to pass a remark on the subject, accompanied by a chagrined smile and a shake of the head. But he found Jaquemar surprisingly unmoved: he stared blankly in front of him and indicated with an almost imperceptible shrug of the shoulders that he did not read the newspapers. Nor did he make any reference to this smear campaign in the course of his subsequent conversation with Goron. In fact, he seemed to have no special reason for coming at all and did not even pay much attention to Goron's report on the steps that had meanwhile been taken against Eyraudt. Sitting and squinting down at the floor, he looked like someone who, while being talked to, is thinking of something else, and it was on the tip of Goron's tongue to ask impatiently whether this was merely a social call—when there was a knock at the door and Montardon, the wardress, entered.

Because of all the loose fat in her face, which pulled her small mouth awry, and down at the corners, she looked offended and ill-humored; and the night-gray eyes above the black lachrymal sacs gazed at Goron with what seemed to be a disparaging expression. She had come about "the new one" and wanted orders from the chief, because she was at her wit's end; Bompard, stubbornly insisting that she was being held illegally, refused to eat the prison food, saying that even prisoners on remand were entitled to provide their own meals and that she wanted a veal cutlet with green peas tossed in butter. As she passed on this request, Montardon gave vent to an asthmatic laugh that set her enormous bosom shaking and heaving to the accompaniment of thin squeaking, whistling, and rattling sounds. "Tossed in butter, eh?" cried Goron. "And what else? Perhaps a few crêpes Suzette afterward, mocha coffee, petits fours?" Anyhow, she could not be persuaded by threats or coaxed to touch the prison fare; yesterday evening, she, Montardon, had silently placed a loaf of fresh white bread, cheese, and a jug of milk in the cell, exceeding her instructions but hoping the delicious sight and smell of the food would break her charge's obstinacy; but everything stood untouched this morning in the same place as last night, and in response to an express invitation to eat Bompard had only shaken her head; "la jeune fille," who was very well behaved basically, was like a cat that prefers to die of hunger rather than eat what doesn't suit it. Montardon was a great cat lover.

"Give her each meal according to the regulations, and take it away again an hour later, regardless of whether she has eaten or not," ordered Goron.

"According to the regulations?" repeated Montardon questioningly, and gave Goron an indeterminate sort of look with her hands folded over her stomach.

"Is that all?" he replied curtly.

No, Bompard wanted her luggage, she needed various things, especially linen.

"Oh, she 'wants,' she 'needs,' does she?"

In her own words, it was "unjust and unkind" to prevent her from using her things; even if, contrary to all common sense, she was to be considered a prisoner in custody, she had a right to them; and it was carrying spite too far to force her to lie naked between "jute sheets on the uncomfortable bed." Naked? Why naked? Hadn't she been given a nightdress? Certainly she had, but she had tossed it aside with her fingertips, muttering that she would rather run naked from one side of Paris to the other than pull other people's things over her "hide."

"We'll pull her hide over her ears!" commented Goron.

"She was thoroughly grumpy," replied Montardon, giving vent once more to her asthmatic little laugh, "as she rubbed her skin this morning, because of the rough bedclothes. 'Conditions are bad in this house,' she said. Shall I have the things fetched? The address is . . ."

Montardon, doubtless searching for a slip of paper, began to rub and finger her black pinafore dress as she looked down over her own bosom. Abruptly, but without looking up from the floor, Jaquemar interjected: "Hôtel des Mines, Rue de la Glacière—they're with me."

For a moment there was silence all around; then Jaquemar slowly looked up to Goron, and perhaps just because the rather strong afternoon sun emerged from behind white clouds and flooded the room with hot light, his face turned crimson, almost as though he were sitting in front of an open fire; even his squinting eyes began to flicker and glint, though his voice sounded quiet and toneless as usual, as he continued: "They were standing in my room yesterday, a trunk and a bag, both marked G. L.; I didn't notice them at first, then I saw them and knew at once what kind of greeting that was. I ran down to Chambron, the landlord. They had been sent from the Villa des Fleurs, 'with apologies for the delay, to Monsieur Edmond Jaquemar.' Have them taken away, I beg you."

"Have them taken away, Montardon," said Goron, without averting his eyes from his visitor. "And come back for further orders when they're here. Thank you."

The door closed behind the wardress; there was silence again, then the lenses of Goron's pince-nez flashed, he laughed a spiteful laugh that set his hamster cheeks quivering, and said: "Very flattering, the trust she puts in you! She has her methods, I must grant her that. But they won't help her! On the contrary: we shall turn them to our advantage. If it's agreeable to you, I shall fetch you at ten tomorrow morning. An on-the-spot investigation in the Rue d'Assas. Perhaps there too she will honor you with her confidences."

Jaquemar suddenly sat with his head tilted and eyes closed, which gave him an expression of extraordinary suffering.

"For the love of God," he said, "leave me out of this business."

"Leave you out!" cried Goron in genuine surprise. "My good friend, you aren't going to let her scare you, are you? Another six or eight weeks and this whole business will be brought to an end in the yard of La Roquette! I'll stake my reputation on it! I give you my word!"

"I wish," said Jaquemar as softly as before, slowly opening his eyes and squinting into space, "I wish I could describe to you how I felt when I saw the trunk and the bag in my room; they stood there so mute and contented, not in the least worried that you had locked the beast up in your cellar. Will you believe me when I say I turned pale? It was as if they were *smiling* at me, with the same innocent, atrocious, empty smile she smiles when she makes her appalling statements and can't see that she is setting your nerves on edge with them."

Goron shrugged, but the young man gave him no chance to speak; his eyes burned into Goron's as though blazing with hate and he blurted out with a kind of sob: "Protect me from that strumpet! She is the most concentrated poison I have ever smelled! It is no good, no good, I tell you, to have to do with such an angel of abomination."

Goron lumbered to his feet and Jaquemar rose at the same time. He now seemed as calm as before his outburst and mumbled something like an apology: of course he would be at Goron's disposal. Goron, somewhat perplexed, patted his arm, gave a short laugh, and looked up at him over the rim of his pince-nez. "You're not used to this sort of thing, my dear chap. You're on edge—do you know, you're beginning to talk like Eyraudt."

"Do you know," interpolated Jaquemar, absorbed in thought, "I'm beginning to talk like Eyraudt."

"Trust in your friends, trust in me," said Goron. "I shall put everything straight."

Jaquemar nodded pensively. Goron shook hands with him, then pulled off his pince-nez and gazed after him as he moved toward the door with his dainty step. His hand was already on the latch, when he hesitated and turned round once more. "You realize, of course," he said, "that what I came about was Bompard's luggage. God alone knows why I couldn't remember it when I was sitting in front of you."

Goron, with a wagging movement of the hand, waved him away, and Jaquemar, after hesitating once more, left.

Drawn by two brisk-stepping bays, the Sûreté prison van drove up the Boulevard Montparnasse—a green-lacquered box of a vehicle with barred, opaque glass windows and a platform at the back enclosed on three sides, in which Soudrais and Montardon sat facing one another, the latter with a childish round black straw hat on her head. Both of them were leaning forward and peering around the narrow rear walls, watching the increasing number of pedestrians who, having caught sight of them, broke into a trot and tried to keep abreast of them—rather surprisingly in view of the fact that the sinister vehicle was no unwonted sight in this district near the Port-Royal—that is to say, near the Prison de la Santé. The swarm of runners in their wake grew visibly larger and managed to overtake them when they rounded the Café des Lilas corner and turned down the Rue d'Assas, where a dense mass of handcarts and delivery vans compelled the splendid bays, tossing their snorting heads, to slow their pace. The people evidently knew where they were going. Some passed the vehicle; others, who had taken a short cut through the Rue Bara, came to meet it; and a crowd of bystanders had already congregated, either because a few particularly wide-awake reporters had already stationed themselves here on the off-chance, thereby drawing the attention of passers-by, or else because word of this on-the-spot investigation, which had been deliberately kept secret, had nevertheless somehow reached the public.

Seeing the throng, the boor Soudrais assumed a stern expression as he clambered down from the platform and immediately turned to the crowd with his left arm outstretched and waving his right impatiently, roughly ordering them to "Make way there, move along, will you!" Meanwhile Montardon, a cumbersome mass of flesh enveloped in black, climbed heavily down the three steps, turning half around on herself and looking unmistakably like a performing bear. When Gabrielle Bompard appeared in the semidarkness of the rear platform, those down below began to push toward the roadway, and something like a sigh of delighted astonishment ran through the crowd as they saw her step forward into the light.

She was indeed astonishingly beautiful, especially as she stepped forward and looked up, with no trace of embarrassment and wearing her usual smile. She was not greeting the spectators, however, but simply the fragrant morning light. She wore no hat; the curly locks of her gleaming black hair, taken up on top of her head in a charming tangle as of flickering flames or little serpents, were ruffled by a sudden breeze and emphasized the audacity of the delicate white face with its little tiger's nose and dimpled cheeks, the curved fans of the eyelashes and the full, deep red, moist lips that were not quite closed. By daylight this face looked both lovelier and more sharply cut and especially much more colorful than in the dusk or by artificial light; indeed, with its tones of white, red, and black it had a painted look, and the gay anguish of the brows that rose and almost met above the nose intensified this colorful quality and gave the whole face the appearance of a clown's mask, without in any way detracting from its naturalness.

At a remark from the narrow-skulled Latrille, who came into view behind her, she nodded as though in eager agreement; she lifted her voluminous skirt over her right thigh toward her lap, looked down, and placed her white boot on the step below; as she did so, she caught sight of the crowd and remarked in a clear and confident voice to Montardon, who went to help her: "Look, Madame, you see how famous we are!" Without replying, Montardon supported her under her right elbow, and carefully setting down one foot after the other, she continued, looking the tiniest bit piqued, but with eyes shining like black diamonds: "It's a great pity Carapin left me in the lurch. I could have done with a nice new dress for this occasion." Yet she was smartly attired in a dress that gave her an aristocratic look because of the high, semicircular ruched collar and the openwork leg-of-mutton sleeves and wasp waist, which threw the well-rounded elasticity of her not very large breasts into prominence and made her seem more slender than perhaps she really was.

Soudrais, who had elbowed his way to the wooden gates and the small door in one of them, found on looking back that the path he had cut through the crowd had closed behind him and the dense throng had turned their backs to him: he was helplessly jammed between all these backs and the gateway and completely separated from the others. After the first two or three steps which she took supported by Montardon, Bompard was pushed ahead by the wardress and wedged in among the inquisitive onlookers; she looked around with a laugh and made a gesture of regret to Montardon, who was gulping for breath with her small, crooked mouth in her fat face, thrust to and fro as though bound hand and foot and unable to reach for her hat, which had slipped forward over her eyes. Latrille was trying to push his way forward to them both, when suddenly a voice rang out from the groaning mob: "Mademoiselle Bompard, how do you like it in the Cité?" At this, dead silence fell, all movement ceased, the groaning stopped, and Bompard answered with a faint, yet ringing cry: "I'm starving, they make me sleep naked, I have to lie between hempen sheets!"

Latrille, hearing this, stopped elbowing his way through the crowd, dropped his arms, lowered his head, and scratched the corner of his mouth. "Have you no legal aid?" called out another male voice. "Oh no," she replied. "I am entirely at their mercy. I'm not allowed to take a walk outside, they refuse me the use of my linen." "What do you say to the accusations Eyraudt has made against you?" She lowered her head, but immediately looked up again with a smile and said: "Who can blame him for putting up a bit of a fight? But it won't do him any good. Should I be here, if I were not innocent?" A small circle had opened around her. She raised her left hand to the back of her head and tidied her curly hair; she looked down with beaming eyes and said: "They take damned little notice of the fact that I'm innocent. They keep me in the cellar, it's damp there, the mice scurry round your feet, and the sanitary arrangements are in an appalling state, they are the same for men and women, and filthy things are scribbled all over the walls. I shouldn't have come here."

All who could, and especially those standing near, gazed breathlessly into her face; then two voices rang out simultaneously from the background, so that neither could be understood, and Gabrielle Bompard shrugged her shoulders regretfully and said confidentially to a young man who happened to be standing in front of her: "Why don't people come and see me—there? Haven't they the courage? Don't they want to know the truth?"

This extraordinary interview would doubtless have gone on for a long time if the police chief's ramshackle carriage had not come around the Café des Lilas corner into the street just at this moment. Latrille caught sight of it at once and suddenly put his foot down: "But, Messieurs, Dames!" he cried. "Be reasonable." Strangely enough, his protest was heeded; he elbowed his way to Montardon without difficulty and pushed her and Bompard through to the green gateway, in which the small door, held open by Soudrais, closed behind them before Goron's wretched jade with the hanging head came to a stop, and Goron, his mouth rounded with annoyance at the unexpected crowd, rose from his seat next to the bareheaded Jaquemar.

Goron looked at the multitude through his crooked pince-nez, his hamster cheeks hanging misanthropically under his top hat, while his companion squinted at the floor, pale-faced and reserved. As Goron stepped down he missed his footing and stumbled against the front rank of the bystanders, which excited laughter and a few handclaps. But a narrow path immediately opened in front of him, and Jaquemar followed unrecognized in his footsteps; they advanced with their right shoulders thrust forward to the little door, in front of which Soudrais, with martial mien and arms crossed over his chest, was now standing guard.

With Goron half a pace in front of Jaquemar, who kept both hands in the pockets of his thin overcoat, they passed an ivy-grown porter's lodge and crossed the forecourt; not, however, toward the flowerpot-flanked entrance, but to the left, through a semicircular arch about head-high and down a few steps into a tunnel. The locality seemed familiar to both of them, for their gait betrayed no doubt as to the way and they traversed the tunnel under the house without hesitation, although it was very dark, with an uneven floor, and lit only by a pale glimmer of light at the far end. Whereas outside there was little movement of the air, and then only an occasional warm and gentle breeze, a steady, cold draft blew through the tunnel that caught at the eyes and seemed somehow mocking, in that it was impossible to tell where it came from; it ended with the tunnel, and after ascending a few steps to the backyard of the house the visitors found themselves in the same mild atmosphere of early spring that they had left on the other side.

The yard was paved with asphalt, bounded on the right and left by a wall and at the far end by a barracklike, single-story brick building, on which the high, rather drab and mournful rear wall of the main building looked down. Yet there was nothing squalid or depressing about the total effect. Even the privy on the extreme right, since it was smothered by creepers, did not disturb the curiously remote and snug appearance of the yard beneath the blue sky flecked with white clouds. Brightly painted, mostly pink, garden furniture stood about in casual groups, and the two steps leading up to each of the rooms in the low annex, spaced out at regular intervals, were flanked on either side by pots and jugs, as well as black iron caldrons and little copper pails, filled with clumps of flowers of the aster type, all with a great many leaves but some of them very badly parched; whenever a breeze struck up, they rustled with a low, grating sound, and this gave an added note of homeliness to the silence that reigned in this place from which the din of the city was shut out.

There was no one in the yard; but the doors at the top of the two flights of steps on the extreme right of the annex, facing the privy, were open, and once again the two unequal walkers went unhesitatingly toward them. Bompard was sitting behind the last window looking out; she was holding the elbows of her crossed arms, which might have made her look cold had she not nodded to the newcomers with such unaffected friendliness the moment they entered her field of vision—a nod which they both ignored completely. They walked straight past the window, and Jaquemar, his bare head bowed and both hands in his pockets, followed Goron up the steps.

So this was the scene of the crime: a not very clean room in the backyard of a medium-priced pension, fairly comfortable but completely impersonal, unless the view out into the curiously idyllic-looking yard could be regarded as giving it a personal touch. A Chinese embroidered silk screen stood three-quarters of the way across the room, which was furnished only along one wall, the long internal wall; but this furniture was reflected in the mirror propped up on the mantelpiece above the bricked-in fireplace and here, because of the angle, it looked more compact and richer.

There was a bunch of peacock feathers on the console at the head of the sofa with its many cushions, a low oriental smoking table in front of this, and by the window the high-back carved armchair in which Bompard was now sitting, her feet in their white boots crossed and drawn slightly back, holding her elbows and smiling with shining eyes and head slightly tilted. Montardon, her vast bosom still heaving and her small mouth still gulping for air, was watching over her from her seat on the corner of the sofa. Goron and Jaquemar walked past them, without a greeting, toward the screen, from behind which Latrille stepped at that moment. They stood there talking in undertones, until Goron turned and said: "Eh bien, Bompard, tell us what happened in this room on the evening of July 25—and without frills, if you don't mind!"

Calmly uncrossing her arms and resting them on the arms of the chair, Gabrielle Bompard leaned slightly forward and looked past the wardress at the sofa. "There," she said with a nod, "that's where he sat, and that's where death overtook him."

Still smiling, she slowly turned and looked into Jaquemar's face, saying: "Will somebody sit there, in his place? If there was a piece of rope handy, I could show you exactly what happened."

Their eyes met, hers shining, Jaquemar's dull with hate; but Latrille stepped forward carrying a piece of rope in his hand, and sat down. "All right, get on with it!" urged Goron.

She grumbled to herself until Montardon touched her elbow, when she rose and allowed herself to be led unresisting to the seated La-trille. She even laughed a little, took the rope from his hand, and twisted it around his neck. She pulled the ends and, looking down at his head, she suddenly took it gently in her right hand and pressed it to her body.

"This," she said, "was done in play, unfortunately, in the red lamp-light, and Gouffé thought no harm of it, although I said to him: 'Look, Monsieur, I could do you in if you don't promise to be good to me from now on.' And it was soon after this joke that Michi, who had been waiting in the other room, unexpectedly stepped out from behind the screen, with bloodshot eyes and dangling hands, and because I could see from the look on his face that there was going to be trouble, I turned away and went over to the window. I raised the curtain a little and looked out for help. But while the fight was going on, with sounds of gasping and grunting, and the table fell over with the jar full of Turkish violet cachous I had bought to give him a treat if he came—while this was happening nobody appeared in the dark yard, and it was only after everything had gone quiet, apart from Michi's panting, that the tall German from the front house came out, the one who always used to wink at me so invitingly when we met; he strode across the yard, disappeared into the closet, and stayed there. Then I turned around and saw what Michi had done. I let the curtain fall.

"Michi stood there panting, with legs apart, and because his tongue was hanging out after his exertion, I gave him cognac to drink from the bottle on the mantelpiece and out of the same glass from which Gouffé had drunk before him. But now Gouffé was lying on the sofa, with his legs and arms stretched out, and he was reflected in the mirror on the mantelpiece, and his eyes were open in the dim light and staring all the time at the same spot. But soon his face was no longer recognizable, because Michi had trampled on it as a precaution. He was undressed, tied up, pushed into the sack and sewn up, and then put in the trunk."

As she told this hideous story, Bompard held the back of Latrille's head in her right hand and unconsciously scratched it a bit. But now she turned to Jaquemar and said with a little bow: "I beg your pardon. This is all very nasty. But we must bear in mind that Michi will pay for it with his life."

"Where did the sack come from?" cut in Goron. "Did you know it was there?"

"Certainly. I made it. Michi came with sackcloth and said: 'Make a sack!' and told me the measurements. So I made the sack, at the open window of this room, over there; everybody who went to the closet saw me doing it, and I sang a song about May as I worked, because I didn't know what the sack was for, and I was very surprised when I saw."

"Well, well, a song about May," snorted Goron, pulling at his collar.

"Yes, I'm sorry," she answered pertly. "I know it was out of place, because it was already July."

Latrille asked: "Mademoiselle, who—'sewed up' Gouffé, he or you?"

She looked down at his head and asked back: "Can you sew? No man can sew."

"You," burst out Jaquemar, "you did it!"

"But he ordered me to!" she retorted, with an obstinate nod. "He was very rough. He often beat me terribly, and when he beat me and I cried and was miserable about it, I thought to myself: You too will be miserable one day."

"So he forced you, did he?" said Goron, shrugging his shoulders. "You *had* to do it, that's what you want to make me believe."

She mumbled something unintelligible, then she looked straight at him with a wild expression in her eyes and cried: "I don't care what you believe! All I want from you is that you should treat me as I deserve!"

"Don't worry! You will be treated as you deserve!"

"Now! Now!" cried Gabrielle Bompard, taking a step forward and pressing Latrille's head close to her. Then, as though coming to her senses, she looked down at the head against her abdomen and continued in a confidential tone: "You can easily see what a brute he is from the fact that as soon as the lid was shut he seized hold of me and did violence to me—on the trunk in which Gouffé lay."

Jaquemar half-turned away with a groan of disgust. Latrille inquired: "He did violence to you? That's unbelievable."

She nodded and said: "Yes, he did violence to me. And I couldn't defend myself, because I was naked, and I was naked because I had taken off my dressing gown, because without the cord it hindered me in the work I was forced to do. All this goes on Michi's account, and he will make sorrowful carp's eyes when he is presented with the bill. Michi, Michi, I have bled red; you will bleed white."

Moved by a sudden uncontrollable impulse, Jaquemar took a step toward her; his fists were clenched and he was quivering like a taut rope that has been set vibrating. "What had Gouffé done to you, the kindest, most decent man who ever lived!? What impelled you to lay hands on him—you destroying angel?"

"*I* lay hands on *him?* And why do you shout? Oh well, I understand. You *must* grieve for your brother-in-law. But it was really mostly his own fault. He desired me, he wanted to have me, and that was perfectly natural; every man has a right to the woman he loves. The silly thing was that he wasn't prepared to love me and have me and atone for it completely, in the proper way."

"Atone . . ." repeated Jaquemar in a whisper.

"Atone?" cried Goron, tilting his head to one side. "What do you mean by that?"

She mumbled something unintelligible; a shadow passed across her clown's eyebrows, and she grumbled: "Another woman stood in the way."

"But you felt no thirst for vengeance?" interjected Goron. "You had nothing to do with Eyraudt's plans for murder, you had no idea about them! Why did you say in London, in Grattan's shop: 'We came to buy a trunk, not a coffin'?"

"Silly nonsense," she said, and looked up with a shrug at Jaquemar, who was glaring at her, his eyes blazing. "The trunk looked like a coffin."

"And why did you say to Chévron, also in London: 'We shall fill it in Paris'?"

"Well, he promised to buy me a whole trunkful of fine clothes when we got back to Paris. Only he was always lying, unfortunately. He also said, when I asked him about the sack: 'We'll put something into it that you'll enjoy.' "

"And the telegram you sent him in London?"

She went on looking at Jaquemar and answered: "He told me to send it. He said: 'Call yourself Geneviève Labodère; take two rooms next to one another in some quiet part of Paris, and when you have come to an agreement with Gouffé, send me a telegram: MUST LOVE BE BEAUTIFUL—then I shall know.' "

"Know what?"

"That I was happy."

"Come to an agreement about what?"

"I wanted to grant Gouffé his wish."

"And you needed two rooms for that?"

"Was Gouffé to live in the yard?"

Latrille intervened: "But when Gouffé didn't respond to the advances you made him, when he didn't want to have you completely— that must have offended you."

Only for a moment did she turn her eyes back to Latrille, then she looked at Jaquemar again and answered: "It was because of the other woman. She kept him dangling, but no one encouraged her to go to him. So he thought he could try it out with me in the meantime. But I'm afraid I don't stand for that."

"Such a flower of infamy," burst out Jaquemar, "for Gouffé!"

She nodded, beaming, and said: "It was outrageous. He should have made up his mind to have one or the other, then he wouldn't have been polished off in that horrible way, because then I should have sent Michi away, and Gouffé could have moved into the room next door. I expect a man to say 'Yes, yes' or 'No, no.' "

Jaquemar sat there, pale in the face, staring at the floor. "I shall destroy her," he said, as though to himself.

"This conversation is very tedious," remarked Bompard, giving her usual little shrug as she looked at Montardon, who had been standing the whole time, with her hands folded over her stomach, gazing at her. "Will someone offer me a seat?"

No one paid any attention to this question, but neither did anyone hinder her when she walked over to the window, raised the curtain a little, and looked out, before sitting down in the high-backed armchair and absentmindedly straightening her dress over her knees. Only Montardon put her hand over her little mouth and tried to suppress an asthmatic, rattling laugh that set her vast bosom shaking and heaving.

"How did you come to know Eyraudt?" asked Goron, stepping forward from the back of the room to the window. "Is it true that you asked him for a job?"

"Certainly," she replied. "I came from elsewhere—"

"Where did you come from?"

". . . and hadn't a sou. But because it always comes down to money or the other thing, I became his mistress the same night. Oh, how he wanted to become my *ponce!* But I had no desire to be his business; and instead of earning money with me, he had to put something in my little bag. He often used to beat me for this and brought me into bad company. But I wasn't submissive."

"Except in the case of Gouffé," remarked Latrille, and joined the group at the window, swinging the rope in his hand.

"Gouffé was different," she rejoined, pulling at her dress. "I wanted things to be serious with him."

"And serious they became," said Goron, pulling at his collar. "Where did Eyraudt go that evening, when he left this room?"

"I don't know. He took the key out of the dead man's trouser pocket and left. But when he came back in the early hours of the morning, he had no swag at all, although he had promised me plenty."

"But you knew nothing about his plans!" yelled Jaquemar. " 'Although he had promised you plenty'—he promised you!"

She rejoined politely: "He said: 'Stay here and don't stir from the spot, you beast; when I come back we shall be rich!' "

"And yet you didn't know what was going on," said Goron, shaking his head and glaring at her from behind his pince-nez.

"I knew he wasn't a man of honor. I took the precaution of hiding his hat, because he had accidentally put on Gouffé's, and because it fitted him very well he didn't notice his mistake. He was wearing it when he tossed Gouffé down the precipice at Marseilles, he wore it on board when we sailed across the great ocean, and he wore it to America. If I'm not mistaken, he is still wearing it, and will be wearing it when they put the handcuffs on him. He'll get a surprise when they take it off his head and ask him: 'How do you come to be wearing Gouffé's hat?' I played this trick on him and in this way I shall avenge Gouffé."

"I wish you would never utter that name again," snarled Jaquemar.

She leaned forward between Goron and Latrille and retorted: "No one else would have avenged him. I bear him no grudge for letting that other woman lead him around by the nose and for taking Michi's money away from him on her account. He deluded himself like a boy. He thought he could have a few hours' fun with me when it suited him. Yes, if he had been an Adonis and twenty years old! Someone who wished him well should have explained to him that a man can't keep a woman like me for his secret enjoyment, not when he has the beginnings of a potbelly and is as overripe as rotten fruit."

Jaquemar was standing, with clenched teeth and closed eyes, leaning his head against the wall, because the enormities that this person was doling out had set his head buzzing and made him feel dizzy; he felt as though an ever more overwhelming, all-enveloping noise was entering with the spring air through the open door; and although Bompard's voice went on speaking as if from far away in the background, the noise swelled to a roar, and it seemed to him to be a confused clangor of sounds that gradually became distinct; it was an excited, ringing, thundering, intermingling crash of bells like the bells of Val-de-Grâce. He opened his eyes, the booming died away, and he saw Bompard still leaning toward him and heard her say: "And because it is I who am responsible for his being avenged—for that is only a matter of time, and a short time—therefore, I ask for the reward to which I am entitled."

"You know," said Latrille jestingly and looking down at the rope he was swinging in his hands, "you shouldn't insist too stubbornly on getting your reward, Mademoiselle—the world is so unpredictable, who knows how things may turn out?"

"You mean," she replied, "because *he*" (and she indicated Goron with a movement of the head) "is trying to keep it from me? Jaquemar will give it to me."

"Enough of this twaddle!" cried Goron. "When Eyraudt went off with the key, did he know that Gouffé had eighteen thousand francs lying in his desk?"

"No!" she cried in amusement. "Did he? I know almost nothing about the business side of this affair. But you can see for yourselves: he was man enough to tan the hide of a weak woman like me, but when he took the big chance he lost his nerve. For although he committed this murder partly to punish me and Gouffé for our intimacy, he would never have had the courage to do it if he had not also intended to rob him. And then he had to be content with swiping his wife's jewelry! That's funny. He will tear his hair—so long as his head is still on his shoulders."

"You'll be laughing on the other side of your face before long!" said Goron, leaning down toward the arm of the chair. "Why didn't you come to the police, when Eyraudt had left you?"

"But he locked the door from the outside!" she retorted with a laugh. Then, still laughing, she turned toward Goron, who was very close to her; the laughter vanished from her face, something savage came into her delicate but now sharp features, and she hissed rather than shouted: "Get away from me! I find you revolting! You're trying to cheat me out of my reward! You are attacking my honor!"

"Oh, don't let's exaggerate," objected Latrille with amusement.

She calmed down and looked at Latrille with her shining eyes and explained: "He wants to pin it on me, because he needs a culprit. He wants to defraud the world of the truth. But he will pay dearly for playing fast and loose with me. He is trying to make me amenable to his lies, he is trying to intimidate me—he intimidate me! That's why he gives me rat's food so that I am forced to go hungry, that's why he makes me sleep between hempen sheets on a hard bed, that's why he keeps me in the cellar."

"God grant that is her last comfortable lodging before the beast is made shorter by a head," said Jaquemar, once more leaning against the wall with closed eyes.

"Do they execute women in this country?" she asked, leaning forward with interest. "With the ax?"

"The woman's mad!" said Goron, slowly straightening up without taking his eyes off her.

"H'm, mad. . . ." commented Latrille. "How did she fix it so that nobody in this house knew anything about her?"

"I always wear a veil," she answered, unasked, with a nod. "I called myself Geneviève Labodère, because Michi told me to. I didn't have to fix anything, because I had nothing to hide. I have nothing to hide. Should I be sitting here, if I had? How can I help the unfortunate complications?"

"Do you call the fact that you enticed Gouffé into the room where he was murdered an unfortunate complication?" shouted Goron, half bending down again.

She stared straight ahead and replied with a shrug of the shoulders: "We had an appointment."

Jaquemar, squinting down at her scornfully, said: "My brother-in-law had an appointment with you, did he? I heard something different."

"Very likely," she retorted, tidying her hair. "You know he tried to keep me secret."

"He had an appointment with Madame Chottin," said Jaquemar coldly to Goron. "They wanted to dine together."

"They wanted to?" she asked, her hand motionless in her hair. "He wanted to. But because it was easy to foresee that she wouldn't want to do what he wanted, but would lead him this way and that by the nose as usual, I said: 'You know where to find me. I shall take my apéritif in the Café des Lilas, in case your evening is empty and you feel like a change.' For I felt sorry for the lonely man who had no one who wished him well, and I bought the violet cachous in the Turkish Pavilion, drew the curtains here in the room, and lit the lamp, so that everything should be cosy if he came home with me—which he did, as I had expected."

"And Eyraudt?" inquired Goron in a threatening voice.

" 'Michi,' I said to him, 'I'm having a visitor this evening, so don't you disturb us!' I warned him beforehand, and if he had listened to my warning, his head would not be wobbling now."

"Enough!" cried Goron, wiping his brow with his handkerchief and turning his face toward the interior of the room. "Montardon."

Gabrielle Bompard was now playing with her curiously misshapen fingers in her lap, watching them with shining eyes. "For a joke," she said, "I also warned Gouffé, after I had twisted the cord of my dressing gown around his neck, and when I looked up, there, in spite of my warning, stood Michi with his bull-neck and his dangling, hairy, thick hands, and the disaster took its course."

"No angel is so pure!" ejaculated Jaquemar, with a savage, sneering laugh.

"Montardon," said Goron, looking over the rim of his pince-nez at the wardress, who came waddling toward the group by the window on curiously shapeless black shoes like webfeet, "take her to the van."

"Is Monsieur l'Inspecteur going to accompany us?" she asked, and kept her gray eyes fixed dreamily on Gabrielle Bompard.

"Come on, we're all going," answered Goron, and turned to the door, immediately followed by Latrille, who for some reason winked at Montardon and then, with a laugh, murmured something into the chief's ear.

Jaquemar hurried after the others. As he passed Gabrielle Bompard, who was still seated, he felt the touch of a hand on his hip; with a gulp he whispered "What impertinence is that?" and stared down at her with his bewildered squint; she was still playing with her crooked fingers and only now did she look up; Jaquemar fled from the room with his dainty walk, but not before he heard her remark: "Monsieur got out of bed on the wrong side this morning."

The sun was now shining straight into the yard, lighting up the creeper that trailed over the privy and casting thin, sharply defined shadows on to the asphalt from the flimsy garden furniture. The three men crossed the yard; but in front of the entrance to the tunnel (which was rectangular at this end) Goron halted, and they waited for the two women, who had just appeared on the steps leading down from the murder room. Bompard lifted her skirt in a gesture that was very womanly and at the same time audacious and, guided by Montardon's hand on her elbow, strode forward with beaming eyes. She was speaking, but too low for the three waiting men to hear what she was saying; Montardon's bosom was heaving with silent amusement, although she kept her face with the crooked little mouth and fat cheeks turned strictly to the front in a way that looked morose.

Goron and Jaquemar led the way down the steps into the passage, followed by the two women, with Latrille bringing up the rear. "Thank you for coming," said Goron. "I hope I shan't have to trouble you again in a hurry."

"I am at your disposal," answered Jaquemar stiffly.

"But there is one thing, Madame," said Bompard's voice behind them confidentially, "that every woman learns who is much loved: men never have simple feelings. They aren't capable of it. That is something you have to put up with, although it is very irritating and causes endless confusion."

"Devil take it," thought Jaquemar violently, his hands in his coat pockets pressed together over his stomach, "How the black draft gnaws at my eyes! Even the glimmer that comes in at the far end hurts me, and I think with disgust of the Hôtel des Mines and the dreams I shall dream there with the aid of Lebigot's narcotics. God, if you exist, help me through this evil time; I should like to go on a long journey (unfortunately I can't afford it) and forget everything."

It was after the strange open-air interview outside the Villa des Fleurs that journalists (making use of an expression in Eyraudt's letter) began to call Gabrielle Bompard by the rather generalized name under which she was to enter the Pitaval of our days; whether it was meant ironically or seriously, whether her beaming naivety was felt to be the antithesis of the demonic, or whether people believed they detected demonic qualities in this very naivety—henceforth she was invariably known as "our little demon." The interview, as was only to be expected, was broadcast far and wide in newspapers of every grade and created a sensation that was extremely unpleasant to Goron. It irked him, in particular, that Bompard's statements were reported without the slightest hint of doubt regarding their veracity. The newspapermen made merry over her terse manner of speech as a man makes merry over the amusing remarks of a very young mistress, and although her attacks on the Cité evoked chuckling comment that rather drastic methods could hardly be avoided in the attempt to render her tractable, this comment was accompanied by complaints that the Press and public were also being somewhat drastically treated by the "stern police chief," who had adopted a very highhanded attitude toward the sightseers in the Rue d'Assas.

As a matter of fact, the incident led to consequences that were diametrically opposed to Goron's plans and finally wrecked them. The reporters became more avid for news and hence more pushing than ever, and dissatisfaction was further increased when Goron reacted to this by a stricter system of interview passes and the punishment of any doorkeeper insufficiently rigorous in the exercise of his duties. One unwanted visitor who succeeded—heaven knows how—in making his way as far as Guillaume, on the morning of the third day, cut a rather ludicrous figure. He was a young man with a large bunch of flowers who insisted that he felt it his chivalrous duty to call on Mademoiselle Bompard, and refused to go until the secretary had promised to see that his flowers reached the prisoner—so long as the chief raised no objections. Goron threw them straight into the wastepaper basket without a word.

Another visitor proved more persistent, however. This was a very elegant gentleman in his fifties, dressed in a pearl-gray frock coat with silk lapels, with a pointed beard, short, curly, graying hair, and flashing black eyes, who gesticulated theatrically with his heavily beringed hands and left no doubt that he would know the correct legal steps to take if his application to see Mademoiselle was rejected. He called on the afternoon of the same day as the young man with the flowers and left behind him a perfectly filled-in form of application for an interview, remarking that there was no need to send the permit by post: he would call personally the following morning to obviate any further "undesirable" delay. Goron was forced to realize that he must accede to this request, if he wanted to avoid unpleasantness, including a possible clash with the Prefecture. The character and identity of the applicant, who declared himself partially responsible for Mademoiselle's fate, gave reason to expect such difficulties: the man's name was Carapin, Edouard Carapin.

He appeared punctually next morning, was at once shown in, greeted Goron with a deep, quick bow, placed his top hat, which matched his frock coat, on the desk, and sat down, holding his gold-tipped cane between his knees. Their conversation was a formality. Goron, suppressing his animosity and rummaging through his papers while he spoke, as though overburdened with work, explained, or rather stated categorically, that it was customary and to the advantage of everyone concerned for the person under arrest to be kept from all contact with the outside world. To the accompaniment of elegant and lively gestures with his beringed hands and with flashing eyes, but with every show of amiability (because he was manifestly flattered by this opportunity to dispute with the famous detective), Carapin eloquently stated his case. The last thing he wanted was to contradict the experience and opinion of a man of Goron's eminence; in any case, it was merely a sense of loyalty that compelled him to do what he could for his young friend, since although she had decided on her own initiative to make the journey that had brought her into this painful situation, he had himself vigorously supported this decision; moreover, he felt all the more strongly that it was his duty to give every possible assistance —also to the forces of justice—because he was convinced that a serious misunderstanding had developed.

Mademoiselle was admittedly full of *joie de vivre*—chivalry forbade him to explain his meaning more clearly—but to look on her as a criminal character was, if he might say so, a crass mistake that must strike anyone who had lived on intimate terms with her as simply grotesque. All the traits of her character, including the *joie de vivre* he had referred to, sprang from the purest of sources, namely her delightful innocence; he had never caught her out in the least lie—on the contrary, she was "a positive little fanatic for justice" and handled her affairs with a childlike respect for fair play that was nothing short of pigheaded and a disregard of other people's opinions that sometimes produced the most comical effects.

Ignoring the cane between his knees, Carapin accompanied these statements by throwing movements of the hands, as though he wished to fling them into his interlocutor's lap or lightly over his head like a juggler playing with balls. Goron gave way willy-nilly and conducted Carapin, who sprang to his feet and swept his top hat from the table with the gesture of a conjurer, into the next room. Since Latrille happened to be there, Goron ordered him to take the visitor down to the vaults.

Latrille went with him as far as the iron-bound door to the vaults.

Down below, the warder, raising the fingers of his right hand to the horizontal patent-leather peak of his round cap in response to the Inspector's order, rattled his bunch of keys and opened the door to the visitor. If he would go down the stairs and straight on, he would come to the corridor where the female prisoners were housed; here, seated at a small table, he would find Madame Montardon, whom he should inform of the purpose of his visit.

After descending the long, steep stairway Carapin entered a circular hall with a low roof and a circle of blue butterfly-flames burning on its walls. Here he found the little table, but no Montardon sitting at it. Three passages opened out of the hall in different directions and led away into the distance; Carapin walked past the little table (on which lay two sections of a black cardboard spectacle case) and took the passage facing the stairs. In his elegant spring clothes he looked very much out of place in this subterranean world, for the corridor along which he hesitantly advanced was bleak, built of massive blocks of gray stone marked here and there by dark rose-shaped patches of damp that had seeped through the stone and gleamed morbidly; small doors of unplaned, spongy wood, which hardly looked as though they were intended for human use, stood side by side along the whole length of the corridor; there was no end in sight, because far ahead of him the corridor turned a corner; up to this point it was decorated at regular intervals by the same blue butterfly-flames as the hall, which burnt without chimneys at the tips of short, sturdy wall brackets. It was deathly still and yet not without a secret life; a rustling as of straw or an occasional sigh from behind one of the doors and then the scurrying of a small animal that darted like a shadowy arrow past the intruder's feet with tail erect and vanished into the wall—or was this only a hallucination provoked by the sounds he thought he heard?

One thing Carapin could certainly hear, and increasingly clearly the further he advanced: a song sung by two voices, which rang out so incredibly thin and high-pitched that it seemed to be forcing its way out through the thick stone from miles away; and yet, as he quickly noticed, it came from a door quite close to him that was only ajar. On tiptoe, he crept to the door, and stood there listening. Because the voices had shriveled up to such an extraordinarily high, thin pitch, the song sounded almost like a soft lament, although it had a lively rhythm and was skilfully harmonized, one voice humming a high-pitched,

rather moaning accompaniment; while the other, sibilating the S-
sounds, whispered rather than sang: "Give me, my sweetheart / A
few pieces of silver . . ."

Nevertheless, Carapin recognized that this was the voice of his
beautiful young mistress, from whom he had parted in anger; he recognized it with emotion, so that he pressed his cane to his heart and
shook his head with closed eyes; to hear that voice again in this place
stirred him to the depths, tears flowed off his eyelashes and ran down
his cheeks into his pointed beard. But then, because the song came
to an end, he pulled himself together, swallowed his tears, replaced
them by a welcoming smile, and knocked more loudly than he had
intended; he pushed the door open and stood half-bent, since there
was no room to straighten up, in the entrance to the stone cell. Bompard, her face dimly lit by the flame on the opposite wall, was sitting on
her plank bed, while Montardon occupied a stool at right-angles to
her; the latter was knitting a woolen stole that poured from her lap and
over her feet onto the floor in an extraordinarily long, narrow stream.
Catching sight of the man, she laid one knitting needle over her
crooked little mouth; but Bompard looked away from the door into
the corner with her pouting smile.

"Gabrielle!" cried Carapin, entering and spreading out both arms,
his hat and cane held in his right hand. "*Ma petite* Gabrielle! Can you
forgive me?"

She mumbled something that sounded like "forgive but not forget"
and immediately afterward looked at Carapin, who sat down dramati-
cally beside her like a stage lover. Her shining black eyes, which mirrored the flickering blue flame, seemed even larger than usual in her
delicate snow-white face.

"See what a mess you've got me into!" she said, and without taking
her eyes off him, she pointed with a yellowish index finger first at the
tiny barred window that opened, high above, onto a narrow, lightless
shaft, then at the washstand with its tin basin that stood below the
window in one corner. "Furniture as though for a servant and no company but Montardon. You must let her show you the water closet
afterward, then you will really see what this place is like."

The wardress looked up at him, shook her head and whispered: "*La
jeune fille est très, très gentille.*"

She bent down to pick up the stole.

"Stay here, Madame," said Gabrielle Bompard, and Montardon straightened up, gasping for breath, sank back into her former posture, and went on knitting.

"Gabrielle," began Carapin urgently, wiping his eyes with the handkerchief he drew from his breast pocket, "we shall put everything right. I believe, in fact I know that injustice is being done to you, that injustice has been done to you." He lowered his voice and whispered with flashing eyes: "Forgive me, my sweetest, the nights with you are unforgettable."

"And what did I get out of it?" she retorted, gazing into his eyes. "They give me a hair shirt for a négligé."

At this the wardress uttered a low, squeaking, rattling laugh of sympathy that set her bosom bouncing.

"Gabrielle," Carapin began again, seizing and pressing the hands in her lap, "it will only be a little while, I shall do everything humanly possible for you, we shall spend the summer at Saratoga Springs, I shall give you a necklace of shimmering pearls, the tears of the ocean, the misunderstanding will vanish like a ghost—the moment I leave here I shall go as fast as I can to Maître Rebattu, the greatest orator in France; not a hair of your head shall be hurt."

Now she held her mouth close to his temple, not exactly kissing him, but speaking so that her lips touched his skin and sent a thrill through him, and said: "I should like a young cockerel. Will you please have it roasted in unsalted butter?"

A throat was cleared vigorously, and Latrille, with his narrow, cunning smuggler's head, stood stooped in the doorway. He said with a laugh: "I see Madame Montardon takes her duties seriously and does not leave her charge unwatched for a minute. You know, Monsieur, we're not monsters here and I'm sorry I have to intrude. But our order-loving chief insists on it, and after all, there must be order. May I ask you to terminate your conversation for today?"

Montardon pouted sulkily and picked up her knitting, Carapin half-rose, put both of Gabrielle's hands to his lips and said: "Mademoiselle, you shall want for nothing."

He gazed deep into her eyes, sighed, and turned away. Ducking his head as he passed Latrille, he went out with a last backward glance, pressing his cane to his heart, followed by Montardon in her webfoot shoes, and the door closed behind them.

Much as this visit with its immediate and later consequences irritated and disturbed Goron, a far more threatening reaction to the interview in the Rue d'Assas began to make itself felt. This was precisely the reaction which Goron had hoped to avoid by giving way to Carapin; he failed to avoid it because the same incident that had led to the elegant gentleman's visit had also given offense both to the general public and the higher authorities. The unrestrained protests of his superiors, brought by express messenger and accompanied by receipt forms requiring his personal signature, now lay before him, one signed with an undecipherable scribble, the other with the strikingly distinct name of Prefect Sallier. That the Prefecture should criticize the "mysterious and obnoxious methods of the Sûreté," castigating the latter for "grossly exceeding its authority," came as no surprise to Goron; such things had happened before, though this time, as he had to admit to himself, twisting his neck round in his collar, his adversaries were at least partially in the right.

But the one short sentence in which the Prosecutor General's Office asked to be informed "immediately" if reports from the Security Police regarding the arrest and interrogation of the prisoner Bompard had perhaps gone astray—this flat rhetorical question, as searing as ice that tears the skin off the fingers, frightened Goron; for, although there was no proof, it was safe to conjecture that it came from Lozé, his patron, on whose supposedly staunch protection he was largely dependent as a defense against the ill-will of the Prefecture. What a good thing that at least Carnot showed no sign of anger! He was the one whom the case directly concerned and he said nothing, he understood. Ought Goron to appeal to him, to his patiently approving silence?

This was the first time since brushes with the higher authorities had become a common occurrence that Goron felt himself to be in danger. The awareness of danger made him cautious: he resolved to postpone his reply for twenty-four hours—and then, unfortunately, a new development rendered him incautious again and induced him to reply to both departments with a discourteous terseness and in identical words, without any excuses or any personal note. The case in question, he wrote, was being dealt with in the customary manner (which was more or less true) and would be handed over to the Prosecution Department, who had raised no objection to the Sûreté's procedure, in about three weeks' time, when the preliminary investigations had been completed. He sent a copy of this letter, with a few lines of greeting, to the Senior Examining Magistrate and, in the pressure of business, overlooked the fact that no answer came either to this copy or to the two originals—until it did come, that is to say, until shortly after Eyraudt's arrival in Paris.

For it was this, when the news reached him, that made him throw caution to the winds and gave him a feeling of triumph which he prematurely interpreted as "victory all along the line," since he naively took it for granted that everyone involved, his opponents as well as himself, was ultimately concerned about the case, and that whoever was right over the case would be regarded as right over everything. Eyraudt had been arrested. What more could anyone want? What more cogent proof could there be of the correctness, the efficacy of his "methods"?

A cable from the Embassy in Washington merely gave the information that Eyraudt had been arrested and handed over and would be dispatched on the *Ile de France* leaving New York on March 8.

So he was on his way, and Goron knew that in a few weeks this case would be over and done with, finished and forgotten like so many earlier ones. In the meantime, of course, it irritated him to find that he could make no headway with Bompard, that on the contrary he was compelled to abandon his policy of intimidation.

It was Maître Rebattu, the celebrated barrister, who compelled him with all the weight of his highly individual and pleasant personality. He appeared the picture of unconstrained dignity in a black frock coat, high wing collar, and narrow patent-leather shoes, the ribbon of the Legion of Honor in his buttonhole; and the most perfect, but at the same time the most natural, the most pleasant French Goron had ever heard rang in his ears with sonorous euphony. He was quite irresistibly pleasant and engaging; his speech, which was almost completely devoid of gestures and in the course of which he frequently rounded his lips as though to utter a conciliatory "Oh," was pleasant; his laugh that came straight from his heart in low, muted peals was pleasant; and the sleek brown hair on his comparatively small head was pleasant. But it was as though, after this first impression of pleasantness, something that had been expected failed to follow; his interlocutor was left, as it were, unsatisfied, and it was not solely due to circumstances, not solely Goron's fault, that he felt a slight sense of uneasiness throughout the conversation.

The lenses of the visitor's gold-rimmed spectacles gave off a highly polished, sharp glitter, and yet there was something odd in this cultured, refined, thoughtful face. The strongly marked eyebrows, considerably darker than the silky brown hair of the head, did not seem properly related to each other; the right one lay at an angle to the left, as though pushed out of position by repressed laughter. The nose above the long upper lip was slightly crooked, as though knocked out of true by an uppercut striking it at an angle. In short, there was a touch of the gallows' bird about this intellectual face, something that aroused a vague distrust, a distrust which was not entirely allayed by the fact that the *soigné* gentleman had tired, nut-brown eyes behind his coruscating spectacles and, when he did not thrust it out in a conciliatory "Oh," a slack, embittered mouth, the mouth of a man who has accepted final disappointment.

The arguments which he presented in support of his highly unwelcome request were as dignified as his demeanor and appearance, and couched in the most pleasantly reasonable terms. He asked that the young lady, whose defense he was thinking of assuming, should be given her legal rights, in particular that of providing her own food and of being allowed to receive the friends who were advising her, whenever she pleased. In any case, it was scarcely advisable to provide fresh fuel for the widespread and unbridled hostility toward the Sûreté, since the period during which they had been left an entirely free hand in the matter must have sufficed to accumulate the evidence necessary for legal proceedings—or was the Prosecution Department of a different opinion? In that event, he would naturally be ready to negotiate with the Department direct.

Goron, his fingers crossed over his waistcoat, looked at the cigar in his right hand and briefly nodded his head, filled with a puzzled feeling that he really ought to be able to speak freely and frankly to this visitor about his difficulties. But all he said was: Maître Rebattu underestimated the prisoner's obduracy, she had disclosed the most hideous details but confessed to nothing whatsoever. At this Maître Rebattu laughed understandingly with his shoulders, but continued to look at Goron with tired eyes through his flashing lenses as he replied that this was certainly regrettable, but only on the assumption that the accused was in a position to confess what Monsieur Goron wanted to hear—after all, she could not confess to a crime of which she was innocent—quite apart from the fact that, according to law, nobody could be compelled to testify against himself. Indeed he, Rebattu, though not personally acquainted with the prisoner, could not shake off an instinctive belief that she was being unjustly suspected, which, incidentally, was the only reason he was considering taking up her defense. This latter remark was all the more credible because it was many years since the famous barrister had appeared in a criminal case, which he would normally have considered beneath his dignity. He was now chiefly engaged in important cases of disputed wills and the like and was the confidential adviser of the nobility and the wealthiest families in the land, especially those who owned mines. If a conversation with the young lady convinced him that his instinct was mistaken, he continued, he would withdraw from the case and leave the defense to someone with more of a—shall we say, sense of vocation.

This appeared to Goron an attractive possibility and, indeed, probability; he laughed amidst the smoke of his black cigar and commented that in that case he feared he would not be seeing Maître Rebattu again for some time. The latter, allowing the smoke of his Russian cigarette to trickle out of his crooked nostrils, joined amiably in Goron's laughter and, protruding his lips like a funnel, responded that there would certainly be occasion to continue and deepen the flattering acquaintanceship. Not until his visitor was on his way to the vaults, conducted by Guillaume, did it dawn on Goron how yielding he had been—in response to the dictates of justice and common sense, it was true, but contrary to his own profound conviction.

Rebattu strode along beside Guillaume through the underground corridor with the little doors of cork-like timber, which looked almost like oven doors in the damp and dripping wall. "Not a very cheerful residence," he remarked, laughing shortly through his nose. "Well, we shall see." Once more, Montardon was not at her table; and, as on the occasion of Carapin's visit, the door to Bompard's cell was ajar. "Don't worry, Madame," a voice full of polite obstinacy could be heard saying, "there is time for everything." When the visitors looked in, after knocking on the door, the wardress was standing with her stomach protruding and a glass of milk in her hand, while Bompard pouted in the corner. "She won't eat her food again," Montardon explained to Guillaume, adding with a repressed laugh: "She says she'll only eat what she feels like eating." "Many thanks," said Maître Rebattu to Guillaume, and, nodding with closed eyes, motioned Montardon with two fingers to go.

In the light of the butterfly-flame the young prisoner looked as pale as death, but more beautiful than ever, especially as the curls piled on top of her head gleamed like blue enamel and (perhaps through undernourishment) a sweet violet shadow lay under her beaming eyes, suggesting, in a way that was both innocent and sensual, past indulgence in the pleasures of love. Rebattu hid his delight at her appearance behind a coaxingly paternal manner, with which he was immediately successful. As he assured her that henceforth she could order whatever she liked in the way of meals, she broke out into merry laughter, seized the glass Montardon had left on the lowered flap table on the wall and drained it in a series of short, quick gulps like a child —which left a comical milky mustache on her upper lip. But her cheerful mood quickly gave way again to her former sulking, and she murmured: "I don't want to live here any longer; my plan was to move into the Hôtel des Mines. Will you please tell Carapin that?"

Rebattu laughed sympathetically. "Well, well," he answered, "we shall see. Monsieur Carapin is doing everything he can; it is thanks to him that I am here."

"That's very kind of him," she replied, with a rebellious nod of the head. "Tell him that the only other company I have is Montardon and the mice."

She looked up with her bold face and cried out in a feeble voice: "I'm nearly at the end of my patience! I shall pay back all those who are trying to get at me."

"You mustn't forget that the circumstances are—what shall we say? —misleading," Rebattu pointed out, looking down at his hands, which he was gently rubbing together. "Quite apart from all the things they are saying and writing about you—and, you know, every Tom, Dick, and Harry, every Grub-street hack, the whole rag, tag, and bobtail have poured their filthy speculations over your head."

"Am I not getting a good press?" she inquired with interest.

"I wouldn't say that," he replied, with protruding lips and tilting his head thoughtfully to one side. "It is two-edged and can be taken either way."

"You," she said gaily, clutching his sleeve as though with claws, "you will make the wicked man sorry for what he's done. He must be punished, he is trying to cheat me of my rights."

"You mean Monsieur Goron? Oh, he's a worthy man. But we shall deal with him. All you have to do, my dear child, is to tell me the unvarnished truth."

"I never lie," she retorted curtly.

"I'm sure you don't," said Rebattu cordially and pressed both her hands. "Well, then. . . ."

The conversation between the two of them lasted a very long time, and the parting, when it finally came, was easy and intimate, although when the famous man, once more calling her his dear child, lightly shook hands with her he was unable to withdraw his hand because, lying back laughing on her plank bed, she held it fast, even placing the nails of her left hand on his wrist as she said: "Don't forget, I don't want to lose anything over this stupid business. Michi, the coward, should have finished himself off properly, instead of having to mount the guillotine. But I have been detained long enough; I want to move on. Tell Carapin I want to go to Saratoga Springs."

She let go of his hands, beamed down at the floor, and murmured: "I have many plans."

Immediately after this conversation, Maître Rebattu informed Goron that he was henceforth to be regarded as Mademoiselle Bompard's official counsel, that within the next hour he would send in the dinner ordered by the young lady, and that he would very soon be in touch with Goron again. He conveyed all this with a touch of impatience, and requested Goron, politely but firmly, not to encroach in any way on the prisoner's legal rights—otherwise he would be regretfully compelled to make a vigorous protest; this, of course, was without prejudice to any protest he might feel compelled to make over what had already happened. Thereupon he bowed, wished the uneasy and disappointed Goron good day, and left.

Within the next hour, as announced, an exquisite meal was delivered for Gabrielle Bompard and served up by Montardon, who first spread out a clean white table napkin (which had been brought with the meal) on the flap table. As she busied herself with the preparations, she kept giggling asthmatically to herself with a rippling bosom, for her young charge's successful pigheadedness seemed to her irresistibly comical. The latter looked at her with shining eyes and finally said: "I shall remind Carapin to see that you do not suffer for your helpfulness, Madame."

So Gabrielle Bompard sat down to dinner in her own way, and while the Press were adopting the unusual practice of publishing each day the menu on which she regaled herself (the expression is apt, since she ate with the same determination with which she had previously fasted), the Ile de France was steaming under a clear sky and on a rough sea toward its destination. Jaquemar thought of it frequently as he sat at dusk in his wing chair at the Hôtel des Mines, and he found it strange and rather eerie to picture the ship, with Gouffé's half-sentenced murderer in her belly, steaming on and on, drawing closer and closer. From the endless distance of the horizon the waves came rolling to meet her, came rolling against the bows with the short jack staff, foamed over them in a turmoil of white spray, and flowed off with a swishing sound, as the ship, solitary in the vast expanse, the steam snarling softly in her funnel, nodding slowly up and down as though giving her assent to justice being done, held firmly and purposefully to her course and carried her cargo to Deibler, to Monsieur de Paris.

The Ile de France docked at Saint-Nazaire on March 22, an exceedingly foggy day, as a result of which she sailed hesitantly into the harbor, past the figure bearing a palm branch that stands in the shallow water, to the accompaniment of repeated blasts from her foghorns and the raucous, ear-splitting hooting and tooting of the launches and tugs that were bringing her in. It must have seemed to Eyraudt, in the brig deep down in the belly of the ship, as though the sounds that reached him faintly from outside were heralding his own fate—gloomy, malignant, and implacable. But not until evening had fallen was he fetched under cover of darkness and dispatched to his ultimate destination in the care of two plain-clothes policemen. On the morning of March 23, around eight o'clock, he arrived at the Gare Saint-Lazare in Paris.

Sitting with handcuffed hands crossed over his abdomen, and wedged between his two escorts, who, in spite of the manacles, held him by each arm, he saw the carriage door open from outside and looked down into the hamster-cheeked face with the pince-nez below (the breath came like thin gray smoke from Goron's mouth), the boorish Soudrais, and the other detective sergeants, and the mute throng of the curious, whom the early hour had not deterred from being present at his reception. Involuntarily he raised his arms and tried to draw back, he looked around over his shoulder as though in search of help, and, almost to his astonishment, heard a scornful laugh ring out here and there among the crowd. Then he looked out again, with his mouth open and his thick lower lip drooping in his beard, and hatred and fear were mirrored in his goggling face. His once-full cheeks, now wasted by vice and chagrin, were marked by two longitudinal black furrows like streaks of pitch, and his whole face presented an indescribably abject and seedy appearance, particularly as the police had confiscated his hat and replaced it with a jockey cap, beneath which his ears stuck out widely.

He shivered in the icy coal-dust dampness of the station, so that for a moment his head trembled violently as though he were saying "No"; this aroused fresh peals of laughter. He looked quickly and malevolently from one side to the other with an indignant gulp, then ducked his head on the enfeebled, slack-skinned neck, behind which, like a broad hump, curved the still powerful back. Goron's hands—first the right, with a beckoning gesture, then the left as well—were stretched up toward him. "Come along!" cried Goron. The escorts pushed him from behind and, staggering half a pace forward, he dropped his manacled hands into Goron's. A senseless grin contorted his foul face and he heard cries of "Fie!" greet him from the crowd—or were these shouts of revulsion not directed at Eyraudt?

He was incapable of rational thought; he was now trembling from head to toe; supported by Goron, and gripped from above by the shoulders of his overcoat, he climbed hurriedly down the steps to the accompaniment of increasingly loud cries of "Fie!" Once on terra firma, he was immediately surrounded by detective sergeants and pushed into motion. His head with its jockey cap ducked between his shoulders, and walking with a tripping step, he was escorted by the encircling myrmidons of the law along the narrow platform, past the puffing locomotive, and through the booking hall, where the hustle and bustle came suddenly to a stop and crowds of people rushed toward the group wildly craning their necks. After this, they emerged into the open air, where once again, to Eyraudt's surprise, thousands of people were waiting to catch a glimpse of him. They were waiting for him, lusting for blood, and the moment he appeared under the projecting roof of the booking hall they gave vent in raucous shouts and yells of "To the guillotine!" "Off with his head!" "Murderer!" to a savage hatred that threatened to degenerate into physical violence.

The police detailed to keep order had to link hands in a protective chain, leaning back with all their weight against the pressure from behind them. It looked as though at any moment the chain might break; it was forced inward, first at one point, then at another, so that some of the detective sergeants had to come to the rescue and exert a counterpressure with their chests and the flat of their hands, while over their heads and far back into the crowd eager heads were craned, threatening fists were shaken, and gradually a kind of savage caterwauling filled the air, punctuated by shouts of "Off with his head!"—a yowl of rage and hate, whistling, and groans of disgust, that rang in the ears of the trembling Eyraudt like the outcry of a host of avenging demons. A terror worse than anything he had ever experienced made his eyes pop out of his head; and although he was held in a viselike grip, he tried to rush forward to the little yellow omnibus, with a uniformed driver on the box, that was standing at the edge of the square. But Soudrais, who was walking in front of him, turned around and struck him such a violent blow in the chest that he staggered back, only to be dragged forward by the rest of the escort; thus punched back and dragged forward, and at the same time doubled up by a retching cough, he stumbled and fell to his knees, after which they hauled him quickly along, cursing him and jabbing him in the back, as though he were resisting—quickly, but not fast enough for him, since in his terror, the ceaseless caterwauling and the dull thud of the milling, shoving multitude seemed to him a threat that the mob would put him to death here and now, that they would quarter him, trample him under their feet, and stamp him to pieces.

He was bundled up the steps of the little omnibus; he landed under the impetus of his own weight on the wooden seat inside and sank sideways with closed eyes. As the two horses moved off, his head struck the wooden seat; he broke into a whimper and wanted to cry, to wallow in his misery and weep like a little boy; but Soudrais, who had sat beside him on his left, roughly dragged him upright, struck him a fresh blow in the chest, and barked: "Quiet!"

"Don't strike the prisoner," came the sharp rebuke from Goron, who was sitting opposite, his arms folded over his chest and a reproving expression on his face. Soudrais stared down at the floor, vacantly smacking his lips, while Eyraudt, whose eyes were wide open and staring, gazed for the second time into the hamster-cheeked face with the pince-nez under the black bowler hat.

Perhaps the piercing eyes in this face disappointed in him some ill-defined hope; anyhow, he quickly looked away again, allowing his thick lower lip to droop crookedly; and now, since cowardice had slightly relaxed its grip on him, the obscene side of his nature broke through, and he growled with a laugh: "They can kiss my arse. I'm only surprised I wasn't led off seated back to front on a donkey. On a donkey—heh, like the Jewboy in Jerusalem in the year dot."

The blasphemy seemed to cheer him up; but only for a little while, then some other feeling took possession of him—perhaps a recollection of the childhood piety we all experience—and he stared down in front of him with dull hopelessness. They were now driving across the Place de la Concorde; no one said a word; then all at once the fine house-fronts on the Quai des Tuileries caught his attention, the trees, the lively yet peaceful bustle in the blue-gray morning light; he stared with eyes that popped farther and farther out of his head, let the hands with the fetters sink lower and lower between his knees, and whispered with closed lips: "My God, my God, what have I done with my life?"

They drove into the rear courtyard of the Cité; and when he looked up, encouraged by Soudrais who was shaking him by the shoulder, the omnibus had come to a halt and Goron had already clambered out. He called back: "At four o'clock—tell them down below!" and hurried off toward the building.

The detective sergeants led Eyraudt across the yard and down the steep stairway into the vaults. When they reached the hall with the blue butterfly-flames all around, Soudrais stepped forward, whistled, and called out, mimicked by the hollow echo: "Hey, Montardon!" Eyraudt saw an obese black-clad figure emerge from the wall of the corridor facing him and come waddling closer. Then the passage on the left-hand side swallowed him up, and, groaning under a sense of irreparable humiliation, he bent down in front of the low hole giving access to the cell and was pushed into the darkness. He staggered forward onto the plank bed; no light was burning, and the last bluish glimmer vanished as though devoured by the creaking of the door, which was shut and bolted behind him.

He was left in the dark—contrary to regulations but on express instructions from Goron, who was hoping that such a blatant demonstration of his desperate plight would fan Eyraudt's rage and hatred toward the woman he held responsible for all his misery. Goron was banking on this psychological reaction. The more bitter the hate between the two accomplices, the more damaging and the more useful would be the accusations they leveled at one another—so Goron thought. But whether because he had omitted some imponderable factor from his psychological calculations, whether, to be more precise, he had once more underestimated Bompard's peculiar power, or for some other reason—the confrontation proved a disappointment, at least insofar as he had looked forward to a defeat for Bompard. In fact, it was terminated prematurely and ended with a breakdown on the part of Eyraudt, while Bompard, with her anguished clown's eyebrows and amidst the rustle of her full skirt, returned gaily to her sumptuous evening meal in the vaults.

At a few minutes to four, Eyraudt heard a key turn in the lock of his cell door, someone entered with bent head and lit the open gas flame on the wall, and he recognized Soudrais, who motioned him with a jerk of the head to stand up. Soudrais fiddled impatiently with the handcuffs without speaking; and Eyraudt, as he watched him with pendulous lips, said nothing either. When his wrists were free he rubbed them, and it was clear from the movements of his flabby mouth that he was muttering silent curses; but then he laughed and growled: "I only hope the slut has also been through the mill!" "Shut your trap!" retorted Soudrais. "Get a move on!" and he pointed with the handcuffs to the door-hole. Eyraudt crawled out; but his gaiety at the thought that his faithless mistress had had an equally bad time continued; and, as they strode along the tunnel-shaped stone passage and mounted the steep stairway, his demeanor was not particularly downcast; without the disfiguring cap, he carried himself almost like an ordinary citizen going freely about his business, even smoothing down the strands of greasy hair that lay across his bald pate.

On the second floor they crossed the anteroom; Soudrais knocked, and went in to Goron, who was sitting at his desk writing and rummaging through papers. But Eyraudt took no notice of him; as though drawn by some mechanism he went between the table and the five empty chairs in a semicircle in front of it to a wretched little mirror that hung on the wall. He stood in front of this mirror and gazed into it as though under a spell. He wiped his thick lower lip with the back of his right hand, moved his head closer, ran the palms of his hands in a circle, first downward, then upward, over his cheeks and nose, and then looked again. He looked for a long time and then whispered: "Good God, I've changed."

"Sit down—there!" ordered Goron, glancing up for a moment and pointing with his finger to the second chair on his left. Then he returned to his writing, while Eyraudt, goggle-eyed and with his loosely-clenched right hand held to his mouth, obeyed the order.

A few minutes later the door opened and Bompard appeared, followed by Montardon, to whom she was just saying, concluding some preceding conversation: "You'll see, Madame!" At the sight of her, Eyraudt sprang to his feet and seemed to be gasping for breath; he raised both fists and his head sank down into the curve of his powerful shoulders as if ready to butt. Bompard, however, stood there erect and elegant, in spite of the long, narrow, white woollen stole that did not seem to go with the firmness of her bosom and the coquettish fullness of her velvet skirt. With shining eyes and her customary shy yet unembarrassed smile she said, as though to herself: "Heavens above. . . . He hasn't grown any handsomer."

Whether it was this utterance or the sight of her radiant charms, of which he had so long been deprived and in happier times had so licentiously enjoyed (with her curly hair on top of her head, her smiling face with its delightfully firm cheeks and the delicious promise of her slightly parted lips, she was totally unchanged, apart from a new and as yet scarcely defined covetousness that now gleamed in her eyes), something or other in her mien seemed to unman his hatred, this diligently accumulated hatred which was suddenly reduced to a mere intention, swept away by a terror that was perhaps nothing more than unadmitted delight, for he unclenched his fists with a sob, let them fall against his thighs, and blurted out in a curiously feeble voice between lips that had turned gray: "Abominable Venus of the guillotine. If only I could get at you."

She turned her face half away, but kept her eyes on Eyraudt as she remarked with calm contempt: "He's not very prepossessing, is he? It doesn't show much pride on my part that I let him—"

Pensively she left her sentence unfinished. Eyraudt now stared down in front of him, white-faced, and whispered: "Why did I have to step into this sweet boghole? He is a lucky man who gets out with a broken leg."

She did not hear him; in her turn, she was now staring down with her head on one side, and she said impartially: "Of course, he wasn't such a wreck then. But now he has more sense. Isn't that so, Michi?" She glanced up. "You wouldn't beat me now, would you?"

She looked at him and shook her head, as though answering on his behalf.

He had to look at her again. An indefinable expression of thirst, such as seems to be visible in the skulls of animal and human skeletons, crept over his face; it had no connection with the reply he uttered hoarsely and as though speaking from outside himself: "If only I had beaten you to death."

"So that I couldn't go off with Carapin?" she asked in a matter-of-fact voice.

"Excuse me, ladies," interrupted an urbane voice; and Latrille insinuated himself into the room past Montardon and Bompard, but immediately came to a stop, crooked his right arm with an ironic bow, and said to Gabrielle: "My lovely one—may I offer you my arm?"

With a little girl's laugh she placed her hand on his arm, stepped boldly forward in her full skirt, and allowed herself to be led to the row of chairs in front of Goron's desk.

Soon they were all seated in a semicircle in front of Goron, with the fat wardress on the extreme left, the boor on the extreme right and Latrille in the center between Bompard and Eyraudt. At the last moment Guillaume joined them and sat down at the end of the desk with his shorthand pad on his crossed knees. Bompard was visibly amused by the arrangement. She leaned forward and looked all around; her gaze seemed to stumble on the goggle-eyed Eyraudt and rest there; she raised her shoulders and eyebrows like a schoolchild making a sign to another; then she turned to the pock-marked Latrille and inquired in an undertone: "Do you think he's worth ten thousand francs? I have kept my word."

"I have only a few questions to ask you, Eyraudt," began Goron, resting on his forearms and playing with a pencil. "There is very little I need to know—you are a convicted man. But what was Bompard's part in all this? Did she seek out the victim, or was she only the lure?"

"I don't know anything about it," answered Eyraudt, staring in front of him. "When I came into the room they had already done for him."

This part of the interrogation is not worth reporting in detail—suffice it to say that Eyraudt dished up his old lies again and obstinately stuck to them, but without verve; he repeated them with a monotonous obduracy, like something learned by rote, and finally realized, as though suddenly waking up, that nobody even thought them worth interrupting—not even Gabrielle Bompard, who looked straight into Latrille's eyes with the trace of an incredulous smile on her mouth all the time Eyraudt was speaking. Perhaps it was the expression on the face of the woman he was trying, with so little passion, to incriminate that made his anger flare up in a shortlived blaze; or it might have been Goron's reminder that he had visited Gouffé's office that same night, "oddly enough" wearing the murdered man's hat—be that as it may, all at once he threw caution to the winds, his pent-up hatred broke through, and with trembling fists he raged at Bompard: "The fiend! The beast! It's all her fault! She engineered it all! She slipped the hat into my hands, so that I should look guilty! She sent me there—she, she, she! I was only her tool, I'm her victim."

"He's squirming," she said, looking into Latrille's eyes. Then she leaned forward and continued to Eyraudt: "Michi, you're behaving like an insect on a pin. But however hard you wriggle, you still won't budge an inch."

He tried to spring to his feet, but Soudrais, with clinking handcuffs in his left hand, held him fast; and he yelled, with his head thrust forward and his bloodshot eyes popping out of their sockets: "I'll do for you! I'll send you to the guillotine! Even if I have to go with you! All right, I did it—but you drove me to it, you kept egging me on, you were randy, you can't see a pair of trousers without getting an itch, you were randy and greedy for his money, you brainless whore, you worked the whole thing, you engineered it all!"

"Because I said: 'He's a pleasant man, unobtrusive and well-to-do'?" she asked with her astonished smile. "But it was you who told me, Michi! Because he withdrew that woman Chottin's money from your business at Jaquemar's request, and I was to beg him on your behalf to leave it there, you told me what kind of man he was and you already had your eye on him. But I talked to him about something quite different. Nevertheless, I gave you another chance: 'Become well-to-do like him,' I said, 'so that we can live decently, and I will stay with you, although you have often maltreated me.' "

" 'His money, chéri,' you said, 'and everything will be all right.' "

"But you misunderstood me—just as you misunderstood me before over the poor baker's boy. Did he ever recover?"

With a silent laugh she put her head on one side, while Eyraudt gulped with fright and then yelled: "You lured him into the house!"

"He beat the baker's boy half to death," she said cheerfully to Goron, "which was quite unnecessary. We were living in the whores' district by the Fortifs, I very much wanted a pastry, and I said to him: 'Order a pastry from Baker Dubocage, order it to be delivered at a particular time in the evening to a fake address C.O.D., then waylay the boy and take it from him.' We were going to pay later, for as usual he hadn't a sou."

"Lies, all lies," moaned Eyraudt feebly.

"But when the boy came along the lonely path in the winter's darkness, he fell on him and beat him half to death. Did he die? I never heard, although there was a lot of talk about it at the time. But that's what Michi is like: in his brain, every joke gets twisted and becomes bloodthirsty. He is incapable of moderation; and when jealousy is added, the situation is really bad. To my great regret, that was what happened over Gouffé. I'm sorry about that nice man. Now Jaquemar has all he possessed and I shall get only ten thousand francs' blood money."

"Didn't you rent the rooms in the Rue d'Assas?"

"The boy's name," she added casually, "was Perrier."

But the hitherto-unsolved case of little Perrier, Baker Dubocage's errand boy, was well known to the police; Guillaume had taken down Bompard's statements unasked in his shorthand notebook, and the fact that nobody questioned him about it aggravated Eyraudt's weakness and despair, so that his subsequent accusations sounded like evasions and are worth mentioning only because they further strengthened Bompard's defense in a way that was most unwelcome to Goron. "Didn't you telegraph me in London?" demanded Eyraudt, wiping his lips in his beard. "Didn't you make the sack? Didn't you entice him into the house?"

"And I was so looking forward to seeing him—I specially bought the violet cachous at the Turkish Pavilion, because they taste very sweet and scented and go well with an hour of love. And because you said to me: 'He collected a large sum of money today,' I was particularly pleased and hoped he would be responsive and in a willing mood, although that other woman had led him by the nose and then jilted him. But I warned you and said: 'Michi, I'm having a visitor this evening; don't disturb us, because I want things to be serious with him.' Why didn't you listen to me? Then there would have been no roughhouse and none of the unpleasantness that faces you now."

"She," blurted out Eyraudt in a kind of gasping tremolo, staring at Goron with his fists trembling against his chest, "she thought it all out, she led me astray, she telegraphed to me in London."

" 'Must love be beautiful,' " she confirmed with a brief nod. "That was what we arranged in the event of my having a prospect of winning Gouffé's love. You were quite concerned about it. 'Good luck to you,' you said."

"She chose the rooms."

"Two, on your advice," she confirmed again. "I thought this idea had occurred to you so that we should be nice and comfortable. Really," she remarked confidentially to Latrille, "really one bed is enough for enjoyment, but Gouffé was a married man, even if retired, and in such cases you have to reckon with a man being a bit worn-out."

Eyraudt ran his curiously stiff, outspread fingers through his greasy strands of hair and slumped back into the chair. Latrille, falling in with Bompard's tone, commented in a half-questioning voice: "You had been with him often, I mean after you went to see him in his office—that's how you got this idea about his marital habits?"

"Certainly," she replied. "I was seriously considering him as a lover; you can see what a shabby piece of work I had got hold of in Michi."

"H'm, in spite of the other woman."

"He has paid dearly enough for that," she retorted brusquely.

"I was completely in her power!" bawled Eyraudt. "She has alienated me from my family, she has bled me white, she has robbed me of my senses with her damned lechery, she drove me half crazy with her fiendish promptings, she is an absolute demon, no one can escape her clutches. I am innocent! Innocent! Why are you holding me? Make *her* a head shorter!"

She looked at Latrille and said: "He was in my power! Yet he thrashed me like an old house dog."

"Why did you let him?" asked Latrille casually.

She smiled down at the floor and said nothing.

"Why did he do it?"

"Because he was afraid, of course!" she explained with a laugh. "Afraid I might run away from him. That tormented him unceasingly! Even on the night when he did for Gouffé and then had his pleasure with me on the trunk, even after this Black Mass of love, he stood in the doorway before he set out to do the robbery and threatened me. He said: 'And heaven help you if you try to give me the slip.'"

"You'd have done it, too, you cat in heat!" shouted Eyraudt in a fresh outburst. "And you would have left me to carry the can, if I hadn't locked you in!"

She leaned forward and said: "Write that down, Monsieur Guillaume: 'if he hadn't locked me in.'"

Eyraudt did not realize the great service he had rendered Bompard with this remark; he looked from her to the secretary and back again and muttered hoarsely: "Of course, was I to let her go away? She had worked the whole thing, it was obvious that at the first opportunity she would rat and try to pin it all on me. It's plain to see. The first moment I let her out of my sight, she ran off with someone else and squealed on me."

She nodded to Guillaume, with eyes closed knowingly and chin in the air, and whispered: "The first moment he let me out of his sight."

Her quiet good humor, Latrille's wary and surprised "H'm," and the piercing look Goron gave him all combined, since he understood none of them, to make Eyraudt's rage flare up again. He tried to jump to his feet, but was again held by Soudrais. Then he bellowed: "The hussy poisons everything! It's an abominable plot! I was a decent man. And what am I now?"

He clapped his hands over his face and burst out coughing and weeping. Goron said impatiently: "Control yourself. You spoke of promptings. What did Bompard prompt you to do? Eyraudt!"

She leaned toward him; he raised his face from his hands; his protruding eyes were wet and sparkling tears welled up and flowed over his lower lids. He sniffed and sighed miserably: "Everything, everything. I was only her tool. I can't describe it. She said: 'Look at Gouffé; he is well off and very unobtrusive.' That meant: 'Nobody bothers about him, nobody will ever notice if he disappears.'"

She glanced at Goron and commented: "It meant: 'He's not like you, he's not a pauper, a ruffian, or a braggart; if I give him what he wants it won't compromise me.'"

But Eyraudt, at whom she was now looking again, continued in his former tone (and with closed eyes): "She was always at me about it, she didn't give me a moment's peace."

"I had to change my circumstances," she said, shrugging her shoulders, and asked Latrille, with her astonished smile: "Can I help it if he misunderstood me?"

He slowly raised his head; he looked at her, his lips hanging slackly in his beard, and said dully, perhaps incredulously remembering it: "I loved you."

"Thank you, Michi," she replied with a polite nod. "And don't blame me if after enjoyment come lassitude and melancholy—in great things as in small."

Latrille laughed like a man of the world; Montardon pressed two fingers over her small mouth and uttered an almost inaudible whimpering giggle that set her bosom wobbling. But Gabrielle, as she took off her stole, folded it, and smoothed it out on her lap, declared with a smile beneath her anguished brows, but in a sensible, serious tone devoid of irony: "You laugh, Madame. Monsieur has nothing to laugh about. It's all up with the yellow head I used to stroke to calm his evil temper."

"To the guillotine!" burst out Eyraudt with a sob. "With me, if needs must!"

"That," she replied alertly, raising the rather crooked and wrinkled index finger of her right hand, which stood out the color of parchment against her dark dress, "that will not happen. You will go alone and without a collar, when dawn is stealing across the sky, and the small audience will be dressed in frock coats and top hats. And you will be shivering so much with loneliness, as they lead you up the wooden steps, that you won't even think of me, neither of the thrashings in America nor of the lovemaking in Paris."

"Well, Eyraudt," cut in Goron, rapping on the desk with his knuckles, as Bompard lowered her still upraised finger, "haven't you any definite facts to relate? Nothing concrete and precise? Did she give you information about opportunities, times, places, did she pump Gouffé as to when he collected large sums of money or where he kept them? These general accusations won't help you!"

"Yes," answered Eyraudt, taking heart, "yes, she did all that! Again and again! I'm meeting him at such and such a time, at such and such a place—he's coming tonight, and don't disturb us! They were all taunts, you understand, and all for the same purpose! She goaded me, saying: 'He's a nice man, I'd like to have it with him; when everything is snug, and flesh glows rosy pink I'll play hide-and-seek with him.' "

"Am I a pierreuse to speak like that?" she interrupted with a laugh.

"Where did you pick up that expression, you hussy?" burst out the stupid Soudrais. "It's unbelievable! Pierreuse! Where did you learn that?"

"The same place you learned it," she retorted, still laughing. "In the dark, when all cats are gray and even stones are soft." A shadow of anger passed suddenly across her face. As though striking with a beak she pointed to Soudrais's lap and spat out: "Ugh! His wedding ring is embedded in his flesh, he has hands like Eyraudt!"

"Silence," cried Goron, and tore the pince-nez from his nose. "Eyraudt! How did you know that Gouffé had collected eighteen thousand francs on July 25?"

Eyraudt looked malevolently to one side, his lower lip drooped crookedly in his beard, but he must have realized that he could not saddle his mistress with this. "I don't remember."

"He doesn't like having his nose rubbed in his own dirt, like a badly behaved poodle," said Bompard. "He was told by his business friend Lévy, it was Lévy, the Jewish furrier, who owed the eighteen thousand francs, and the dolt went to him of all people to borrow money from. Lévy said: 'I'm sorry, but I have to pay off eighteen thousand francs in cash to Gouffé.' He told me this himself, and he mentioned it again the same night, when dawn was breaking and he came back without any money and I asked him: 'What made you think he would have the money in his office?' He answered me and said: 'He had an appointment with Lévy, the Jewish furrier at five, when the banks were already closed.' But because he hadn't been able to find anything, we came to the conclusion that Gouffé must have taken the money to a private banker and deposited it in his safe. Because we couldn't imagine that such a meticulous man would simply put it in a cardboard box in his office, as Maître Rebattu tells me he did." She leaned sideways and said confidentially: "Just think of it, Michi!"

"Well, Eyraudt?" urged Goron with his right hand half raised.

"I don't remember having discussed this point with Lévy," muttered Eyraudt, staring at the floor.

"No, you don't remember," she retorted without irony. "Do you remember when we lived in the whores' district by the Fortifs, where you beat Dubocage's errand boy half to death or maybe to death (we could find that out from the police records)—do you remember how you were always trying, by hints and bringing me into bad company, to make me go out on the streets like the other women? Just think hard and remember: you were always trying to make money out of me and you thrashed me black and blue when I refused to do what you wanted. Brutality instead of brains! The only time when a favorable opportunity occurred and you really went the whole way to take advantage of the fact that, without meaning to, I turn a lot of men's heads, you made a mess of it."

She looked at Latrille and said: "He doesn't remember! Lévy will remember. He used to live quite close by and probably still lives there —in the Fourteenth Arrondissement, Rue Delambre."

"It was of no interest to me," said Eyraudt, glancing at Goron as though caught out.

"Heavens above—of no interest!" she interjected. "He was in such a hole that I had to call myself Geneviève Labodère, just so that his creditors shouldn't get on his track! For everyone knew that Mademoiselle Bompard was his mistress; but nobody knew who Mademoiselle Labodère was, and I always wear a veil. Of no interest! He was simply waiting for an opportunity and made use of my credulity! It was all planned! Hence all the preparations! Hence the two rooms under an assumed name, hence the trunk, of which I was suspicious straight away, because it looked like a coffin, the long coil of rope and the sack, which I had to make and into which he pushed Gouffé, after tying him up, like a swollen finger into a glove, because I had made it rather narrow."

Goron lost his temper; he threw the stub of pencil on the desk, planted his pince-nez on his nose, and shook his head, so that the lenses oscillated in front of his black buttons of eyes: "But you, you couldn't imagine, you didn't know what all that was for?"

"Would it have dawned on you?" she replied in smiling astonishment. "Now I understand. He was waiting his opportunity the whole time, with his tongue hanging out. He was probably planning a *coup du Père François*, a method that was much talked about at the time and that always amused him when he heard about it. (We often laughed over it.) He thought Gouffé would be carrying the money in his pocket—and in case things turned out badly, the shroud and coffin were ready."

This hideous description had the effect of causing Eyraudt to shut his eyes, drop his chin on his chest, and let out a long-drawn wail that sounded like the anguish of a guilty conscience and almost amounted to a corroboration of her accusation. But just at this moment a timid knock at the door made all of them, including Eyraudt, prick up their ears. Goron stamped his foot angrily and shouted: "What the devil is it?"

Créneau, the shabby Sub-Inspector, who was still caged up resentfully in the Press Service and was only temporarily replacing Guillaume in the anteroom, came in and approached Goron, his face twitching with aversion, and a sickly smile. He bowed slightly and whispered in his ear.

"Are you out of your mind?" yelled Goron, seizing him by the collar. Then he thought better of it and continued in a calmer voice: "Wait a moment. . . . Yes. Show him in."

It was none other than Monsieur Carapin who immediately afterward made his entrance, with fluttering dove-gray frock coat and matching top hat pressed to his chest in preparation for a gesture of greeting, which he made, sweeping his hat in a wide arc to the right and making a deep, though brief, bow, as he began: "Monsieur Goron, I have the honor, I felt that it was time, on account of Mademoiselle's move—"

He was so involved in his project that only now did he notice the presence of the others—Créneau had doubtless merely indicated in a general way that the chief was busy. Taken aback, he glanced first at Gabrielle, who tilted her head to one side in amusement without looking at him, then at Eyraudt, and as he looked at the latter he pressed his hat to his chest and even took a step backward. Eyraudt leaped up with a snarl; Soudrais seized him by the arm and, as he struggled to free himself, rapped him hard over the knuckles with the handcuffs so that he whimpered with pain, rubbed his hand, and stood where he was. "Randy dog!" he snorted. "Deceiver—wait till I get at you. I'll teach you to steal other people's women!"

"You can see," said Goron with a wry laugh, "that you are heartily welcome."

"Monsieur is welcome," said Bompard, with a touch of haughtiness. "I'm glad you've come. I'm glad you were not ashamed of me in my trouble and that you still wear the souvenir I gave you. Look at his tiepin, Michi—do you recognize it?"

Everyone looked, and Eyraudt gaped, as the sapphire surrounded by brilliants which Carapin wore in his sumptuous red silk cravat and which he himself fingered, at first uncomprehendingly and then with a smiling movement of the head. "I would never be parted from it, Mademoiselle," he breathed.

"Not even for a little while?" she suggested roguishly. "While it served another purpose? It is the stone from Gouffé's ring, you must know, which Michi was too much of a coward to pawn. To keep me, he had it made into a brooch for me, and after I had worn it for a time I had the brooch made into a tiepin for you, to give you pleasure. The jeweler Simmons in Springfield broke the stone and the splinters out of the ring, and he made a good job of it, for he said: 'This stone is worth taking trouble over.' "

No wonder this statement by Bompard, who was now tugging her skirt straight with her fingers, shocked Eyraudt. But it also shocked Carapin, and pained him; twisting his head with its short, curly hair several times, he glowered down at the floor beside him with a deeply injured expression, and raising both eyebrows he said: "If I had known where it came from . . ."

"Are you like Jaquemar?" she asked to the astonishment of all those present, shrugging her shoulders slightly. "Do you want to see to the bottom of things? I thought you loved pleasure."

"A certain delicacy of feeling should have prevented you from making use of this object," came Carapin's reply in a low voice, as he pulled the pin out of his cravat and placed it on Goron's desk, closing his mouth and eyes.

"I'm sorry I've hurt your feelings," she answered, with a polite little bow from the waist.

"Perfidious beast," whispered Eyraudt, with blank, goggling eyes, sinking back into his chair like a broken man.

But Bompard did not hear it. "Men. . . ." she said with a slight shake of the head to Latrille. "They can't have it dirty enough, and all of a sudden they're as sensitive as a raw egg and put on airs."

This, then, was how the first confrontation between the two actors in the Gouffé case went off. At this point it was terminated, with the result that Eyraudt, prostrate with horror and despair, had to be positively dragged away, his greasy locks hanging down, his eyes closed, his head swaying from side to side with closed lids, and his knees continually buckling underneath him; Soudrais, linking his arm in Eyraudt's, hauled him off in this condition along the corridors, cursing through clenched teeth and making occasional unsuccessful efforts to bring him to his senses by digging him savagely in the ribs with his elbow. Bompard, on the other hand, handed her stole to Montardon, stood up, pulled her velvet skirt toward her lap over her right thigh and with a pretty gesture said to Goron, smiling under her gaily anguished brows: "How much longer, Monsieur, are we going on with this comedy?" "Get out!" yelled Goron, quivering with rage. Glancing back at Montardon with an indeterminate smile, she moved off as though Carapin were not there, walking, with an unhurried gait that was nevertheless somehow gay and dashing, toward the door and out.

Goron had good reason to be angry. The interrogation had not produced the slightest evidence that she was an accessory before the fact, let alone an accomplice; and if he had secretly hoped that the

meeting between her and her protector would cause the latter to
withdraw his support, in this, too, he had been disappointed. It was
true that the elegant gentleman took his leave quickly and rather
shamefacedly that afternoon, without returning to his proposal that
Gabrielle should be allowed to move from the police headquarters to
his hotel; but he did return to it the following day—unsuccessfully, of
course, since, legally speaking, there was no serious argument to support it, whatever nonsense might be talked by the public and the
newspapers, whose interest in the idea Maître Rebattu had found it
useful covertly to whip up in preparation for more important cam-
paigns to come.

Incidentally, Carapin did not call on Goron until after he had paid
a visit to the vaults, where he met with a cool reception from Gabrielle. As he made his stooping entrance she took no notice of him
whatsoever, but continued to stare fixedly into the corner, impervious
to the protestations which he made with darting juggler's hands on
which the rings clinked, at first in a reasoning tone, then beseeching
—until finally she did turn her face to him and said curtly: "You
don't appreciate my good intentions—leave me." Then the incredible
happened: after talking for a long time about yesterday's "misunderstanding" without receiving any reply, Carapin suddenly went down
on his knees (which drew a little cry from Montardon, who was present throughout the scene) and with his hand on his heart, begged
to be forgiven for his unconsidered reaction; he knew how overwhelmingly generous she had been to him, and he would remain eternally
grateful for all she had given him, if only he could hope that she
would give herself to him again as she had given herself during those
unforgettable days and even more unforgettable nights. Bompard
looked down at him in a not very friendly way but with her eyes
shining as usual, tugged pensively at his short, curly hair with her
rather withered-looking, crooked, yellow fingers and murmured:
"We'll see. . . ."

This young person had an amazing gift for bending hearts to her
will, for robbing men of their reason and turning order into chaos, by
means of her beauty and her secret qualities. The above was only a
minor example of her power, to be immediately followed by a greater
and more serious instance, by those incidents to which a passing
reference has already been made in this report—in short, by the events

those manifestations turned the on-the-spot investigation held three days later at Marseilles and Millery into a scandal without parallel, not only in the story of the Gouffé case, but in the whole history of crime.

Whether Goron himself was wholly or partially responsible for these events, as he was subsequently held to be, remains an open question. The possibly ill-considered and provocative orders he conveyed to Beaujean, the local police chief, through his emissary Latrille, may indeed have contributed to them. One thing is certain: he had an unlucky touch at this period, and everything he did proved either useless or harmful, as though personality traits, inalienable characteristics, which hitherto had faithfully helped him to success, had deserted to the other side and allied themselves with suprapersonal forces opposing him. Everything seemed to be conspiring to produce the most ludicrous distortion of the facts, the grossest animosity. For example, certain voices in the Press were impudent enough to proclaim to the public that Goron had cordially shaken Eyraud by both hands the morning he arrived at Saint-Lazare station, doubtless in the hope of gaining the murderer as an ally in his hatred of "our little demon," the young and beautiful Gabrielle Bompard; the writers claimed that this demonstration had been greeted by the bystanders with cries of "Fie!"

A worse blow than this libelous rubbish, however, was the imperiously worded order from Senior Examining Magistrate Carnot that arrived on the eve of Goron's departure for Marseilles and instructed him without delay to transfer the prisoners Bompard and Eyraud to the custody of the Prosecution Department—an order that spoke for itself and was not deprived of its sting by Goron's failure to comply with it under the pretense that it had not arrived till after he had left. The true time of its arrival was communicated by Soudrais to Latrille, by Latrille to Delattre, by Delattre to his chief Sallier, and by the latter to his colleague Carnot, whose short-lived smile at once changed into an expression of sour displeasure.

In short, Goron, the tubby little fanatic for truth and justice, enjoyed no good will, not even in his home town and the scene of his fame. How much less, then, in Marseilles, where the lame Beaujean raged and roared through his yellow teeth in his sparse prophet's beard, because Paris had "once more" seen fit to order him about like a lackey! But everyone could see what the gentlemen thought of themselves and of Marseilles from the unforgotten utterance: "You old wag, who do you think you're kidding? We're not from Marseilles!" Beaujean made this statement at a conference of representatives of the local Press, called by himself, omitting, perhaps because his memory played him false, to add that it was not Goron, but Latrille, who had jokingly made this remark. It was now attributed to Goron, who was credited with general hostility toward the people of Marseilles and with being determined, in his blind hatred, to bring down the beautiful, demonically beautiful and possibly innocent young Gabrielle Bompard, no matter what the verdict that was whispered and shouted by the voice of the people, the voice of God.

On the merrily windy morning of March 27, 1890, the party of travelers from Paris arrived at Marseilles on Express No. 3, the same that Eyraudt and Bompard had used on an earlier occasion. In the meantime, the grizzled police chief had had almost two days in which to create an atmosphere of antagonism, which was further intensified by the last-minute preparations forced on him by Latrille, on Goron's orders, with the unmistakable threat that if Beaujean did not carry them out Goron would have them imposed by "another authority" —meaning the Prefect of Police. With his blackish lids lowered in an expression of tragic suffering, noisily swallowing his saliva and drumming on the floor with the rubber tip of the walking stick in his trembling hand, Beaujean thundered "So be it!" and turned away in disgust, hiding his head with its flamelike aureole of hair in shame that the upstart from Paris should once more have usurped the authority of the Marseilles police.

It is true that these preparations went far beyond their purpose; they were too sweeping and too ostentatious. Intended to preserve law and order, they achieved exactly the reverse. For a large proportion of the Marseilles police force, six hundred men in all, was detailed to line the streets along which the group from Paris would pass and to surround the squares in which they would stop—all of which, coming on top of the existing mood of exasperation, inevitably had a provocative effect.

Beaujean, rendered malicious by mortification, managed to play one trick on the intruders which, coming as it did at the eleventh hour, they could do nothing to counter. When Latrille came to meet his colleagues, he found waiting at the station not the prison van he had ordered, but three elegant open carriages, each with two well-groomed, glossy, and powerful horses, which were pawing impatiently at the ground and tossing their heads till the harness jingled. They belonged to a private coaching company, as he learned from the first coachman, who bent down to him with his beflagged top hat held respectfully in his white-gloved hand and explained that the prison van had gone out in the small hours on an errand for which the order had been given earlier and, through an oversight, not countermanded, so that it was not available; hence his employer had been asked to provide transport from his famous coach-house—at *Monsieur l'Inspec-teur's* service.

Latrille looked at the carriages and their drivers, the latter dressed in patent-leather top boots and white leather trousers, uttered a thoughtful "H'm" as he rubbed the corner of his mouth with his little finger, but saw neither possibility nor reason forcibly to alter the arrangements now; for the throng of sightseers gathered around the station exit gave no cause for alarm, it could not be compared with that outside the Gare Saint-Lazare in numbers or excitability; and they would just have to wait and see what happened when they got into town, he thought with a shrug of the shoulders.

In fact, the party of travelers were met with silence as they emerged from the station hall; the bystanders craned their necks and shuffled closer, but were easily held back by the police cordon. As Gabrielle Bompard, supported by Montardon, mounted the second carriage, however, something like a sigh of mute wonder went up from the crowd. Holding her skirt bunched up over her lap in her little yellow claw, she stood upright for a moment before taking her seat and looked out with a beaming smile, even giving a sketchy nod of greeting. Turn-ing back to Montardon, who was breathlessly heaving up her heavy mass of flesh topped by her childish black boater, she said: "It is shyness that makes them so quiet."

The windy spring morning by the sea, whose salty tang she seemed to be sniffing with sensitive nostrils, afforded her a perfect setting. Especially as her black traveling costume, with which she wore a matching derby held with a veil and which looked almost like a riding habit, fitted closely to the upper part of her body, and billowed out below in a way that made her wasp waist, bust, and head appear to blossom forth as though modeled in black foam. The total effect was one of loveliness combined with austerity and a touch of the school-marm, because the collar of her white blouse was embellished with a black bow tie, and, at the same time, of entrancing youthfulness, because the enamel-blue, glossy curls fluttered gaily in the wind around the brim of her hat and were from time to time blown back to reveal the faintly veined temples.

With his goggling eyes and thick, pendulous lips, the handcuffed Eyraudt, who was pushed into the third carriage by Soudrais, looked by contrast the embodiment of everything base and despicable; and as he sat there with hunched shoulders it was as though in craven despair he were offering his still fat neck to the sword of justice. Finally Goron, clambering up in front of Latrille in the first coach, cut a comical figure, a shopkeeper in his Sunday best: he had donned for the journey a black and gray checked frock coat, badly cut and too short at the back, adorned with two buttons high above the loins, which he was evidently not used to wearing and found irksome.

He kept thrusting his face up out of the flat turned-down collar and tapping his detachable cuffs back into place with his fingers; altogether he presented a picture of nervous and misanthropic dis-comfort—despite the purposeful way in which, the moment he had sat down, he replied to the glacial greeting of the coachman with an impatient "Get going, get going!" accompanied by a violent gesture of the hand, which threatened to send his detachable cuff flying onto the back of the coachman's neck. Warned by the wind, he pulled his bowler down over his forehead with both hands and folded his arms over his compact chest, and the horses, urged on by clicking of the tongue, set off at a cracking pace.

The three coaches proceeded in lordly fashion uphill through the narrow streets of the working-class districts on the outskirts of the town; the cool sunshine came down over the roofs of the low houses, and the rubber tires of the carriages rumbled quietly over the cobbles, across which silvery dust eddied.

Not until they turned into the great Rue Cannebière did the scene change. Here the waiting crowds were so dense that the broad pavements were barely wide enough to hold them, and anyone wishing to walk along had to push and wriggle his way through; but the road-way was completely clear of traffic because it had been closed to the public. As the carriages with their fiery steeds now turned into the unimpeded space, an inarticulate whirr rose above the many thousand heads and swept down to the far end of the street, rather like the beating of giant wings. Yet it continued, and now had a fluctuating, surging character, like a storm tide listened to with stopped ears. Out of this dull but mighty flood of sound there arose, yelled by a single male voice, a long-drawn "Fie, Goron!" that imposed silence for the fraction of a second and then released the many-voiced cacophony of general disapproval. Goron, not believing his ears, looked at the public through his little pince-nez under the brim of his bowler that was pulled down low over his forehead, his mouth rounded with indignation, while Latrille, taking off his hat, ran his hand pensively over his hair and leaned back against the cushion.

Goron did not see this, nor did he see that, in the carriage behind his, Gabrielle Bompard leaned forward with interest and nodded to the crowd with a smile, which, because of the way her brows rose toward the middle, may have looked melancholy, as if she were saying, "Well, there it is, what can one do?" In any case, her smile gave a new direction to the excitement; all of a sudden a multitude of voices rang out from different points, rising like jets of spray from the dull thunder of the surge, high-pitched cries of "Bompard!" "*Bonjour*, Bompard!" and in gradually increasing unison "Hello, Bompard!"

The carriages drove on and came unimpeded to the Hôtel Keiler, beneath whose glass porch a wedge-shaped space had been kept free between the milling throng held back on either side by close-packed lines of police. The entrance, as in many hotels, was carpeted in red. Goron climbed briskly out of his carriage, but for safety's sake stood aside for Bompard and her waddling escort; the manacled Eyraudt, his shoulders hunched, was also taken up the steps and into the building in front of Goron by Soudrais, and soon there was nothing left for the crowd to stare at but the three empty carriages.

What happened in the Hôtel Keiler is of comparatively little interest—though it was surprising that it should have been the Hôtel Keiler in which it happened, the same hotel Goron had chanced to pick for his stay a few months ago, completely unaware that he was thus choosing for himself the last European quarters of the criminals he was so ardently seeking. In any case, this on-the-spot investigation (and the one at Millery) was a fundamentally superfluous attempt to

complete the picture. Considering how dearly poor Goron paid for
it, and that he carried it out in defiance of Carnot's specific instructions and solely in response to his own pedantic overconscientiousness, coupled perhaps with the stubborn hope of bringing to light
some conclusive evidence against Bompard, it all looks in restrospect
like a trick played on him by his own perfectionism. This perfectionism blinded him to everything that was going on around him and
seems to have provoked the irony of fate. Whatever he may have
hoped to find, he in fact found nothing.

Of the two hotel employees who had carried down the coffin-trunk
three-quarters of a year ago, the page boy was now employed elsewhere and could not be got hold of, while the boots, though still
there, was no help. He remembered nothing but the appearance of
Gabrielle Bompard, and no matter how furiously Goron, mopping
his moist forehead, pressed him, he was completely unable to say
whether it was Eyraudt or she who made the remark about the broken
bottle of dye. Indeed, he could not even remember the remark itself
or the bloodstain on the floor, doubtless because he had no eyes and
no mind for anything but the young woman's beauty—he seemed still
to have no mind for anything else, since he kept repeatedly looking
away from his questioner and staring at her, as, holding his cap in front
of his green baize apron, he shook his head and uttered his "I can't
remember."

The one and only clash between the two accused that took place
on this occasion was also valueless from Goron's point of view. When
first Eyraudt and then Bompard were called upon to give an account
of their first night in this hotel (which was otherwise uneventful)
she corroborated his statement, but added: "Once during the night a
noise came from the trunk and I pulled at Michi's nightshirt and
said: 'Michi—he's alive.' But he answered angrily: 'Silly goose, the
corpse is relieving itself! Leave me in peace!'"

"It was she who said that," bellowed Eyraudt in despair.

She looked at Goron with an incredulous smile and finally retorted:

"Would I have mentioned it, if I had said it?"

Goron dismissed the subject with an impatient gesture of both
hands. "Enough!" he cried; he jammed his bowler on his head and
terminated the disappointing interrogation.

When the party emerged from the glass porch, with Goron at its head, palpably increased excitement reigned among the dense multitude outside; people were grunting, pushing and shoving, and trying to climb on to one another's shoulders in order to get a better view. A muttering came from the struggling mass of pale, heated faces with blazing eyes that ceased only for a few seconds, as though paralyzed with shock, when Bompard came into sight. As she descended the steps, supported by Montardon, she gazed down at the red carpet beneath her. She had barely advanced two paces from the bottom of the stairs, when a curiously effeminate and shrill male voice screamed, as though in unbearable physical pain: "They are doing violence to her."

Gabrielle Bompard stopped in her bold and rustling walk; she took half a step in the direction of the voice, smiled with her chin up over the shoulders of the police cordon, and called back: "Violence? If I screamed like a woman in labor, who would hear me?"

Montardon stood waiting beside her, her eyes above the black lachrymal sacs gazing at her dreamily, but Goron turned around abruptly, seized her by the elbow, and dragged her forward. "Come along, if you please!" he snarled.

No one heard his words, of course; they only saw the angry gesture with which she was pulled away. As she tripped off, she turned with a shrug of the shoulders to those whom she had been addressing, and a deafening howl, a thousand-voiced outburst of indignation and disgust, whistles, yells, catcalls, immediately filled the quivering air. It grew louder and louder and finally developed into a rhythmic chorus of "Fie, Goron! Fie, Goron! Fie, Goron!" At the same time, the mob pushed more and more forcibly and the police cordon began to give way ominously. Another cry mingled with the continuous shouts of "Fie, Goron!" and was quickly taken up in rhythmic unison by the chorus: "Set Bompard free! Bompard free! Bompard free!" His head down between his shoulders and punched by Soudrais, the goggle-eyed Eyraudt hurried with an almost hopping step along the red carpet to the carriages in which, heaven be praised, they were now all seated, only a few hundred yards from the tree-lined square in which stood the Prefecture and the Security Police headquarters. The thought flashed across Goron's mind: How wise of Jaquemar to refuse my invitation to come down here!

Meanwhile, the horses began to pull the carriages out into the road.

way in a curve. They did not get far, however; the howling suddenly rose to a roar and an indefinable rattling, cracking sound became audible, like a vast mass of water smashing into a barrier of rotten timber and thundering down into the depths. Goron sprang to his feet and turned around, crying "Stop! Stop!" to the coachman, and saw that the mob had now really gained the upper hand. They had swept away the cordon of foot-police and engulfed the few on horseback, who were being pushed backward and forward in short jerks as though caught up in some piece of machinery. Around these frightened men elevated above the crowd by their mounts, a struggle was raging: fists were raised to threaten or strike, outspread hands like those of a drowning man were thrust into the air, umbrellas and sticks waved and stabbed, and heads and torsos were thrown up as though by the billows of a spring tide and sank down sideways. The clattering hooves of reinforcements of mounted police made themselves heard above the din as they passed Goron, but they were not noticed by those rushing Bompard's carriage in an attempt to free her until the rearing horses with their flailing hooves were upon them.

"We want Bompard!" came the yell from all sides. Police reinforcements hurrying to the rescue accidentally opened a passage for them through the ranks of the foot-police, and the battle raged more fiercely still—for it was a battle, a revolt, a revolution.

The mounted police struck out with the flat of their sabers; one of them was dragged down from his horse and disappeared beneath a hail of blows; another, also on his way down, was caught up in his saddle and hung head down with a face that was immediately covered in blood, until finally there was nothing to be seen amidst the raucous screeching of women but the one leg suspended foot uppermost in the stirrup. Bompard was laughing; Montardon was crazily twisting her head this way and that, scared to death, clutching with her fingers at her vast, soft bosom; but Bompard was laughing, heartily amused, her head to one side. Finally, she bent forward slightly and cried still with laughter in her voice, yet loud enough for the crowd to hear that she was shouting: "Enough, Mesdames, Messieurs! Enough!"

The crowd paused to hear what she was saying; there was an instant of hesitation and questioning, a turning of heads and even some laughter; the movement lost momentum and died away for a few seconds. This was enough to allow fresh reinforcements of mounted police to cut into the multitude like a snowplough, so that the mob foamed up and flowed away in all directions, screaming and whimpering beneath cracking saber blows. The carriage, freed from its besiegers, immediately set off, spurred on by the terrified coachman's whip. They were moving fast again, all too fast unfortunately, for their departure looked desperately like flight, as though they hoped by galloping to escape with whole skins from the disaster they had brought upon themselves. A few minutes later, the procession had left the raging and shouting behind.

The on-the-spot investigation at Millery was as fruitless as that in the Hôtel Keiler, since the shattered Eyraudt merely nodded dully in corroboration of Bompard's description of how they had driven themselves here in a coach, disposed first of the body and then, after driving three miles back, of the trunk. Perhaps he was lost in contemplation of his old crime, which had not aged with him, perhaps he did not feel the fragrant breeze that blew here on the hilltop, perhaps he did not hear the snorting, stamping and scraping of the horses, or even the questions Goron kept asking him so insistently.

With Soudrais holding him by the sleeve, he stood beside the whitewashed stone parapet staring down the overgrown slope, at the bottom of which could be seen the foaming mountain torrent, but not the footpath, the fateful footpath from which the presence of his victim had first been noticed through the mephitic stench of putrefaction in the heat—because, in Beaujean's melodramatic phrase, death has its language just like life and wished to call out to the living: "Do justice to my memory!" Did he see himself tipping him out of the trunk and down the slope "as though out of a garbage can"? "And she," he suddenly yelled, shaking his clinking handcuffs in the direction of Bompard, "she helped." "Certainly, Michi," she answered in a friendly voice. "Because when I refused, you said: 'Don't forget the whip on the coach box!'" But Eyraudt stared down the slope again as though he had not heard what she said.

Goron, at the end of his patience, tugged at his collar and cried: "Come along, that's enough of this aimless nonsense—if we waste any more time we shall miss the train as well." As a matter of fact, he had already cut things very fine. He had forgotton the hilly nature of the terrain and, hoping to avoid the assembly of large crowds again, he had arranged to arrive at the station just before the afternoon express left. Fortunately he had sent Latrille to reserve two first-class

compartments while they were waiting at Security Police headquarters, to obviate last-minute difficulties over finding seats. The city
streets, especially the Rue Cannebière of unhappy memory, were
lined by reinforced police cordons and closed to normal traffic, their
three coaches protected by half a hundred mounted men; preparations
had been careful and complete—why was he on edge? What could
happen?

Nothing. That is to say, nothing that did any immediate harm,
in other words: nothing of a violent nature. What did happen had an
almost festive character, to which the brilliant blue cloudless sky and
the silvery sunshine, the gentle breeze, the aromatic smell of seaweed
drifting in from the sea, and the resinous scent of sun-warmed conifers all contributed. But the factor that contributed most to this festive
spirit was the perfect orderliness with which everything took place,
the orderliness of a parade, in which the military contingent seemed
to be serving exclusively as decoration.

When they turned hurriedly into the Rue Cannebière, surrounded
by their guard, they found the pavements on both sides just as
crowded with onlookers as before; but this time they were in an unexpectedly peaceable, in fact festive, mood and the spring air was
charged with an electrifying enthusiasm—if enthusiasm is the right
word for the frenzied outburst that greeted Bompard's coach the
moment it turned into the street. Single cries of joyful recognition
were immediately followed by many thousands of voices united in a
roar of welcome and jubilation that filled the wide street. "Vive
Bompard!" cried the multitude of men, women and children. "Vive
Bompard! Vive Bompard!"

And yet there was nothing to be seen of her behind the guard of
cuirassiers with their gorgeously fluttering crests—or nothing until,
after beaming hesitantly into space for a moment, she rose and stood
upright, supporting herself on the arm of the seat, so that her metallic blue curls streamed out behind her (in her satisfaction at what was
going on, she had removed her riding hat and shaken her hair free).
Even now, however, there was very little to be seen of her, because
the mounted men in their glittering cuirasses and red trousers, with
their sword belts bouncing regularly up and down and their flashing
spurs, hid the object of the ovation. About all that could be seen was
the black veil she had detached from her hat and was holding in the

air as a greeting to the cheering multitude and of which they caught an occasional glimpse between or above the silver armor. Feeling flattered, Montardon gazed up with folded hands at the young woman standing beside her. Still the shouts of "Vive Bompard! Vive Bompard!" rang out on the trembling air.

Goron, who was sitting with arms crossed grimly over his chest in the first carriage, exclaimed for the second time: "The rabble are out of their minds!" Latrille, who had put one hand over his mouth, no doubt to hide it, because he could no longer hide the smiling crow's-feet appearing at its corners, also heard the cheering and took note of it. But neither of them heard the cries that were striving stubbornly to gain attention behind the jubilation, strange cries in the cracked voices of half-grown newspaper and street boys: "J'accuse!" they were calling out. "J'accuse!" Their cry was out of keeping with the festive occasion and perhaps for that reason was not perceived by those who were cheering the black veil as it drove past, waving handkerchiefs, throwing their hats in the air and flowers into the street, so that her way should be strewn with them even if she could not see them. Now they were shouting in strict unison "Vive Bom-pard! Vive Bom-pard! Vive Bom-pard!"

The insistent, pounding rhythm sounded like a demand, almost like a threat, and fear stole over Goron's otherwise fanatically courageous heart and rage and hatred sent the question circling round and round in his head: Why did I come here? Why did I have to come here? And something similar was boring into the goggle-eyed, bull-necked, and cringing Eyraudt's bewildered brain: Why? Why?

But Bompard continued undisturbed along Marseilles's show street, encircled by the glittering silver of the cuirasses and canopied by the festive sky of spring. Only once did she interrupt her enjoyment of her turbulent popularity, when she looked down at Montardon, shrugged one shoulder, and shouted, to make herself heard: "I told you they were only shy, Madame." So saying, she looked straight ahead again and kept her veil aloft in acknowledgment of the people's ovation.

Goron might have known that the Marseilles incidents would be talked about, and he should have at least suspected that his handling of the affair would be made to appear at best ridiculous and at worst as very nearly criminal. There could be no doubt that in his hate and injured pride Beaujean had reported at once to the Ministry of the Interior, that is to say to Lozé, and also that he had laid the whole blame for the bloody riot on the chief of the Paris Sûreté, stressing the fact that this riot was not only terrible in itself but calculated to shatter public respect for the authorities—in other words, that it went beyond the sphere of police matters and entered that of politics.

The fact was, the Marseilles incidents had aroused an unexpectedly loud and discordant echo in the metropolis. Even the most highly respected editors had been unable to resist the temptation to pass on to the public the sensational news that had just reached them by telegraph or telephone, and since the regular evening editions were already out they printed special editions. Apart from the inflammatory effect automatically produced by this form of communication, the contents and treatment varied with the outlook of each editor; some chose the noisy reception accorded to the Paris police chief as being the most interesting angle, others the jubilant ovation given to Gabrielle Bompard, and yet others the bloody clash in the Rue Cannebière; and they devised their headlines accordingly, so that the public's thirst for scandal was liberally satisfied in a variety of ways, all of them unwelcome to Goron.

It goes without saying that the hurried manner in which the news was printed, which gave neither the reporter nor the subeditor time to read the proofs properly and eliminate sources of error, combined with the overwrought local pride of the Marseillais to bring about all kinds of omissions, exaggerations, and distortions—thus, for example, several reporters described the violent efforts of the mob to free Bompard as an attack on the life and person of the unhappy Goron, who escaped the people's wrath only by "panic flight." Only one report, however, made a fleeting and unexplained reference to the strange cry that had tried in vain to make itself heard above the noisy jubilation of the multitude at Marseilles, the ominous "J'accuse" which, from the next day on, was to enrich and enliven the scandal in Paris.

"J'accuse"—remember that this was the slogan under which the tempestuous Zola later carried on his one-man battle for truth and justice in the Dreyfus case; it was a powerful slogan, and even now it sounded somehow like a clarion call to enlist in the militant ranks of justice, when shouted up and down the streets and boulevards, not-withstanding the fact that on this occasion it served as a title and slogan for the most disgusting piece of libel. It served its purpose supremely well. The nauseating pamphlet sold like hot cakes and in-jected into the morbid excitement over the Gouffé case a new and abominable note of cheap obscenity and spine-chilling horror.

Be it that the author, a hack writer of the meanest type and, natu-rally, anonymous, "because in a thorny matter like this it is not proper to become personal," had some grudge against Goron and Jaquemar, be it that he had fallen victim to the universal morbid infatuation inspired by Gabrielle Bompard, or be it that he was merely an astute businessman, he certainly had his finger on the public pulse. Yet he had really done no more than assemble all the rumors, conjec-tures, and slanders that had sprung up around the Gouffé case as time passed, quite indifferent as to how vile or how absurd they might be, heedless of whether his statements were mutually consistent or whether they were in crass contradiction, and not caring a straw whether anyone could believe this farrago of filthy lies—and therein lay the main strength of his effusion; for it is a mistake to suppose that people mind whether they can seriously believe a thing; what matters to them is something different, something more deep-seated and more secret; on the contrary, truth has very little chance against any trickery that panders to these murky lusts. The anonymous author of *J'accuse* had a brilliant grasp of this fact. What he offered for a few *sous* was a welter of gore and pornography leavened here and there with a feeble outburst of moral indignation; a few obscene drawings would have rendered it complete. Instead, the text was broken up by appropriate subtitles in heavy type: HEIR RECEIVES MURDERESS IN HOTEL BEDROOM or POLICE CHIEF AND MURDERER ARM IN ARM.

It would be impossible to trace any logical order in this hodgepodge of mudslinging and calumny. Suffice it to say that the author, con-sistent in this one respect alone, harped from beginning to end on the Sûreté's "extraordinarily significant" unwillingness to reveal the facts to the public and that he linked this attitude on the part of the 'police scum' with the munificent heir, the sole beneficiary of the crime, a man who appeared mysteriously allied with the only witness —didn't it therefore seem plausible that this witness was to be dis-couraged from divulging her knowledge to the public, discouraged in fact by every legal and illegal means, including medieval methods of incarceration and torture, that, moreover, all "interested parties" were straining every nerve to silence her forever? She, Gabrielle Bompard, played the most fascinatingly contradictory rôle in this penny dreadful; it was suggested on the one hand that she was involved with everyone in the case, that she was, so to speak, the gallant *huissier's* most coveted heritage, the first cause perhaps and the instrument of the whole gruesome melodrama; but at the same time she figured as the epitome of persecuted innocence (NAKED IN THE VAULTS OF THE CITE!), as the victim of circumstances that had been subtly planned and stubbornly maintained; in short, she served on one page as a stimulus to lechery and on the next as a means of appealing to the reader's chivalry and sense of justice.

Let us repeat: the author had made no attempt to achieve credibility, every individual calumny could have been easily refuted and was not even worth refuting, but the obscene quality of the whole production, in conjunction with the excitement aroused by the incidents at Marseilles, had its effect—an effect that was all the more corrosive and dangerous because there was no straightforward means of combating it; in the upshot, there was nothing that could be fought with logic or law, it was a kind of atmosphere which—regardless of truth—threatened to envelop the victims of the slander like a seething fog and draw down upon them the vilest back-street gossip. This rendered immediate countermeasures all the more necessary; but Goron did nothing. Perhaps he told himself that if he made any move, popular ill-will would interpret this as proof of a guilty conscience; perhaps he believed that the General Prefecture of Police, which, in his view, was the proper authority to deal with the situation, would not go so far in its antipathy toward him as to look idly on at these activities—he certainly believed that the police section of the Ministry of the Interior could not avoid coming out into the open and rallying to his defense. A whole day passed and yet another, a roaring trade was done with the libelous pamphlet in the streets, and no one moved a finger.

Goron gritted his teeth and continued "not to notice anything." Meanwhile, however, he became hourly more unbearable. He hurried through the long corridors of the Cité, panted up and down stairs, burst into offices, and soured his subordinates' ill-concealed delight in

his difficulties with the most venomous faultfinding, rummaged recklessly through their papers so that they fluttered down to the floor,
and left behind him, in addition to intensified ill-will, his half-smoked
black cigars that smoldered away forgotten on desks and in pigeonholes and burnt ugly holes in the wood. Apart from Guillaume, there
was not a single employee in the whole of this great building, from
the janitor to the Chief Inspector, who did not wish him to blazes;
even the charwomen, over whose mops and brooms he stumbled,
cursing, in the early morning, detested him; and Guillaume himself,
who took it all with exemplary patience and an impassive face, was
roughly hauled over the coals several times.

For the first time, Goron became fully aware that he stood alone
within a wide field; the realization rendered him calm and obdurate to
a point at which obduracy almost assumes the appearance of gentleness. With head thrown back and staring through his pince-nez into
space, he walked unhurriedly along the corridors. His demand for
loyalty had been rejected—rightly, he could see that. "What will
you do when the Gouffé case has been settled?" Carnot had put this
question to him months ago, benevolently at the time; now that it
came back to him it sounded sinister, malicious. He beckoned a cab
and climbed in. "Cité," he said, and continued his train of thought:
But the Gouffé case has not been settled yet! It is my case, I shan't
allow it to be made the center of unscrupulous machinations. I shall
rescue it for justice and clarity, I shall neutralize the poisonous atmosphere that has been built up around it. I must act; I shall issue a
report, seize the obscene pamphlet, arrest the anonymous author,
put him behind bars for libel against official and private persons. I
must talk to Jaquemar about it.

He looked out from the smooth-running cab at the street; something was making him uneasy, and had been making him uneasy for
some time. Now, with a feeling of disappointment, he realized what
it was: outside in the amorous early-summer afternoon (for this was
the hour of love) life was going self-indulgently on its way, the
women in beribboned dresses with bustles at the back and wide-
brimmed straw hats or little hats with flowers on their hair, the
young and elderly gallants confidently pursuing their everlasting hunt
for female flesh; but nowhere, near or far, the provocative J'accuse.
The whole scandalmongering turmoil, which yesterday had kept

everyone busy, had died away as though it had never been. Of course, he could still intervene; but would it not look like starting to shoot after the enemy had made a victorious withdrawal, would it not do more harm than good and excite ribald merriment, misinterpretation, and derision after this infamous calumny and humiliation? He sat there in consternation. "Coachman!" he cried, as though struck by a sudden thought. "Not the Cité—the Hôtel des Mines, Rue de la Glacière!"

The young leaves on the trees in the Rue de la Glacière were already rustling with a kind of nostalgic whisper, and the black-and-gold inscription on the Hôtel des Mines glowed massive and inviting through the whitish-green flicker of the foliage. The coachman looked down at Goron's bald pate and scratched his cheek in amusement; Goron handed him the fare with a meager tip and disappeared into the stone-floored entrance to the hotel. He did not so much as glance at the hive of activity in the large bistro that opened on his left, but went straight through to the spiral staircase and ascended it purposefully.

On the second floor he found the door of room 12a open, but his path was blocked by the medico Lebigot, who stood in the doorway with his back to him. "Excuse me," he said, and tried to push past him, but the other thrust him vigorously back with his shoulder, turned around nonchalantly, and looked at him under blinking parrot's lids. "Keep out," he said. "No visitors today. Some other time." Goron saw that he was holding a glass vessel with a rubber tube attached, an enema to be precise, and to the intruder's astonishment he raised the vulcanized rubber tip of the tube and said with a trace of an ironic smile on his hard, emaciated features: "Shall we have a go?" "Excuse me!" rapped out Goron, decisively rather than angrily, but at the first step forward he had the other's great red hand with five outspread fingers on his chest. Now he could see the whole of the room, however; it seemed even emptier or bleaker than usual, because the screen in the left-hand corner had been removed, disclosing the bed and the rickety bedside table, on which stood a lot of little bottles and some very beautiful flowers.

In the bed lay Jaquemar, propped up with several pillows, his face turned to the wall with closed eyes, and his hands and arms hidden under the blanket; which greatly increased the impression of sickness and seclusion. Beside him on the edge of the bed sat young Madame Chottin with a white chambermaid's apron over her smart red dress; she turned around, whereupon Jaquemar opened his eyes, turned his head slightly, and looked at Goron with his melancholy, squinting gaze. "H'm," he said, as though to himself, "the crapule de police with whom I am hand in glove." He closed his eyes again, turned his head back to the wall, made his silent munching movement of the lips, and added in a low voice, but politely: "Please come in. I'm glad to see you."

Lebigot no longer stood in the way. Goron went to the bed and greeted Madame Chottin, who had risen and now said in a very low voice: "But we must avoid any conversation that will excite him." At this, Goron, feeling somewhat irritated, looked over her shoulder and noticed that Jaquemar, his eyes still closed, was smiling. "I'm so glad you're here," she went on in her customary warmhearted, frank manner. "You will help me with your authority, won't you? Edmond must go away and rest—he's so terribly pigheaded."

"Leave him alone, Germaine," said Jaquemar with a laugh from his bed. "You all fall upon the good man as though he were a stranger entering a hostile country. And I'm sure he has all sorts of exciting news for us." "As a matter of fact—" began Goron. But Lebigot, who was busy at a table in the opposite corner of the room, shaking bottles and rattling his enema, took up the phrase: "As a matter of fact—your Edmond will not be disappointed, if he hopes to suck poison from that heart. May he enjoy it!" "I don't know, Madame," said Goron more coldly than he had intended to answer the charming young woman, "whether I can promise you my support."

Meanwhile, Lebigot came up with the wing chair, which he carried in front of him with striking ease. Holding it by the arms, he put it neatly down beside Jaquemar's bed, looked at Goron with his unwavering bird's eyes, and remarked: "Deign to place as much of your posterior end as you wish upon this noble piece of furniture and give your wit free play. After fifteen minutes I shall throw you out!"

"Welcome," said Jaquemar, but without bringing his hand from under the blanket in greeting. He watched Goron sit down and continued: "As you see, I have turned this dwelling, which once served for a tête-à-tête with my accomplice, into a sickroom. Rich people can indulge in such transformations."

"You've read that wretched pamphlet?" asked Goron hastily. "It has vanished!"

"What did you expect, Monsieur?" came the reply, not from Jaquemar, but from Lebigot, who was now standing at the foot of the bed, his thumbs in the armholes of his waistcoat and his fingers moving stiffly but playfully in front of his chest. "Our universally admired and beloved Dr. Lebigot called at the Prefecture and gave the fat Sallier a prod; he did not shrink from threatening the worshipful department with an action for gross dereliction of duty, and this brought the indolent brute to his feet. The matter is over and done with, further discussion is unnecessary, forget it."

"Go away, Lebigot," said Jaquemar in a tired voice. The other gazed up at the ceiling and went away sighing "Heaven, is not ingratitude the world's reward?" while Jaquemar continued: "He is right. And the vile intrigue has been silenced—for the moment."

"Yes, for the moment," confirmed Goron and his black eyes behind the pince-nez met the questioning gaze of the sick man, who finally asked: "And—what else is there?"

"What else?" repeated Goron, looking thoughtfully down at his lap. "I don't know. Only that we are lagging behind, our cause is in a bad way. I employed all the tricks of the trade to squeeze the truth from Bompard—to no avail; on her account I exceeded my powers, swallowed abuse, ignored orders, put up with countless pinpricks, and allowed bucketfuls of filthy calumny to be poured over me. I remained blind to the mudslinging of the Press, deaf to the catcalls of the mob —all to no purpose. The case has been taken out of my hands, belatedly, but prematurely. And now? You know how things stand: the lascivious rabble are wringing their hands for fear some harm might come to their darling. The mood of the public is imperious; what will the authorities do about the Gouffé case under these circumstances? It will be a tremendous humiliation for the police, a slap in the face for truth. The trial will be 'rushed through,' that woman the most unmitigated scoundrel I have ever come across in the whole of my career, the most shameless criminal—will get away with a mere scratch on her white skin: she may be given two or three years as an 'accessory after the fact,' or else she will be put on probation, and the applause of the intoxicated populace will greet her everywhere. That must not be."

During this statement Jaquemar lay motionless, with his eyes on the ceiling. "No," he said, "that must not be."

"Don't you understand," broke in Goron impatiently, "there are people in whose interest it is. The fire has been vigorously stirred, the 'soul of the people' is on the boil, now they are in a hurry to cool it down—at our expense. Not a word now about justice, no time for a thorough preliminary investigation, a hurried process hardly worthy of the name *trial*. New Caledonia or maybe the guillotine for Eyraudt and for her a triumph; I can just see her shameless exhilaration, I can hear the 'vivas' and 'hallelujahs'; the gentlemen in robes will wash their hands in innocence, for 'What is truth?' "

"I understand," rejoined Jaquemar, with bitter calm. "Maître Rebattu will also understand: he has got a good case."

"He has an impossible case," contradicted Goron with foolish obstinacy. "Legally speaking, he has nothing but popular sympathy on his side. Everything is on the side of lies! I don't even know how the charge has been put. I know only one thing: it will all be at our expense. We have gone through the whole filthy business for the sake of truth; how shall we bear it when truth is cast down in the dust?"

"Really," said Jaquemar, with a dry laugh. " 'What is truth?' "

Goron glowered at him incredulously—and as the other turned his face toward him, it flashed across his distracted mind how unruffled and becoming his hair style seemed, even in bed.

"I beg your pardon," said Jaquemar, with dispassionate insistence. "I ask you, what really is the truth? Whence comes her mysterious fascination, the sympathy she enjoys? What is it about her 'shameless exhilaration' that holds people in thrall even from the depths of the Cité vaults and through the flyblown newspaper reports? She is dull rather than demonic, at best she stands up for herself in a way that has a certain grimly comic appeal, she refuses to be browbeaten, she butts like a young he-goat and doesn't stop to wonder whether she has horns under the wiry fuzz. But that doesn't make a person a 'demon,' not even a little one."

"What a lot of philosophizing!" cut in Goron, looking thoroughly peevish with his pendulous cheeks. "A woman who stirs up the universal lewdness, disregards all convention, is utterly ruthless, and does not shrink from the most shameful abominations, in short is morally insane—how could a woman like that fail to appeal to the rabble?"

Madame Chottin, now without the chambermaid's apron, which she had doubtless taken off in honor of the visitor, sat down on the foot of the bed; she held her hands in her lap and remarked with a certain pensive roguishness: "Messieurs, she is very beautiful."

"I know," growled Jaquemar.

"She has sharp features and crippled fingers," objected Goron, with spinsterish finality. "Pretty faces are two a penny. No, it is her moral insanity that hypnotizes the rabble! And anyhow, why this—pardon the expression—sisterly esteem? You have no reason for it, Madame. I warn you, she will persuade the court that it was you who drove Gouffé into her arms."

"Suppose that is true," said Madame Chottin, looking down at the bedclothes. "Dear God, nothing was further from my mind, and yet—"

Jaquemar drew his right arm out from under the blanket and rubbed the back of his hand across his lips. He turned his head to the wall and said in an undertone, as though to himself: "Her picture frightened me the moment I saw it. No one who has seen her can ever forget her. People's lives are too poor for them to be able to forget her; we have to have something to dream about."

"Why are you in bed?" demanded Goron out of the blue. "What's the matter with you?"

"An indisposition," Jaquemar answered curtly.

"We have to have something to dream about?" repeated Goron, as though there had been no interruption. "They could have found something more appetizing."

"More appetizing?" inquired Jaquemar, with a smile.

"Devil take it!" exclaimed Lebigot, with a snigger from his table in the background. "The policeman is choosy. As far as Papa Lebigot is concerned, he would like to lick his thin lips, roll up his shirt sleeves, and get down to business."

"Appetite," commented Jaquemar, now completely serious, lying back on the pillow, "appetite—that's just it. There is a hungry void in everything." He laughed sadly. "Oh, you won't admit it, you say 'unmitigated scoundrel,' you say 'moral insanity.' Hunger doesn't bother about that. Morality, justice, truth—people want to satisfy their hunger, even if it is only in their dreams. Hunger gnaws, bores, becomes an obsession, at last it catches sight of food—do you expect it to ask, 'Is it just?' "

Goron fixed the recumbent man with his black eyes. "I have devoted months of my life to bringing the truth to light, my energy, all my thoughts; am I now to have the prize snatched from me by that gutter Clytemnestra?"

"It's disappointing," said Jaquemar.

For a moment Goron remained silent, breathing hard; he buttoned up his jacket as though preparing to leave and said: "I understand. It doesn't shock you. The matter doesn't interest you any more."

Jaquemar looked calmly at the indignant man, without a movement in his gray face, and said: "If it should cost me my whole fortune, if it should cost me my life, I shall not let go of this affair. I shall go on to the end, even if it horrifies me."

This remark cheered Goron considerably; he actually laughed with pleasure, took his pince-nez from his nose, his handkerchief from his pocket, and wiped his eyes:

"And I thought . . . forgive me! I should have known you better, I am bewildered, too much has happened during the last few days."

"What did you think?" asked Jaquemar, with his impassive face.

"Well, that you too—had been infected, no offense meant; that you too had picked up the softening of the brain and will with which this hussy is poisoning the masses, positively driving them to fornication and whipping them up into an unparalleled state of raving jubilation—you should have seen them at Marseilles—it was incredible, unimaginable! Has there ever been such a mass aphrodisiac? I tell you that if it were nothing else, it would be a matter of personal pride to keep one's head high. You are a man of breeding, I don't need to say any more to you."

The lanky, gaunt Lebigot was standing at the table in the far corner of the room staring at the group around the bed, or, to be more precise, at Goron, and before pronouncing between leathery lips: "Suspicious knave." He actually wagged his right index finger threateningly before returning to his potions.

No one was speaking now; Jaquemar lay with a look of exhaustion on his face, his lids lowered and his lashes like shadows; his nose stood out rather sharply against his narrow cheeks and the soft, though firmly shut mouth, and his unrumpled brown hair, shot through with strands of a lighter color, looked somehow "arranged," like that of a head on a coin. Young Madame Chottin gave him a look that combined loving concern with a certain gaiety and which was so incomprehensible to Goron that he felt the ground was slipping from under his feet, that he did not belong here, that his efforts were in vain.

He countered this feeling with fresh resolution and energy, planted his pince-nez on his nose and was about to expound his case: "Let's get down to business!" when Madame Chottin immediately interrupted him.

"You agree with me, don't you?" she asked, slowly turning her eyes away from Jaquemar and looking with her old candor at Goron. "Edmond is in no condition to be subjected to all these atrocious excitements and misconstructions. Who would gain from it? In six weeks or two months the whole hateful turmoil will be forgotten! He can go abroad, Venice is a nice place to stay, or if that looks too much like running away, the Riviera, or even some remote little village on the Normandy coast. Must he let himself be drawn into their game? There are calumnies too base even to refute."

"I can't agree with you at all, Madame," contradicted Goron even more angrily than he himself felt to be justified—and as he spoke he was surprised to see how little impression his protest made on her, for her gaze remained fixed on Jaquemar. "The cause is too important, the situation too critical, this is no time for such . . . sensitive considerations. One must make a stand, that's just it!"

"For my part," she rejoined, with just a trace of acerbity, "I consider that self-torture. Perhaps I do not altogether understand male standpoints; there seems to be a code of honor the significance of which eludes me. The cause is important, you say? But in what way does he serve the cause by not withdrawing?"

"Your question hits the bull's-eye," replied Goron with satisfaction. "It is not enough not to withdraw. One must take action, must openly and effectively intervene. I am almost sorry that Sallier was forced to put an end to the goings-on in the street: we should have done it. That was my mistake. I shall make good what can still be made good. But now that Carnot has given me to understand that the trial will be 'rushed through' I realize one thing: the scandal will be transferred from the street to the courtroom! Just consider the situation: the jurisdiction of the Sûreté does not extend to the courtroom; the Prosecution Department, which is preparing the charge, is bound to give way to the Prosecutor General's Office; the Prosecutor General's Office, in complete collaboration with the Prefecture, is swayed by considerations that have nothing to do with justice; the jury represents a public which, to the silent satisfaction of the authorities, has risen in an unparalleled revolt against justice and truth. What is the outlook for justice? What guarantee have we that this court will pronounce *justice*? That it will not sacrifice justice to nefarious aims and foul impulses, behind the mask of a histrionic moral rectitude à la Beaujean and certain of universal acclamation if it tramples truth beneath its feet?"

Jaquemar was now lying with his eyes open, there was a tension in his face, a readiness to spring to his own defense that did not, however, cause him to look at the man who was speaking. "What can I do about it?" he asked in a low voice, attempting to smile. "Start a revolution? I'm no Camille Desmoulins."

"You should appear as co-plaintiff," said Goron. Jaquemar did not move, and this seemed somehow to aggravate Goron so that he bent forward, spread out both hands, and shouted rather than said: "Do you understand that? It must be so! There must be someone present who is on the side of justice, someone who will open his mouth and protest when lies and slander strike an attitude and speak in favor of scandalous injustice! You understand what I mean, don't you?" In his zeal he nodded toward the prostrate man. "Someone who with all his wits about him. . . ."

"To take the kicks that are meant for the police?" asked Jaquemar, without looking at the other.

"You owe it to yourself," said Goron in a curiously feeble voice, and only then replied: "For the police? You know as well as I do that when the harm has been done, people will come to their senses, the police have nothing to fear. People always come to their senses— afterward."

"Quite right," replied Jaquemar.

"But by then it will be too late for the cause of justice! It isn't I, that is to say the police, who matters, it isn't you who matters; what matters is the cause of justice! Remember, too, that we are both in the same boat."

"Are we?"

"Can you ask?"

"People want to have us in the same boat! I'm not sure that I shall accept their friendly invitation."

"Didn't you say just now: 'Even if it costs me my life, I shall not let go of this affair'?"

But at this point Madame Chottin suddenly intervened in the conversation. "You can see," she cut in, with a harshness unusual in her, "that Monsieur Jaquemar wants nothing to do with this business. I can't understand why you go on tormenting yourself, yourself and him."

"Perhaps," said Jaquemar, with a slight laugh, propping himself up on his elbow, "perhaps he doesn't want any harm to come to Mademoiselle Bompard?"

Thereupon, as Goron looked from one to the other, the young woman rose to her feet and retired to the far end of the room by the small table, where she seemed to be whispering to Lebigot, who shrugged his shoulders indifferently.

"So you refuse," stated Goron grimly, and buttoned up his jacket again.

"I have other methods," responded Jaquemar, lost in somber thought.

"Just now you solemnly declared . . ."

All at once, Jaquemar placed his hand on Goron's knee for a second: "You mean so well. I am very grateful to you. Why did you not immediately seize the other side's propaganda pamphlet, the noble *J'accuse?*"

"Because I considered it beneath my dignity."

"Exactly," said Jaquemar.

"But it was a mistake!" cried Goron. "And the position is different now—this is our last chance!"

"Yes, if I act as you want me to."

"In any event. A verdict is a verdict."

"I could have the case reopened—if I do not interfere now."

"Only if you can prove that a formal error of procedure has been committed."

"It will be committed."

"Bompard will show you a clean pair of heels, never to be seen again."

"I shall know where she is."

"You've thought of everything," remarked Goron, with a spitefulness that was intended to be ironic and did not suit him.

"Yes, my friend," replied Jaquemar with a thoughtful nod. "I have thought of everything."

Now Lebigot, who had approached unnoticed in the excitement of the moment with the vessel which he had refilled, stepped between them and declaimed in a loud voice: "Now *taceant mulieres in ecclesia*. . . . For behold, the Consummate One has appeared unto us, to distribute his benison among his faithful flock. . . . Ladies first."

So saying, he dipped the tips of the fingers of his huge right hand into the soapy solution in the enema and, glancing at him under his brows, flicked them at Goron. The man thus sprinkled wiped his forehead with his handkerchief indignantly, while Lebigot commented with a hard, unmoved face: "I warned you: twenty minutes. The time is up."

"Where's my hat?" asked Goron, looking around and rising with a haste that clearly revealed his anger.

"You didn't have one, Monsieur Goron," replied Madame Chottin maternally from the background.

"We could make you one out of newspaper," proposed Lebigot. "We have several sheets taken from *J'accuse*."

Goron made a brief bow of farewell to Jaquemar, who looked at him calmly with his melancholy, squinting eyes and said: "I wish that you, at least, did not misunderstand. Instead of pondering what I have not said, will you ponder what I *have* said?"

"Certainly, of course," answered Goron acidly. "I found it very interesting. I wish you a quick recovery. Good-by."

But when he came to Madame Chottin, he paused again, looked beseechingly into her eyes, and said in a low voice: "Madame, it is not yet too late."

"I fear it *is* too late," she replied in an equally low voice, folding

her hands over her bosom in a charmingly ingenuous gesture and looking down at the floor with a helpless smile.

"Try, anyhow," insisted Goron.

She parted her hands, stretched out the right to him, and said with
a melancholy but candid little smile: "I haven't had much experience,
Monsieur Goron, but this I have learned: delicate men are more stubborn than robust ones. My chances are very small."

Goron descended the spiral staircase; he stared at the uncomfortably
curving steps and noticed that his knees were almost giving way, as
they had in the Chévron Private Hotel in London. "Pull yourself
together!" he exclaimed angrily. Then he came to a sudden stop. He
thought to himself: "Of all the kicks I have had to put up with, today
and recently, this is the worst."

The Eyraudt-Bompard trial, together with the events that immediately succeeded it, was the final sensation derived by the public from
the violent death of poor huissier Gouffé. Then all the actors in the
drama vanished from public view and hence from public consciousness: the two accused for a start, Goron pretty soon afterward, and
above all Jaquemar, who disappeared so completely that, if people
remembered him at all, they might well have thought him dead.

In the meantime, they heard that he was ill, although they did not
believe it for a moment. His illness was given as an excuse and explanation (a pretext, as they said) for the fact that, although invited
to appear as a witness, he did not attend the trial; nor did Goron, but
he had not been invited. But there was so much that was odd about
this trial, and the outcome was so universally regarded as a foregone
conclusion, that no lasting heed was paid to any detail—apart from
the fact that, on the second day of the trial, one of the jurymen declared himself prejudiced and therefore unable to carry out his duties,
because he had fallen desperately in love with the defendant Bompard. This incident was greeted with great delight, though everyone
wished that all the jurymen were in the same position, without,
however, renouncing their right to reach a verdict.

Furthermore, the prevailing excitement, an excitement directed
toward a single purpose, was far too strong to admit of clear judgment.
This excitement was intensified by the fact that—by design or otherwise—a courtroom of only medium size had been chosen for the

drama's final apotheosis, so that thousands were unable to enter and gathered in the street outside, where they had to be content with a kind of telepathic participation. This participation made itself felt in a mysterious way: events in the courtroom were immediately greeted by the invisible audience outside either with enthusiastic jubilation, laughter, and clapping, or with discordant catcalls, hissing, and long-drawn cries of "Ee-ee-ee," all of which was difficult to explain and constituted a rather weird contrast to the cool and rational atmosphere in the courtroom with the white candles of the chestnut blossoms dancing peacefully outside its windows.

There was nothing remarkable about this long, narrow room; it held some four hundred persons, and the only view of the world outside was through the windows just referred to; these occupied the whole of the longitudinal external wall and were kept open throughout the proceedings, except when the Presiding Judge ordered them to be shut because the ghostly din outside had reached an intolerable pitch. The walls were decorated with snow-white lacquer paint, which gave the whole interior the soberly scientific appearance of a lecture room, apart from the low platform at one end bearing a dais and the judges' table and seats, a triangular composition of black ebony with the high-backed chair of the Presiding Judge forming the apex and looking from a distance like an altar; it recalled the simplicity of Protestant churches—an impression strengthened by the cross standing in the center of the large table—a cross of modest dimensions to be sure, but extremely solid and made of pure gold. Immediately in front of the dais, and a good deal lower, stood the desk and chair of the Clerk of the Court; to the left of these, with a space for the barristers in front of them, the docks, square stands surrounded by a waist-high wooden railing like a play-pen, and facing these the Public Prosecutor's seat at the head of the double row of jurymen's chairs that ran in a diagonal line toward the external wall with the windows.

In its unembellished simplicity, the whole arrangement was dignified and practical, and calculated to encourage cool thinking, as ought to be the case where truth and justice are concerned. Less practical, because it gave rise to disturbances, was the fact that the benches for the public were not raised progressively toward the back of the court, but were all on one level. Before the end of the first day's hearing, the Presiding Judge used this as a convenient pretext to clear the court of all women, on the grounds that their hats, many of them as big as wheels, blocked the view of the other on-lookers. Very probably, in his ignorance of feminine nature, he considered the intimate, not to say extremely obscene, details that were being disclosed unfit for feminine ears and liable to offend the modesty of the gentle sex—although any child could have seen that the ladies present belonged chiefly to the more expensive demimonde and had turned up in their smartest clothes as though to a gala performance at the theater.

Of the judicial personnel, Massicot, the Public Prosecutor, was by far the most imposing figure, a man of about sixty, almost bursting with malice, who seemed incapable of speaking in any way other than vehemently and to the accompaniment of a generous spray of saliva. He hissed as he spoke, like an enraged snake about to strike. His head was small and looked as though it had been compressed by the excessively vigorous application of a lever, so that the coarse gray goatee was thrust aggressively forward, like the bristling inky-black brows that twitched nervously above his spectacles whenever anyone, even if it was himself, compelled him to remain silent.

As regards the Presiding Judge, Deist, one could hardly speak of a face at all; it was white, puffy, and spherical, and the eye slits gave it no expression other than one of offended indifference, especially as, whenever he was not wriggling about in his chair seeking a more comfortable position in which to lounge, he propped up his chin, turned his head to one side, and covered his face with his hand, as though he had no interest in events or persons and was sitting there only as a burdensome formality. Finally, the jurors were middle-class men decked out stiffly in their Sunday best, trying to defend the dignity of their judicial function against their natural shyness and unable to restrain themselves from goggling wide-eyed when intimate disclosures were made, particularly by Bompard, at the sight of whom an incredulous, delighted, and increasingly lecherous half-smile suffused their coarse faces.

The whole trial centered on Bompard, from first to last; Eyraudt's fate was sealed in any event, and he himself was little more than a picturesquely hideous supernumerary; even the officially appointed Counsel for the Defense, the mild Chantegrei, who did his job honestly and well, spoke in his restrained way of the "instigator" almost as much as Maître Rebattu did—at any rate, he spoke more of her than of the perpetrator, and when she was not being discussed the public treated this almost as an interlude, an interlude between bouts of intense watching and listening.

Not only had the ladies brought their lorgnettes, fine tortoise-shell instruments on long gold chains, but the gentlemen had also brought opera glasses in leather and plush containers, which they trained on her; many of them held their horn-rimmed pince-nez with the myopic lenses a few inches in front of their eyes, turned their heads and half rose in order to get a clear view of her—and, after all, what is more worth seeing in this sorry life than beauty? She was more beautiful than ever, and in her long black taffeta dress with the high fan-shaped collar and the heavy piece of antique jewelry (gold set with beryls —a gift from Carapin for the occasion) she looked positively queenly, far more aristocratic than any of her judges, not to speak of the rest of the assembly; compared with her, even Maître Rebattu lost in stature and gave the impression of being an adroit secretary or at most a diplomatic *chargé d'affaires* in her employ, for his distinction was cool and measured, while hers was without self-consciousness and completely natural. Her regal bearing was visible at the very beginning of the hearing, when she removed her long white stole and, turning her shining eyes toward the public, held it out behind her with a careless, friendly gesture to Montardon, who took it and folded it neatly on her lap. She displayed this quality later the same day. She repeated the remark she had made once before, "He should have known that he couldn't keep a woman like me for his secret enjoyment," whereupon Deist, the Presiding Judge, his face still averted and speaking with his thick lips into his hand, asked: "Why? What do you mean by that?" and she replied politely: "If you would trouble to look at me for a moment you would not need to ask." Applause mingled with laughter burst in through the open window, and even the spectators in the courtroom clapped, until Deist, furious both at this rap across the knuckles and the resulting applause, rang his bell for silence.

There is little more that need be reported here concerning this first day of the hearing (during which the ladies were still present). After the jury had been chosen by lot, the rest of the day's session was occupied by the cross-examination and the confrontation of the two defendants, and produced practically nothing that has not been related before in one form or another. It must be said, however, that if Eyraudt had not recovered physically, at least his fanatical hatred of his former mistress had gained a fresh lease of life. He threw everything into the balance, and was evidently less concerned to save his own skin than to drag her to perdition with him. He had been nothing but her tool, he protested; he acted solely in response to her promptings and suggestions and committed the whole crime "in a trancelike state," in fact he was half insane at the time, continually urged on and encouraged by her by word and deed—all of which he was unable to substantiate with a single concrete fact, so that rage had to serve as a substitute for cogent reasoning.

As usual, Gabrielle Bompard listened to these outpourings of hate and fury with the hint of an astonished smile, turned around to Montardon several times, shook her head slightly or shrugged her shoulders, and once cried out in the midst of his torrent of words: "But, Michi, you're only making things worse for yourself with all that blather!" After Deist had called her to order for this interruption, exclaiming "Silence, defendant!" she quickly remarked with a wink to the jurors: "You can't blame him for trying to wriggle out of it!"

When she was cross-examined in her turn, she stuck to her earlier statements—affecting to be surprised that the matter was still thought worth discussing—showing little desire to incriminate Eyraudt further than was necessary to her own defense, and beyond this contented herself with the two old arguments: on the one hand, there was absolutely no proof of her having instigated, let alone assisted in, the "nasty" crime; on the other hand, her innocence was proved by the fact that she came voluntarily to Paris, "without any necessity," and reported to the "unpleasant" Monsieur Goron—why did she do that, if not because she was completely confident that no one could touch her? It was impossible for her to denounce Eyraudt sooner, because, in his fear and jealousy, he never let her out of his sight for a moment, employing "very drastic" methods to keep her under his thumb, till finally she managed to give him the slip, when she came hotfoot to Paris precisely for the purpose of denouncing his crime.

And did not the gentlemen of the jury agree with her that it was a breach of faith that, instead of the promised reward, she had been repaid for her trouble with treatment that cried out to heaven? She placed the main emphasis on the "disrespectful" way in which she had been treated, returning to it again and again, until, a second Danton before the Revolutionary Tribunal, she seemed more plaintiff than defendant; in this she was assisted by the ghostly howls of indignation and enthusiastic cheers from the invisible audience outside, while Montardon every now and then shook her huge white face, with the corners of her mouth hard, as though hearing all this for the first time.

There was really nothing new either in Bompard's statement or in Eyraudt's; it had been heard and read a hundred times; but apart from the fact that a tall story gains rather than loses by repetition, they were now hearing it from the mouths of those who had acted in it; the story was taking place before their eyes and moving on toward its final climax—no wonder the spectators were thrilled! And every now and then something really new did come their way, as, for example, when the cross-examination dealt with a past that had barely been touched on till then, with the defendants' origins and early life.

As regards Eyraudt, what emerged was very much what might have been expected: the son of middle-class parents; grew up in Paris; involved while still at the *lycée* in rowdy, indecent, and near-criminal escapades and therefore expelled; theft of petty cash while apprentice in a bank followed by flight to Algeria; five years in the Foreign Legion and then return to Paris; last attempt at respectability through marriage with irreproachable young woman of means; squandered his wife's fortune in riotous living and increasingly fraudulent undertakings; another flight, another return home, forever veering between dubious respectability and fraud and dissipation; irredeemably addicted to women, at one moment squandering his ill-gotten gains on them, at the next exploiting and beating them till they respected this ponce whose brutality was not to be trifled with; punctuating these activities with the establishment of factories and trading companies whose operations were limited to cashing the shares paid in by credulous investors—and so on, until finally, the crowning event in his career, Gabrielle Bompard appeared in his office, "of all women the most depraved, every man's ruin, a golden chamber pot."

By comparison with this catalogue of sins—in which, incidentally, only a passing reference was made to the crime against Baker Dubocage's errand boy, since it had been excluded from the present proceedings to be dealt with separately at some future date—by comparison, we say, the information given about Bompard sounded very unexciting, indeed drab—chiefly, no doubt, because in the hurry to press on with the case and bring it to an end, little attempt was made to obtain closer details. After the very early death of her parents, she was brought up in *Au Sacré Coeur de Jésus*, a girls' home at Angoulême, not in the public boarding school, of course, which was a benevolent institution, but in the School for Children of the Aristocracy attached to the convent, in which, according to her mumbled statement, a place had probably been "bought" for her with the remnants of her parents' estate. The nuns had tried to persuade her to take the veil, but after a prolonged inner conflict as to whether she felt the call, she had "renounced the plan" and run away to Paris, "where I immediately fell into Michi's hands." That was all—and it was not much, although there was a certain piquancy about the idea that she had almost become a bride of Our Lord.

The confrontation was equally unproductive, but naturally far more dramatic. It took place below the tribunal, that is to say in front of the Clerk of the Court's little desk and at the feet of Deist, who remained seated on his lofty throne and whom even the proximity of the defendants did not induce to take his puffy face out of his hand; only now he also played with the gold cross, which he first fingered with outstretched arm, then drew toward him and turned, weighed, and stroked with his left hand, like an idling schoolboy. Bompard entered with rustling, almost-dancing steps and an air of youthful vigor, followed rather than accompanied by the waddling wardress, took up a position near the desk of the testy Public Prosecutor, and watched the approach of Eyraudt, who was led in by a court sergeant of the Soudrais type, meanwhile tidying her hair and beaming as though the whole procedure seemed to her like an amusing game of forfeits.

Eyraudt, on the other hand, stood with fists on hips and head lowered as though to butt, and glared at her with his bloodshot eyes, muttering unintelligibly and once groaning loudly, as though his hatred was too great to bear. His feelings were clearly beyond his control. Time after time Deist (grumbling into his hand) admonished him: "Don't shout!" Eyraudt went on shouting, stopped with a gulp, and stood there breathing heavily, without ever taking his little protruding eyes off his adversary. It was a good thing that the Sergeant, leaning his posterior against the Clerk's desk, was standing between them! They began to quarrel from the very first question, put in a tone of contemptuous boredom by the Presiding Judge: on the occasion of her first visit to Eyraudt's office, was it Bompard who "invited him to indulge in sexual intercourse" or he who invited Bompard? "She, she," yelled Eyraudt, "she set me on the downward path, she started practicing her arts straightaway and gave me a lesson in the hotel that made my hair stand on end!"

Her eyes still shining, she clicked her tongue and asked: was she supposed to have learned these things from the nuns at Angoulême, where they even had to wear a long chemise in the bathtub on Saturday evenings because of the sinfulness of the flesh? "He, on the contrary," she said, looking up at Deist and indicating Eyraudt with a movement of the head, "is an old whoremonger, saving your presence, a filthy swine." "Perhaps," commented Deist into his hand, "you will try to respect the dignity of the court and use less objectionable expressions." "It isn't easy," she answered dryly, "in this case."

Deist turned his eye slits toward her, but she was already looking at Eyraudt again and asked politely: "Will you describe that night? But don't forget that you borrowed the album of photographs from the hotelkeeper (her name was Madame Bergasse) for two francs fifty, so that under your instructions I could study the positions, and that later you went down again and fetched a special erotic appliance, and I had to kneel on the edge of the bed and watch with my head twisted round what you were doing to me. It had very little resemblance to the love I had learned about at Angoulême: you pulled me apart till it hurt terribly and was a disgrace and I saw myself naked, as naked as it is possible to be without having your belly slit open." "You slimy fish, you made me do it; all the whores in Paris put together couldn't think up tricks to compare with your depravity! Whose idea was it with the pin?"

This was the point at which (while the jury goggled as though hypnotized and a deathly silence lay over the courtroom) Deist suddenly rang his bell as though in anger, thrust the cross away, threw himself back in his chair, turned to the ushers, who were standing, also breathless with expectation, by the doors, and blustered: "Clear the court of all women—their large hats are an inconvenience to others!"

Inside the court this order was greeted with a single outraged yell

from all the women present, their indignation being far greater than
if he had cleared the court entirely on the reasonable grounds of a
threat to public morality; at the same time a caterwauling burst forth
from a thousand invisible throats outside, turmoil broke out in the
court, which became the scene of a veritable hand-to-hand battle;
women's voices screeched and shrieked, many ladies had to be dragged
struggling from the benches and hauled with outstretched legs along
the center aisle, large and small hats slipped off disheveled heads and
over angry faces; but the tubby Presiding Judge had at last once more
taken up his customary position, his averted face resting in his hands,
his lips thrust out contemptuously; Eyraudt was still glaring at Bompard with his head down; and she alone gazed at the uproar with
friendly eyes and a regretful shrug of her shoulders.

When order had at last been restored, the conflict between the two
defendants switched to less delicate, or at least more serious, matters. The Presiding Judge stated with finality: "Bompard—so he
seduced you, did he?" "And because he is unfortunately a completely
depraved man," she said, nodding her head to emphasize her words,
"and because he was down to his last sou, he moved with me to the
whores' district by the Fortifs, so that I could earn money for him."
"Lies!" howled Eyraudt, with quivering fists. "Nothing but lies!" "He
picked the prostitute Bernard to introduce me to the trade."

For an instant there was silence, Eyraudt gulped without speaking,
she leaned over to one side and called out in a low voice to Maître
Rebattu: "I forgot to tell you about that," and with a shrug of the
shoulders went on: "But although I had to degrade myself for his
pleasure, I refused to earn money for him; on the contrary, he had to
slip money into my purse; I had to put up with a lot of beatings and
thrashings because of that, but since pain passes and disgrace remains,
I bore it and thought to myself"—here Bompard roguishly, but rather
aggressively, raised her yellow index finger—"Today I am weeping, who
knows who will laugh later? I said this to him many times, as a
warning. Do you remember, Michi, before we ate the pastry that time,
for instance, when you got rough with Baker Dubocage's boy?"

"You filthy limpet! It was the other way around!" bellowed Eyraudt
and began to pant, so that his words were interspersed and distorted
by gasps. "No one can ever shake you off until you've sucked him to
death! You ruin everyone you get hold of! You stick tight, no matter

how much one scratches! Why did you stay with me, you crab louse?" And Deist pressed her: "Well, answer, defendant. Why did you stay with him?" "But he loved me," she replied astonished. "A funny sort of love," exclaimed the Presiding Judge, guffawing into his hand. "No," she replied without a trace of humor. "It wasn't funny." "Then I suppose you loved *him* too?" commented Deist. Now it was she who laughed, a brief, gay laugh; she looked the bull-necked Eyraudt in the eyes, and said: "Every woman loves her seducer."

Later, discussion centered on the deed itself. Eyraudt repeated his accusation that Bompard was the instigator of the crime with such vehemence that those who heard him were forced to believe that, at this moment anyhow, he was completely convinced of the truth of this statement: how else could she have acted as she did, how could she have rented the two rooms in the Rue d'Assas, drawn Gouffé into her net, sent the signal to London, made the sack, enticed Gouffé to her room at the crucial hour?

"You mean," she rejoined, "why did I obey these orders? Because I had long ago ceased to pay any real heed to you. It was Gouffé I was thinking about. Of you I thought: let him talk, as long as he doesn't make a nuisance of himself! To my indifference was added a touch of the weakness a woman always feels for the man who first deflowered her—it was pity, Michi, for I knew very well that you would go completely to the dogs if I threw you over, as I firmly intended to, once the new man had seen sense and broken with the woman who was then leading him by the nose. Never for one moment did I think of the beastliness you were already up to." "Who was it, if not you, serpent, who put the cord around his neck?" "You had been warned not to disturb our rendezvous." "Who, I ask, put the cord around his neck?" "I did, for a joke—do you think I should have wanted to throttle the man to whose wealth and friendship I had taken a fancy?"

Bompard's aside was greeted with approving laughter from without, but Eyraudt, undeterred, continued to press her, his fists quivering: "Why didn't you come to his aid? You generally start hissing at the slightest provocation and you've got claws like a wild cat!" "But this was a man's fight," she said in surprise. "What had I to do with it?" "What," cut in the Presiding Judge, "you had nothing to do with it?"

"I can't be expected to join in when two grown men are fighting, both of them weighing over two hundred pounds!"

Once again there was laughter outside, and some clapping, but Eyraudt stuck to his point. "I thought you had taken a fancy to him," he yelled. "Was I to assume that someone I had intended to give myself to wasn't man enough to look after himself? Besides, I couldn't do anything in my dressing gown with no cord, and anyhow I was annoyed. If Gouffé had shown himself willing to become my sweetheart the way *I* wanted it, the whole disaster would never have happened." "Ah, hah," cried Eyraudt (and his voice turned into something like a howl of triumph), "you say I came in unexpectedly!" "You don't understand what I mean," she said sulkily.

"The court doesn't understand either," broke in Deist, clearing his throat and shifting about in his chair. "I should have locked the door!" she cried. "That goes without saying! Perhaps I should even have gone into the other room and thrown Michi out, if he had been in there. What right would Michi have had to be in the room that was now to belong to *him?*" "But because he refused to become your sweetheart, as you wanted, you intended to punish him—Gouffé, I mean?" asked Deist. "Good heavens, no!" she rejoined. "I was just careless. I was only playing around with Gouffé; if we had been going to do the real thing I should have thought of locking the door, because a woman always shuts out the world from her true love."

Eyraudt snorted uncomprehendingly. Deist answered indifferently: "Aha, so you stick to your story that Eyraudt appeared unexpectedly. Why didn't you at least shout for help, when you saw what was happening?" "There wasn't a soul in sight, it was a very discreet little room. By the time the tall German came out into the yard, the panting had ceased and the fight was over, Michi had his hands free— was I to anger him by crying out and have my neck wrung like a chicken, as I had just seen him wring Gouffé's? To calm him a little, I even had to give him a glass of cognac, and even so, after he had made Gouffé unrecognizable and packed him up, he was still in such a rage that he took hold of me, with his eyes popping out of his head, threw me on the trunk, and misused me with such violence that it made me blind and deaf. Gentlemen, a woman will make allowances for a man in the throes of passion, but one who celebrates such a Mass she will expect to shrink from nothing."

During the last few sentences, an ever more overwhelming growl of indignation rose from the invisible throng without and echoed through the open window like a lament. Eyraudt made as if to charge at Bompard head down; the Sergeant pushed him in the chest, so that he staggered back and only managed to force from his throat something like the yelping of a lap dog; Gabrielle nodded with an expression that seemed to say, "Serves you right," as she looked into his hate-contorted face above which the strands of greasy hair projected like spikes. A murmur of indignation broke out within the courtroom too, but it was silenced when the Presiding Judge, turning his chin on the hand supporting it, swept the room with flashing eyes from which darted a lion tamer's stern glance. To some extent appeased, he shifted in his chair and proceeded in a bored voice: "Well, were you still frightened after he had gone?"

"Of course I was frightened. He is a spiteful character, as suspicious as he is brutal. How was I to know that he wasn't standing outside waiting to see whether I should cry out?" At this point Massicot, the Public Prosecutor, could no longer restrain himself, and a spray of saliva spurted out above his straggling, jutting beard as he burst out: "Is that your only excuse?" He stopped himself, and his black brows twitched above his spectacles. She turned to him, made a grave little bow, and answered: "It occurred to me I might use the closet in the yard as a pretext, and I softly tried the door. But he had locked it. Then I saw that I had better keep quiet, if I wanted to get away with a whole skin."

Deist commented: "You seem to have adapted yourself to the situation pretty well." "The love-making under these hideous circumstances had somewhat confused me. I wandered around the little room, tidying up a bit." "What were you thinking as you did that?" "I pictured to myself what a shock a man would get, who forced his way in because he was lusting after me and saw me there with the dead man in the trunk and the needle and thread with which he had been sewn up still sticking in the armchair. But above all, I thought to myself that it was all up with Michi now, sooner or later, whatever happened, and I made up my mind to deliver him to justice when the time came."

"When the time came!" hissed the Public Prosecutor, his brows twitching, and Deist added laconically: "It took a long while, didn't

it?" "I'm not impatient," she replied, shaking her head and looking
into Eyraudt's face. "If Carapin had not fallen head over heels in love
with me—and Michi had not had to give way to him, because he
hoped to rob him like so many others before (although he thrashed
me on his account)—it would have taken much longer, and I should
still not have grown impatient." "Perhaps," snarled the Public Prosecutor, "the time would never have come?" "It has come," said Bompard with a radiant obstinacy and without taking her eyes off
Eyraudt's face.

Immediately, a completely senseless roar of applause went up outside, an outburst of clapping, shouting, and cheering that poured in
through the window and was enthusiastically echoed by the public
inside; the Presiding Judge rang his bell furiously, and the uproar
slowly subsided.

The second day of the trial was devoted to cross-examination of the
witnesses, which went, if possible, even less deep than the cross-
examination and confrontation of the two defendants the previous
day. Yet even this act in the drama had its thrills; indeed, it began
with one, since the first witness called was Eyraudt's wife, the only
person in the whole proceedings who spoke cordially in his favor,
very surprisingly, and with such unquestionable candor that the scene
was profoundly moving, especially since the moment she appeared
Eyraudt shyly lowered his head, later covered his face with his hands,
and finally laid his forehead on the wooden bar in front of him and
sobbed bitterly.

She was a homely, careworn woman in a decent but threadbare
dress, and the fact that she wore a black shawl around her head in place
of a hat gave her the appearance of a woman of the people and at the
same time a Mater Dolorosa. She straightaway pushed this shawl
back onto her shoulders, and although she spoke quietly and continually cast her eyes down to the floor, she was free from any shyness,
perhaps because after all the trouble she had been through, this interrogation was no ordeal.

She had been called by Chantegrei, the officially appointed Counsel
for the Defense, a conscientious young man of seraphic appearance
with brown doe's eyes, a sensitive nose, and a slightly cleft chin; he
had a curious habit of terminating his comments and questions with

a half-inquiring, half-confirmatory "H'm," a thin, inarticulate sound in the throat, which made his conversation sound rather like a monologue. He treated the careworn woman with almost filial consideration, although any understanding that had been reached seemed to be on his side only; for all these strange people appeared to mean just as much, or as little, to her; she merely spoke the truth, her truth, and it was a truth of astonishing simplicity—thus when, having been formally apprised that, as the defendant's wife, she could refuse to give evidence, she replied that she would give evidence, "because he was a good husband to me."

Naturally, she could say nothing about the crime itself, she had first heard of it from the papers, and from the papers, too, she had first learned of the existence of Bompard, about whom, for this reason, she refused to express any opinion. "I don't know anything about the young girl," she said. "I can't estimate what influence she exercised over my husband." Hence what she had to say was important only in a general sort of way, only insofar as, after sharing with him twenty years of her life, she now stood by him with quietly saddened fortitude—in spite of all the trouble, in spite of all the humiliation she had suffered through him, in spite of the fact that he had again and again abandoned her, and in spite of the abominable crime of which he was now accused; for she denied nothing of what was said —especially, in a carefully considerate tone, by Maître Rebattu—about his evil mode of life. "That's possible," she said, or: "Yes, that's true, that's true—he got into bad company and it spoiled his good intentions, but although he was quick-tempered and thoughtless and easily led astray, he was also good, he would have liked to be good."

"Were you happy during the first years of your marriage, Madame?" asked Maître Rebattu, with gentle urgency. She nodded, her eyes glued to some spot on the floor, and finally answered: "I didn't know it was possible to be so happy." In short, if the aim of this question was to strengthen Bompard's defense and detract from the value of Madame Eyraudt's evidence by proving that she was led to speak in his favor by nostalgic recollection of the only happiness she had ever experienced in her poor life, she for her part did nothing to refute it, either not noticing the implication or ignoring it.

To Chantegrei's almost shamefaced question: "Did you have to put up with rough treatment from Eyraudt, later, did he, forgive me for asking, ever beat you?" she replied, for the first time raising her big black eyes, which were lit by a sudden fire: "Oh no, nothing like that ever happened between us. When he was at home, he was a quiet, well-behaved man. He loved our daughter, and I believe he loved me too." It was at this point that Eyraudt let his forehead sink down onto the wooden bar in front of him and began to sob bitterly. But as he did so, the Public Prosecutor, Massicot, snapped that it was asking a great deal to expect anyone to picture Eyraudt as a good husband and father. Again she nodded and replied: "I know, but it is as I say."

Had she not felt some scruples, the Presiding Judge wanted to know, when Eyraudt turned up in the middle of the night to take away her jewelry? "Scruples," she repeated pensively. "I heard him hurrying along the passage, he pushed the door open and cried in a low, breathless voice: 'Rachel!' . . . 'Rachel,' he said, 'I'm in difficulties, give me your jewelry!' I got up, gave him the jewelry, and went back to bed. With my head on the pillow, I watched him as he made his way hesitantly to the door in the darkness, only a little light from the street lamp outside entered the room; at the door he stopped and came back once more. He knelt beside the bed and we looked at one another, a glimmer of light from the street lamp outside was reflected in his eyes; he took my hands, but he couldn't speak, in the end he kissed me on the forehead and said: 'They're on my heels.' Then he tore himself away and hurried off."

"And although he said: 'They're on my heels,' you felt no scruples?" shot out Massicot, and twitched his black brows. "I knew his creditors were after him," she replied. "He had to turn to someone in his need." So transparent, however, were the honesty and the veracity of the witness that at this point she was told she could stand down. At first she appeared not to understand; the gentle Chantegrei took her by the arm and wanted to lead her to the witnesses' bench or out of the courtroom; but she looked up at him, freed her arm, and went over to Eyraudt, who lay sobbing with the upper part of his body across the wooden bar of the dock; she stood in front of him for a moment, touched his hand, and walked quietly out.

The invisible multitude without had no share in the emotion aroused by the appearance of this witness among the audience in the courtroom; they remained silent, while Bompard, straightening her hair with an amused expression on her face, leaned down to Maître

Rebattu, who for his part reacted cheerfully and reassuringly to what she whispered to him: he laughed with his shoulders and shook his head with protruding, rounded lips. If he meant to imply by this that the slight gain in public sympathy that had accrued to Eyraudt was no cause for alarm on the part of his client, he was only too right: the wife who still loved him in spite of everything had manifestly been Chantegrei's star witness for the defense, he had been unable to dig up any other intercessor of comparable weight, and the remainder of the witnesses he called did his client more harm than good.

In any case, there were only three of them. Franquet, a barber by trade, a man whose features were at once handsome and weather-worn, with bold, beautifully waved, fair hair above hard, colorless, pale eyes and a wiry figure, had lived by the Fortifs at the same time as the defendants. He testified that there could be no question of Eyraudt having tried to induce Bompard to engage in prostitution; they had all been surprised at his having burdened himself with such an extravagant, stuck-up creature; he was wax in her hands and at her beck and call. Though perhaps inclined to be hot-tempered and jealous, he was always a "jovial" man and friend, a heart of gold beneath a rough exterior, and even if he occasionally exclaimed with a significant gesture, "So and so should have his neck wrung like a chicken," his bark was worse than his bite, he was quite incapable of carrying out a premeditated murder—he, Franquet, would vouch for that. This Franquet had a quick, resolute way of speaking, frequently raising his shoulders as he talked; with a dark frock coat he wore very narrow, brightly checked trousers and held a narrow-brimmed bowler in his hand.

Maître Rebattu, to whom the witness was handed over after making his statement, asked briefly where he was working. He had no fixed employment at the moment. He had said "they were all surprised"—whom did he mean when he said "they all"? Well, their acquaintances. Of course, but what acquaintances, people of both sexes? Could he name a few and say what their trades were? But the witness could not remember as clearly as all that: they were simply "the people in the district." "Women too, if I understand correctly?" asked Maître Rebattu, with an encouraging little nod, adding, after Franquet's awkward concurrence: "And the ladies found it extravagant that Mademoiselle Bompard refused to make herself useful in the same way as they themselves—is that what you meant? Yes, I can quite imagine that. Professional pride is to be found everywhere. Incidentally, were you without fixed employment at the time of the crime? I mean, otherwise you would probably have helped your friend Eyraudt out of the difficulty in which he happened to find himself?"

"I was away," answered Franquet. "Where were you?" "I was busy elsewhere," replied Franquet, after some hesitation. "Were you by any chance busy in the Poissy penitentiary?" "Yes, yes, yes!" yelled Franquet in sudden anger. "It was Poissy!" "Oh, it was," said Maître Rebattu regretfully, and sat down with a gesture of thanks to Chantegrei.

Chantegrei's next witness, the furrier Samuel Menuchim Lévy, was considerably more dignified, almost venerable in fact. His appearance, combined with his carefully weighed utterances, were well calculated to assist the defendant's case against his co-defendant Bompard. He was a grizzled old man with watery eyes, dressed in a long black frock coat, and he invoked his advanced age when he replied in the negative to the Defense Counsel's question as to whether he remembered having told Eyraudt on the evening of July 25, 1889, that he had to pay out the sum of eighteen thousand francs in cash to Gouffé that same day (as Bompard asserted). "I'm an old man, it's possible I may have told him, how should I know, I can't remember. I don't think so. I definitely don't think so."

This much he could remember and testify: the accused was an honest man, in his experience. "Not even Michi's widow claims he is honest!" cried Bompard, laughing, thereby arousing ghostly laughter outside the windows and Deist's anger. "Hold your tongue!" he barked, and the old man murmured: "Is that the woman of calamity?" "Go on, please," admonished Chantegrei gently. In his experience the defendant was an honorable man, he had had business dealings with him for many years and had not lost by it; if he said he had not heard about the eighteen thousand francs from him, Lévy, then he had not heard. "I have nothing for him, I have nothing against him," he said in his hoarse, mournful voice. "God be with him."

"Did the defendant have an interest in the fur trade, Monsieur Lévy?" inquired Maître Rebattu. "I didn't know about that. I lent him money," replied the old man, spreading out both hands. "I lent

him money, he paid it back." "I see, you're also a banker. At what
rate of interest did you lend it?" The old man swayed backward and
forward: "These are hard times," he answered plaintively. "They are
indeed. Interest rates are high, I know—how high, if I may ask?"
"Five percent!" replied the other, striking the air with both hands.
"But that's cheap," said Maître Rebattu wonderingly. "You mean five
percent per annum?" "How could I—" cried Lévy clutching at his
chest, "with *that* risk!" "You mean per month? Five percent per
month? That is not cheap, Monsieur Lévy."

After this intercessor, too, had been pretty thoroughly discredited,
the last witness for Eyraudt's defense was called: a medical expert
named Dubois, a man quite unknown in professional circles. Dr.
Dubois most emphatically asked his audience to visualize the suggestive intimacy of the scene that presented itself to Eyraudt's eyes as
he entered the cozy little room, a scene which, though admittedly not
entirely unexpected, went far beyond his expectations. In a man
subject to bouts of morbid jealousy, the shock occasioned by this
vision might well have induced a state bordering on frenzy and led
him to commit an act far more horrible than anything he had originally
contemplated. On these grounds, it seemed hard to sustain the thesis
of a *premeditated* capital crime; indeed, this thesis ought to be rejected, while the supposition of a limited degree of free will and a
corresponding limitation of responsibility inescapably imposed itself
—even Bompard had expressed the view that he had originally planned
only a *coup du Père François.*

Questioned by the hissing Massicot as to how he reconciled the
preparations for removing the body made days and weeks ahead—the
purchase of the trunk, the making of the sack—with this psychological
argument in extenuation of the crime, Dubois, speaking with a good
deal less confidence, launched into an obscure discussion of the psy-
chologically still-unexplained phenomenon of "duplicated thinking"
and the inscrutability of human impulses in general, and on being
told he could stand down (since Maître Rebattu considerately forbore
from putting any questions to him) he withdrew rather hurriedly,
while Chantegrei stood with his hands folded over his flat abdomen,
his seraphic face bent forward, biting his lower lip.

The stage was now Maître Rebattu's; but it could not be said that
he had gone to great trouble to assemble an impressive array of wit-

nesses or even that he made very thorough use of those available; he treated the whole thing rather casually, contenting himself with a few questions put in a conversational tone, thanked the witnesses politely, and handed them over to Eyraudt's defense counsel with a nod. Chantegrei asked very few questions, either because he attached no value to cross-examination at all, or because he felt it better to rest content with the information already elicited.

What could he have gained, for example, in the case of the first witness, who had come in person from London, instead of giving his evidence by affidavit, perhaps less out of concern for the truth than in order to pay his tribute as a man of the world to the heroine of the drama? With light yet measured tread, Monsieur Chévron, the *soigné* fox, approached the bench, made a brief but courtly bow with deferentially closed eyes, and corroborated the statement of Mademoiselle Bompard's counsel that she had stayed from June 24 to July 5 of last year in his humble house, the Hôtel-Pension Chévron, Hallam Street, and had been an unexceptionable guest, polite and no trouble to anyone, on the contrary an "asset," as they say over there; the old ladies, who formed the majority of his English guests, had positively fallen in love with the young girl, whose friendly reserve and stimulating naturalness at once revealed, if not the *Au Sacré Coeur de Jésus* convent school, at least a cultured home background; Madame Chévron had taken to her as much as he had, and even the chambermaids peeped around doors and corners of the landing to catch a glimpse of the lovely young woman.

As to her remark about a large trunk, which had been the object of so much special comment—the remark that she was going to fill it in Paris, not in London—he had repeated this to Monsieur Goron, "who was slightly unwell at the time," without the slightest thought that there was anything wrong in it. "Not," he said, lowering his lids again and letting a smile of long experience play over his gourmet's lips, "not, heaven forfend, that I credit myself with being able to see through the feminine heart; but I cannot for one moment believe that there was anything insidious in this remark." On the other hand, he could very well believe that, in her charmingly pensive way, Mademoiselle had been thinking of the beautiful clothes she was going to buy in Paris, with which, as he heard, Eyraudt had promised to fill this trunk, again very credibly, since it was hard to see with what other attractions he could have held such a youthful and much-admired mistress.

It was a pleasure to hear Monsieur Chévron conversing in this fashion with the no less *soigné* Maître Rebattu, who either supported the ingratiating, insinuating, rambling worldly wisdom of his witness with a few additional elucidatory questions, which betrayed an even more mature and sound grasp of the issues; or he simply corroborated what had been said with a slight nod of complete agreement. In any event, this witty and urbane discourse could only serve to display their qualities and those of their subject, Gabrielle Bompard, in the best possible light—though, strictly speaking, the exchanges cannot be said to have been important, let alone patently necessary, to the matter in hand.

Yet everything remained in proper proportion; the scene lasted a bare ten minutes, then Monsieur Chévron was followed by Miss Priscilla Evergreen, and whereas he was a Frenchman running a *hôtel-pension* in England, she was an American woman running a boarding-house in Paris: she was the landlady of the Villa des Fleurs. It must have been eccentricity that led her to adopt such a profession, and abroad too, "in order to have company," as she put it, in a French that was pretty free from mistakes, but extremely odd, so to speak pickled; at one moment the words came out linked in their normal short cadences, at the next they were uttered with a distinct gap between each word, her high-pitched voice thrusting them out through protruded lips in a jerky rhythm, as if she were spitting a crumb of tobacco from her lips and tongue at each one, nodding as she did so.

She was eccentric in every respect; with shortsighted, pale-blue eyes and lashless, inflamed lids; she had almost blood-red dyed hair, with dun-colored skin smothered in rice powder (which recalled withering white rose petals); and at an age that must have been approaching senility she wore a girlish spring frock over her skinny little figure that looked as though the wind could blow right through it; the frock was of tulle with veil-like, foamy Brussels lace filling in the V-neck and a comically pompous taffeta bow at the small of the back; on her head she wore a gaudy flowered hat, and she carried a small sunshade which several times fell from her hand, so that the dignified Maître Rebattu had to bend down and pick it up.

Every time he did so, she thanked him at great length and with a very sweet, ladylike smile; for, eccentric in this too, she was obviously as anxious to see herself as being treated with chivalry and gallantry —in short, as a lady—as she was to depict the God-given superiority of the female sex as an absolutely self-evident fact, despite the sorry way in which this sex was generally downtrodden. This, at least, seemed to be the essence of the rather confused statement that issued now in a smooth flow, now in fits and starts. She thought that—here —as—so—often—in this world ruled by men—the woman—was—once —more—being called upon to pay for the misdeeds of the man; once more the crimes of the baser sex were being visited upon the gentler —she, Miss Evergreen, could say plenty about that—

"Come to the point, witness," said Deist, speaking into his hand and tapping with the toe of his shoe on the wooden floor. "People— do—not—like—to—hear—the—truth," she replied clearly. "It—gives —offense." Then she did come to the point, however: Mademoiselle Labodère was a refined, retiring young lady, it was—masculine madness to brand her a criminal, Mademoiselle Labodère. For some reason Miss Evergreen could not bring herself to call Bompard by her correct name. In reply to Maître Rebattu's gentle correction: "You mean Mademoiselle Bompard, don't you?" she dropped her sunshade, thanked him with a sweet smile for picking it up and continued: Naturally Mademoiselle Labodère had to do with the "brutal man" only because she was forced to by his roughness and by prevailing social conditions.

"A—few—times—he beat her," and she had wept and lamented and made so much noise that the tenants of the front building—"the front building, mark you"—had complained, especially a German gentleman, Herr von Schweissheim, and she had had to overcome her reluctance and speak to Miss Labodère about it; the young lady —in her womanly way—was of a courageous nature, a superior character, she had smiled with her mouth (the rest of her face was hidden by the veil), had consoled her, Miss Evergreen, and said: "Don't worry about it, Miss. We either have to remain continent or accept the fact that they all have their quirks. But I'm soon going to exchange this one for another." So Mademoiselle Bompard, if Maître Rebattu understood correctly, had announced her decision to break with Eyraudt? "Oh—very—definitely," agreed the witness, pecking at the words, "a few days, or perhaps the very evening before her departure."

There could be no doubt that this was the point for which Bompard's counsel had called this queer individual as a witness; tension in the court was tremendous, and even Eyraudt gripped the dock and stared as though against his will at the autumnal speaker in the schoolgirl frock. "The man" had settled the bill shortly before, so that there was nothing of a business nature outstanding; nevertheless, Mademoiselle Labodère, returning home from shopping with a small parcel, had looked in at the front building and made—the—following—remark: "I was sitting at my desk writing. 'Miss Evergreen,' she said, 'we shall soon have a new tenant for the room next to mine—perhaps —already—tomorrow.' That's what she said: 'Perhaps—already—tomorrow.'" "That is very interesting, Madame," commented Maître Rebattu, raising his crooked eyebrows and nodding his head earnestly, adding in conclusion: "I thank you." But she seemed unwilling to accept such an abrupt dismissal. "What is it you want me to tell you?" she asked, with an anguished smile. "Thank you, thank you very much," replied Maître Rebattu, "that is all—unless Monsieur Chantegrei wishes to ask you any questions?"

Eyraudt's counsel contented himself with one question: Did she not think it odd that her young tenant always wore a veil? This was not in the least odd; when she thought, for example, of the perseverance with which the aforementioned Herr von Schweissheim, in the ordinary way of a man who kept strictly to himself, had continually asked about Mademoiselle, even hinting that he would like to be introduced to her, she could—understand—only—too—well that she should have kept her face veiled, in order—so far as possible—to— elude—such animal—lust. With this, the witness was finally released. Once more she dropped her sunshade, which this time Chantegrei picked up with the ghost of a smile around his fine, grave mouth. "How—clumsy—of—me," said Miss Evergreen, looking up at him flirtatiously as she fanned her face with a little batiste handkerchief. Then she stumbled as she stepped down to the witnesses' bench, causing a loud, wooden clatter with her shoes, but fortunately no other harm because the gallant Monsieur Chévron sprang to her aid in time.

That morning a court sergeant was sitting behind Bompard, holding the young defendant's white woolen stole on his lap; at first he had been a trifle self-conscious and clumsy, but now all this was forgotten in the fascination of the statements being made to the Bench. He had taken the place of Montardon, and it was she who now entered the witness box in her black wardress's uniform, her straw boater dangling from her forearm by its elastic chin strap. The corners of her crooked little mouth in her big white face were hard, and her multiple chin trembled with repressed emotion as she declared: Mademoiselle bore with dignity and fortitude the "cruel" treatment to which she was subjected in the vaults of the Cité and which she, as the wardress, was able to mitigate only in a very small way; Mademoiselle had left the little additions to her starvation diet untouched, but had responded with childlike gratitude to attempts to alleviate her tedium—in short, she was the most irreproachable, the most admirable, prisoner she, Montardon, had ever had under her charge.

What had Montardon done to relieve Mademoiselle Bompard's tedium? Maître Rebattu inquired casually. Well, Montardon had kept her company and provided her with harmless entertainment—for example, la jeune fille had tried to learn knitting from her, to their great amusement, but in vain, because her fingers were not made for "coarse" work; they had sung duets together and, kneeling on the damp flagstones, had prayed together. This statement caused amusement in the court; Bompard naively joined in the laughter, but Montardon was not to be intimidated. Mademoiselle was of a religious turn of mind, she had insisted in introducing her, Montardon, to the ritual of the Roman Catholic Church, demonstrating it with the aid of the washstand, which served as an altar, while Mademoiselle herself took the part of the priest, murmuring Latin, singing monotonous melodies, and bowing before the washstand.

It was for this purpose, that is to say as a chasuble, that she had knitted in the cell the white woolen stole which Mademoiselle, in accordance with her naturally grateful character, was wearing today; for there was no trace of arrogance in her, she knew no distinction of class, and even under those wretched conditions she was equally gay and friendly toward everyone, with one single exception (here the witness's vast white chin twitched and quivered as though she were on the point of choking), with the exception of Monsieur Goron, of whom she had said that he was seeking to cheat the world of the truth.

Maître Rebattu ignored this declaration and merely asked whether Mademoiselle Bompard had ever felt afraid, whether she had not, from time to time at least, been worried about her ultimate fate.

"Never!" cried Montardon, with a somehow scornful laugh and in a voice so high and shrill that it almost broke. "God forbid! Never, and why should she! She radiated innocence!" With this, Maître Rebattu handed her over with a gesture of invitation, rounding his mouth into an O, to Chantegrei, who looked at her with his doe's eyes and asked mildly but insistently: "You spoke of the 'cruel' treatment suffered by the defendant in the vaults of the Cité: did the cruelty of this treatment exceed usual police practice and, if so, in what way?"

In great excitement, Montardon retorted: "It is quite a different matter, Monsieur, whether you are dealing with a proven criminal or with a fine young lady who positively radiates innocence! Just look at her! Does a person with a guilty conscience look like that? Is she a person who can be subjected to pressure? Isn't it a sin—" "Remember your asthmatic heart, Madame!" cried Bompard, with a laugh. Maître Rebattu rose to his feet and began to turn toward her, no doubt to warn her not to interrupt; but she checked him with a hand on his shoulder and continued: "Don't excite yourself! Is it worth it for these people?"

This interjection produced the most varied effects: outside there arose a murmurous sigh of compassion, the public in the court showed emotion and the officials of the court indignation; even Deist turned his spherical white face with an expression of extreme incredulity toward the defendant, who now leaned down and spoke to Maître Rebattu with a shrug of the shoulders. But it was Montardon herself who seemed most affected. She rose, with her hat still dangling from her forearm, shook her folded hands toward the dock and, overcome with emotion, broke into violent, whimpering sobs; she could not control herself, tears gushed out between her fingers as she covered her face with her hands, her vast, shapeless body shook and jerked all over—so that at last the gentle Chantegrei renounced further cross-examination and a court sergeant had to lead the weeping woman away by the arm.

He doubtless intended to take her to the witnesses' bench, but as soon as she had stepped down from the platform, she pulled and tugged in the opposite direction, and the man let go; still sniffing and dabbing and wiping her face with a handkerchief, she took the woolen stole from the warder in the dock and sat down in her old position, behind Bompard, who did not so much as glance around at her.

Instead, she replied to Deist's thundering admonition kindly to show proper respect for her judges, with a polite, boyish little bow from the waist and the comment: "I wanted to spare us a scene. You can see for yourself how right I was."

Maître Rebattu's next witness was a dashing figure in a mouse-gray cutaway, with a red carnation in his buttonhole and an azure-blue cravat between the white silk lapels of his waistcoat. It was Monsieur Carapin who now took his place before the tribunal, bowed very low, if briefly, to Bompard and then rather less deeply to the judges, and made his heartfelt statement to the accompaniment of whirling, beringed juggler's hands that seemed to be tossing his words now to the bored Presiding Judge, now to the jurors—a statement that at the outset tallied word for word with the one made earlier to Goron but culminated in the declaration that he could only confirm "completely and utterly" the evidence of the preceding witness.

In corroboration of this evidence, he wished to state that Mademoiselle was the most delightfully innocent, the most entirely truthful, person he had ever had the undeserved good fortune to get to know, and to get to know intimately, which meant that in respects not altogether suitable for discussion in the present setting he could amplify the character testimonial supplied by the previous witness; in fact, the defendant was a positive "little fanatic for justice," with a childlike stubbornness that was often comical in its effect.

Carapin, a man not devoid of vanity, was obviously flattered by this opportunity to figure as a forensic speaker and to challenge this exalted court. With great emphasis he advanced his view that to accuse Mademoiselle of being an accessory before the fact, let alone the instigator and accomplice, in a murder committed for filthy lucre, or of any crime at all, would be, if he might say so, a crass judicial blunder and utterly at variance with psychological probability; if the court stuck to this view and, led astray by the maneuvers of a particular official body, actually condemned her, this—as true as he stood here and was speaking nothing but the pure truth—would go down in history as a judicial blunder—no, a judicial crime.

A burst of cheering rose from below the windows, but the public in the court remained quiet, perhaps because they expected the hearing now to turn to the "maneuvers" of the official body and show up the scandalous behavior of this body (to wit, the notorious Goron); but this did not happen. Maître Rebattu ignored this remark and merely wished to have a few factual details above and beyond the witness's admirably clear and enlightening statement. For example, while they were in America, was it he who persuaded Mademoiselle Bompard to leave Eyraudt, or Mademoiselle Bompard who persuaded him; was it her wish or his to go to New York; in short, which of them was responsible for the preparations to return to Europe?

Carapin assured him, with his hand on his heart, that the journey to New York, and even more so the trip to Europe, had been extremely unwelcome to him on business grounds alone; she had begged him to take her away and save her from more of the savage maltreatment with which the atrocious ruffian had forced her into obedience and silence, and the traces of which she still bore on her face and body, yes, she implored him to take her away, and he readily did so at the first opportunity, an opportunity which chivalry and decency forbade him to describe, as he indicated with eloquent regret and much shrugging of the shoulders and elegant gesturing of the hands—moreover, she had often told him that she had "another bone to pick with Eyraudt." Mademoiselle was addicted to such understatements, and he had foolishly supposed that she merely wished to get her own back for the aforementioned brutalities, and only when the matter was really ripe for discussion did the significance of her various hints dawn on him.

Maître Rebattu thanked him amiably, and the seraphic Chantegrei stepped forward: "Monsieur Carapin," he said slowly, lowering his head thoughtfully as he spoke, "you say: 'when the matter was ripe for discussion'; it became ripe for discussion when you came across the defendant's photograph in the newspaper, during breakfast at the Waldorf-Astoria Hotel—that is correct, is it not?" And with a "H'm" that sounded less inquiring than corroborative, he seemed half to withdraw his question. "Quite correct, Monsieur," replied Carapin, with a quick nod, and continued ebulliently: "Because—in my reprehensible blindness!—I had urged on several occasions that we should leave New York and go to Buffalo, where business was calling me. Mademoiselle waited until circumstances convinced me of the necessity of casting all such material considerations to the winds and accompanying her to Paris. Mademoiselle knows what she is doing, Mademoiselle is an exceptionally determined and patient character.

"Yes?" rejoined Chantegrei undecidedly, looking up at the witness reprovingly. "And yet we hear that later, in Paris itself, there was dissension because the defendant reproached you with not having considered the unpleasantness to which this return to Paris would lay her open, in other words, you ought to have advised her against making this journey." "How right she was!" cried Carapin, with flashing eyes, and threw this cry up to the bench like a rocket. "How very right! It was my duty as Mademoiselle's protector to advise her against it—must I remind you of what the honorable Madame Montardon, who, as a member of the staff of the Cité, might be expected to be somewhat hardened to such things—what even Madame Montardon said about the cruelty to which my poor young friend was subjected . . . and the mud that was slung at her! Oh, how absolutely right she was! I am ashamed, I must confess, gentlemen, I am ashamed." And with an expressive gesture, Monsieur Carapin spread both hands over his face for a second with the little fingers outspread (which showed off to advantage the heavy signet ring on the little finger of his left hand).

Meanwhile, Chantegrei calmly went on with his questions. "On the other hand, you want to make us believe that the defendant worked with energy and foresight to persuade you to bring her to Paris?" "Yes, indeed! Of course! Certainly!" cried Carapin, with a gesture as though he were flinging the objection back at Eyraudt's Defense Counsel in little pieces. "On that morning in New York she already knew the ship on which we were to travel, she had made full inquiries, her trunks were packed." "Dr. Dubois's famous duplicated thinking!" shouted a wit from among the public, thereby disturbing Deist, who was on the point of reaching for his bell, but not Carapin. Shaking his head he continued: "I don't know what you are getting at—or am I seriously to understand that you see a contradiction between Mademoiselle's wish to make the trip and the fact that she subsequently reproached me for having given way to her, for having indeed strongly encouraged her? It is not for me to enlighten the gentlemen of this worshipful court on the subject of feminine psychology; but everyone, even the least experienced, knows that the most contradictory ideas may live side by side in the female heart. Mademoiselle was resolved to lodge her accusation against the murderer Eyraudt in Paris, she regarded that as her civic duty—and she was quite right. Mademoiselle was angry with me, because I, her friend, had not warned and protected her against the adversities which this accusation would bring upon her, as a woman she felt neglected and hurt—and once again, she was quite right!"

Chantegrei opened his fine mouth to reply, but the witness gave him no chance. "Oh, I beg you!" he cried, with an anguished twist of his curly head. "You must not conclude from this that, if I had warned her, if I had tried to dissuade her from making this trip, Mademoiselle would have accepted my advice and changed her mind . . . no such thing! I can assure you from rich experience that what she has once got into her head, she puts into effect! When the poet exclaimed 'Frailty, thy name is woman!' he was not thinking of Mademoiselle Bompard." Once again, loud applause rang out from below the windows, while Eyraudt's Counsel sat down with an expression of disappointment. Carapin made a series of quick bows to the jury and the Presiding Judge, and a separate, very deep one with his hand on his heart to Gabrielle Bompard (who responded haughtily, with a barely perceptible inclination of the head, without, of course, allowing the smile to fade from her face). Then Carapin withdrew, with a springy step, and left the field to the witnesses for the prosecution.

But the prosecution had made, if anything, even less effort than the two defense counsels, whose choice of witnesses at least revealed the unambiguous aim of exonerating their clients. Naturally Massicot had to aim at the opposite, but it was impossible to see what he hoped to achieve in this direction by calling on the good Dopffer, Gouffé's former head clerk and now managing the *huissier's* firm on the Boulevard Saint-Michel as executor, who had never consciously set eyes on either of the defendants before. Or was the object in cross-examining him to arouse sympathy for the victim of the crime that was being tried and thus to render it all the more repugnant?

Dopffer, a tall man of sixty, who held a large white handkerchief in his soft right hand and every now and then slowly wiped his forehead with it, seemed indeed still to be mourning Gouffé; from time to time he shook his bent head with the fine gray moustache, as though plagued by memories; it was as if he could still not grasp this thing that had happened almost a year ago; this painful awkwardness on the part of a man who was obviously, in the ordinary way, clear-thinking and upright introduced a note of human sadness, which the proceedings otherwise lacked and which the case itself, in consequence of its disgusting vulgarization, had long since lost; for the essence of a man's life and end is remembered only in a faithful heart.

But if Massicot attached any value to the introduction of this human element, his irascible watch-dog's temperament militated against his own plans, since it prevented the development of a more contemplative mood; perhaps he wished to use the excellent impression made by his witness further to blacken the defendants, to draw from his loyalty to the murdered man some angry outburst that would reinforce the belief that the murder was committed with malice aforethought. In practice, however, his efforts drove Dopffer into a defensive position that was more helpful to the defense than to the prosecution.

Dopffer did not know the defendants personally; all he knew about Eyraudt was what everybody knew, and even the fact that it was Eyraudt's business from which Gouffé had withdrawn a sum of money belonging to Madame Chottin, a few months before his death, had come to his notice only recently. At the time, he merely gathered from a chance remark by Monsieur Jaquemar that it was an apparently unsound enterprise showing an excessively high profit and offering insufficient security; and the insignificant transaction did not go through the books, because Monsieur Gouffé regarded Madame Chottin not as a client, but as a personal friend, and the transaction itself as a trifling favor—this was the reason why Eyraudt's name did not appear on the list of creditors and debtors subsequently prepared for Monsieur Goron.

Since it nevertheless involved several thousand francs, commented the saliva-spraying Public Prosecutor, the withdrawal might be presumed to have aroused a desire for revenge in Eyraudt? He stared with twitching black brows at Dopffer, who looked back at him over the rim of his horn-rimmed pince-nez. He did not understand what he was expected to reply. "It would be pure speculation, if I were to express an opinion on this point. I don't know the man, Monsieur le Procureur, and God forbid that I should attempt to put myself in his shoes."

But he knew that Bompard had called on Gouffé to persuade him to cancel the withdrawal? No, he didn't know that either; Monsieur Gouffé hadn't told him about it; for his part, he had never seen her, at least not consciously—"which, of course, doesn't prove that she did not call on him. I understand the young person usually wears a veil; veiled ladies are no rarity at the office in the Boulevard Saint-Michel; it is quite conceivable that she called once or several times; I can neither affirm nor deny that."

Did he consider it possible that an intimacy had developed between her and Gouffé that was calculated to arouse Eyraudt's jealousy, that is to say, to intensify his lust for vengeance against Gouffé? The witness threw out his chest and chin; some harsh retort was probably on the tip of his tongue, but he thought better of it and merely replied: "Monsieur Gouffé was a reticent man. I did not have the privilege of being acquainted with his personal affairs." "But you knew his temperament!" cried Massicot, his beard bristling. "Was he a sensual man, given to drunkenness, was he interested in women, had he a taste for adventure?" "For adventure . . ." reiterated Dopffer, lowering his head. "Perhaps he was once interested in passing affairs. I only know that he was very happily married and that later, after his wife's death, he took an interest in Madame Chottin, of the most respectable kind, of course." "You mean, it is unlikely that there was any intimacy between him and Bompard?" Once again the witness looked up at Massicot between the rim of his pince-nez and his brow and replied with a touch of acerbity, "I mean no such thing, Monsieur le Procureur. I have said I know nothing about that."

In short, the cross-examination produced no result whatever, apart from making the total incompetence of the prosecution unequivocally manifest. Massicot was as muddleheaded as he was bellicose; instead of a clearly conceived plan, he abandoned himself to the turbulent irritability of his natural disposition, and if he had any effect on the jury it could only be one detrimental to his case. An unprejudiced observer could not fail to wonder why the Prosecutor General's Office had not chosen a better man for such a much-discussed and thorny case—a case, moreover, that must have been handed to him at the eleventh hour, since there could be no other explanation for either his indignant helplessness or his meager collection of witnesses. Was he, at bottom, concerned only to complete the picture? Why else had he called, perhaps in the place of the sick Jaquemar, on young Madame Chottin, who, like Dopffer before her, had never seen either of the accused and had nothing of the slightest weight to say against them?

Naturally, the curious and sensation-hungry spectators were delighted that she should have been called. She was the second of the two leading female figures in the closing period of the life of "L'huissier galant," closely connected in an obscure way with the much-discussed Jaquemar, a most charming person, and above all involved in a mysterious rivalry with the lovely Bompard, the piquancy of which only dawned on the public (and perhaps even on Madame Chottin herself) on this occasion.

When called for cross-examination, she handed her poke bonnet with a friendly whisper to the old servant sitting next to her on the witnesses' bench, whose company she probably tolerated on grounds of propriety rather than protection. She rose, smoothing the hair over her right ear, approached the dais without shyness, and gathered her crinolinelike skirt in one hand as she mounted it; over her dress she wore a white silk bolero embroidered with threads of gold and bright colors, in which the hills and tips of her young breasts formed warm shadows and gay highlights. Opera glasses, spectacles, pince-nez, and even feminine lorgnettes—doubtless left behind by wives who had been turned out so that their husbands could get a better view and give them a detailed report later—were trained on her.

She walked confidently toward the altarlike tribunal, not with a girlish walk, in spite of her youthfulness, but with the step of a young woman who knows love and loves it; on reaching the Bench, she made a very slight curtsey, a gesture of acquiescence and unobsequious reverence before the dignity of the occasion that deliberately overlooked the fidgeting behavior of the Presiding Judge—anyone could see that she was used to good society and felt at home in it. But she did not so much as glance at the defendants. Eyraudt was staring into space with drooping lips. Bompard sat bolt upright with her face demonstratively averted, so that if anyone wanted to compare the two women, only the backs of their necks and their hair were available for the purpose: the defendant's neck obstinate and snowy white, but almost entirely hidden by the fan-shaped collar, and above it the enamel-blue curls that flickered at every breath of wind, and by contrast the luxuriant chestnut tresses of the witness, shot through with lighter streams of gold, clinging like tendrils around the little shells of her ears and emphasizing by their fulness the delicacy of the nape of the neck, which looked touching in the upright collar of the bolero.

With this the spectators had for the time being to rest content, as they had also to rest content with a series of rather haphazard questions put by the hissing Public Prosecutor and correspondingly unsurprising answers from Madame Chottin, who, however, gave them with the most charming unconstraint. She listened carefully, and when the twitching brows of her expectant interlocutor invited her to, she gave the information requested intermingled with conciliatory little rhetorical questions—"You can understand that, can't you?" or "I was bound to think that, wasn't I?"—and quite unperturbed by Massicot's frequent interjections.

"Poor Monsieur Gouffé," she said. "He was such a good-natured, reliable man, he must have been very craftily lured to his doom. I can't imagine anything wanton in his life—except that he was perhaps more desperate than I could grasp. It is difficult to imagine such a quiet, sensible man becoming so desperate that he loses his self-respect." What was that, what did she mean by "loses his self-respect"? She meant that Monsieur was a fastidious man, and although he once admitted to being in a state of exasperation that was clamoring for an outlet, she took it in a vague general sense and not as meaning that he was seriously considering a dubious adventure, some liaison lasting for a few weeks or a few hours, which would have been contrary to his moral principles, quite apart from the danger of any such liaison, of which he must have had some kind of presentiment.

She meant, Massicot suggested, because the woman in question had been the mistress of a man of evil repute, who felt he had suffered a business loss through Gouffé, did she? So Gouffé had a feeling that blackmail or something worse awaited him if he became involved with Bompard? "You misunderstand me, Monsieur le Procureur. I didn't know that anybody felt he had suffered through Gouffé; and I need hardly stress that he did not talk to me about loose women, need I?" "Then where did you get the idea that he had a presentiment of the danger of a liaison with Bompard?" "I named no name, Monsieur le Procureur. I said: I took his remarks in a general sense." "Which remarks?" "Well, for example, that his life was empty and desolate. Of course I knew he was fond of me, and you must attribute it to a certain womanly weakness if I found such utterances rather flattering. I thought they were intended to prepare me for a particular proposal—which, however, never came."

"Surely you can't conclude from the fact that a person says 'My life is desolate' that he has a presentiment of danger?" "I was merely trying to give you an example of the general terms of our conversations. Only after the appalling event had taken place did this and other remarks he had made come to assume, upon reflection, a deeper significance. As when he said that evening outside the Véron: 'And I thought that this evening my fate would be decided!' Poor man . . . he had no idea how terribly right he was. But it sounded to me like a gloomy foreboding." "And from that you conclude—well, what do you conclude?"

"No, one cannot conclude anything from it. But when a reasonable, mature, experienced man says that on a particular evening his fate will be decided—isn't that strange? Doesn't it remain curious, even if he meant nothing more by it than that he had expected to hear my 'Yes' or 'No' to a proposal which he never made? Is it not a very strong expression?" "I don't know what you are getting at." "I'm sorry, what I am saying is perhaps not quite logical. But later on, it seemed to me that the fate of a man of that age should no longer be decided by a woman's 'Yes' or 'No,' flattering as that would be for us women . . . and then something else he said appeared in a new, sinister light. He was speaking of the monotony of his life and said: 'Edmond wouldn't believe it, but I often feel like leaping into the abyss!' "

"Now she has come into the open at last, the infamous pedlar of souls!" Bompard suddenly shouted, whipping her head around. "Are we to sip her poison like a liqueur? No wonder her 'poor' Gouffé kicked over the traces! Who wants to be sent to the slaughterhouse to the accompaniment of a siren's song?"

Maître Rebattu started to spring to his feet, but she put both hands on his shoulders and pushed him back with sudden, unexpected strength; curiously, no one called her to order. A deep silence reigned, in which her anger still echoed, while young Madame Chottin hesitated for a second and then slowly looked away from the Public Prosecutor to face her. Madame Chottin's gaze fell first on the yellowish hands on Maître Rebattu's shoulders, then rose to the chalky white face with the blood-red lips, little tiger's nose, and flashing black eyes. Then her eyes opened wide, and it was as though the blood was drained from her cheeks. She whispered so softly that, in spite of the prevailing deathly silence, not a spectator in the courtroom could make out what she was saying: "I can see that he was bound to fall into your snare."

"Of course! And to hell with your fluffy charms! Never more than titillation, no one is satisfied with that, and other people have to face the music in your place. Look, Michi"—as she said this she kept her eyes fixed on Madame Chottin—"just look at her! That's what the 'decent' woman looks like, who sent you your customer: she will sip her chocolate when she opens the newspaper and reads that your head has fallen off—for her!"

"But," said Madame Chottin softly, somehow shamefacedly and at the same time in a tone of horrified foreboding, "this person is mad."

"That would just suit you! You stand there bubbling your sickly sweet boudoir simperings that make a person's ears curl up to listen to—and you say I'm mad! Where an apple has been nibbled, it rots, I say, didn't you know that? You should have thought of that in the case of your 'mature' Gouffé! But your palate was itching for something else. Your appetite will be spoiled for you! Mad? You'll weep, when I laugh!"

That this scene should have been permitted, that neither Massicot, nor more particularly Deist, the Presiding Judge, did not intervene to put a stop to this scandal, was an unparalleled breach of regulations. It was as if they were all hypnotized; even Maître Rebattu was now holding his chin in three bent fingers as though lost in thought, his uncomfortably crooked brows knit with consternation; Chantegrei was staring at the ground and biting his lower lip as though looking at something he had never seen before; Deist sat leaning far over the judges' table with both fists under his chest; and even Eyraudt, forgetting his hatred, was staring at Bompard with his mouth open.

The silence in the room was as complete as if it had been empty, and it was not broken by the slightest sound from the invisible audience outside, who seemed to be holding their breath in telepathic rapport with those inside. But the glasses were still trained on the drama out in front, and if anyone had taken note of it in the tension of the moment, he might have been surprised to see that the enchanting young woman who was being subjected to this unheard-of and incomprehensible abuse made no move to look for the aid to which she was entitled. She faced her insulter, who was glaring at her with flashing hawk's eyes, erect and unintimidated, though with heaving bosom; the blood returned to her cheeks, her delicate shell-like ears, especially, took on a pinky color and gradually a deeper glow, as though in childlike stubbornness; independence and determination rang out in her voice as she now demanded, as though bringing the scene to an end on her own account: "What do you want with me, Mademoiselle? I don't see why I should converse with you."

"No, she doesn't want that!" cried Bompard with a laugh. "She'd rather spoon and pout and make eyes at the men, trousers or robe—it's all the same! It's in her blood! But what's the use of softening them up? To put me in the wrong? Be your age! I'm in the right, any child can see that! But what about you—just look at your admirers! The first had to throw away half his fortune, just to wriggle out of the dreary marriage bed! The second, a dead-and-alive old codger, got led around by the nose so long that he tripped over his own feet and fell face first into a pool of blood! And the third, who is meant to come crawling to your scent of milk and diapers like a fly on a flypaper? There isn't going to be a third—you can reckon with a long spinster-hood, you blighted love!"

"Do you presume to criticize my life?" cried Germaine Chottin, but really more in astonishment than anger. "I thought you would be glad if your name went unspoken!"

"She says that! She throws the lover she has nibbled at onto an innocent person's shoulders and then says— She says he was 'craftily' lured to his doom. Why didn't she hold him back? He threatened he would leap into the abyss!"

"How could I?" demanded Madame Chottin, with as calm a voice as possible, though the agitation and the profound feminine anger were unmistakable as she retorted: "I'm not the sort of woman who can be forced to love."

"But you're the sort who can say 'No,' aren't you? Did you say 'No'?"

"I wasn't asked. You can't reject a proposal that hasn't been made, can you?"

"Lord above! What a stuck-up bitch, what a palaver! He said straight out that his fate must be decided! And yet you couldn't bring yourself to say 'Yes' or 'No'! You knew perfectly well you were condemning him to death."

"How could I ever have thought such a thing! And what good would it have done if I had said 'No'?"

"You think I would have been good enough for a man to work off his mortification on, and give me nothing in return, do you? You think a man can have me when he feels like it and keep me secret from the world? You make me laugh! Do you expect me to let him dream of you in my arms?"

"That's your affair, Mademoiselle—I don't know the code of honor that prevails in your circle."

"If he had known where he stood, I should have taught him to forget, he wouldn't have wasted another thought on you, and he would have blossomed out for just so long as it lasted. And that man there, Michi, who is now going down to the grave with him, I should have chased away, perhaps to you—his specialties are no use to me anyhow, I can't be beaten into submission, I weep and afterward I'm just the same as I was before, but you need a hard hand!"

"You will admit, won't you, that there is no need for me to listen to your reproaches and insults and all these wild accusations? I'm not used to such language anyhow. But I want to try and make you understand. God knows, I say, that I wished the poor man no harm—"

"A hair shirt on your body! So that you find out what your own wishes really are!"

"God knows, I say, that I wished the poor man no harm, and God forgive me if I nevertheless acted wrongly. Yes, it may be that I acted wrongly! I didn't realize."

"Death by strangulation and all his goods acquired by another—it suited her fine, but she didn't realize, God forgive her, she just acted wrongly."

"Are you trying to hold me responsible for the murderous trap into which the unhappy man was lured?"

"For the desperation that drove him to destruction!"

"Am I responsible—"

"Am I? Am I to pay for your confounded *demi-vierge* dallying?"

"She *is* mad!" cried Madame Chottin. She took a step backward and repeated in a low voice: "She is mad. Only a madwoman could accuse me like that."

"Look at her!" cried Bompard, pointing her crooked yellow index finger. "Look at her, Miss High and Mighty, Miss Respectability—too respectable to be responsible! And I have all the vexation, I get maltreated by that fat copper in the Cité, I have to put up with the bad manners of that man up there, I have to sleep alone—I, I, I! Why not her? Is that goose to sit in the center of the hurricane, where it's quiet, preening her feathers, while I have the filth slashing around my ears? All this damned petty-bourgeois rubbish? That would be nice!"

"I didn't say it was your work," burst out Germaine Chottin. "I could have said so!"

"You'll take care not to! It infuriates me that you can't say 'Yes' or 'No'! What do you hope to gain by your soft cow's eyes? You won't get your Jaquemar, you know! Listen, I'm warning you: he has already swallowed the hook! If you tug at it, don't ask yourself for the second time, 'Am I responsible?' You won't get him, deeply as he is in your debt!"

The blood had left the young woman's face, which was now almost as pale as Bompard's, who continued to glare at her with eyes blazing with hatred; before this look, she once again staggered a pace backward and cried out in a voice that was both wild and toneless, a despairing voice: "Where am I, that no one silences this harlot!"

"Too bad for you!" mocked Bompard in a jubilant voice like ringing glass. "Your Jaquemar isn't here, Monsieur is keeping to his bed, he's ill—between ourselves, they're always ill when there's trouble, you have to get used to that in good time. Did he give you that old woman there for your protection? How thoughtful! But she can't protect you—you can see for yourself, no one protects you, not a soul anywhere, not even the men in the black smocks."

Madame Chottin raised her right hand and turned toward the Bench, but at this very moment Deist, too, had recovered his senses, his white ball of a face turned lobster red and he thundered: "Hold your tongue, will you, you— Be quiet! Silence!" Then he rang his bell, as though tugging furiously at a rope; but at the same moment a tumult had arisen in the court, in which the individual voices that were raised did not ring very loud, but which in its total effect was deafening, so that the jangling of the bell seemed merely to float on top of the mighty wave of sound, like the helpless ringing of a bell buoy on a stormy sea; from outside, too, murmuring, growling, laughter, and excited exchanges of opinion among thousands of people poured in through the open windows like a tidal wave; it was a popular commotion against which Deist's tinkling availed nothing, although he shouted at the same time: "I shall clear the court! Silence! Silence!"

The excitement gradually died down, but everyone was still talking, even the lawyers. Massicot was addressing the Presiding Judge, gesticulating with outstretched arms; Chantegrei leaned forward and whispered in Maître Rebattu's ear, while the latter shook his head. Only Bompard sat there as though nothing had happened, straightening out her gold and beryl jewelry with her fingers, her white and red face with the anguished clown's brows half submerged in her fan-shaped collar. Madame Chottin, her eyes wide, was led by a court sergeant to the witnesses' bench—the barristers were not even asked whether they wished to cross-examine her—and order was on the point of being restored, when the incident already referred to occurred among the jurymen.

The foreman of the jury stood up and announced to the Presiding Judge that a substitute would have to be found for the juror Louis Dufréty, the latter having resigned his judicial function on the grounds that he had fallen passionately in love with the defendant Bompard. This announcement was greeted from outside the windows with wild delight, clapping, shouts of "Bravo!" and general exultation; Montardon, her arms folded over her enormous bosom, nodded with a smile of fatuous complicity to the jury, and the public in the court could also not refrain from expressing their approval of the incident.

True order, that is to say a serious concentration on the few events that followed and brought this second day of the trial to a close, was never restored at all; the spectators' heads were full of impressions that had to be digested—and they did not lose very much as a result. For the statements by the two medical experts, whom the prosecution had called as a matter of routine and who declared the two defendants both fully responsible for their actions, deserved no special attention, since there was no doubt about the premeditation as far as Eyraudt was concerned, or about legal responsibility in the case of Bompard; according to one expert opinion, the "neurasthenic hypertension" of the latter's vital impulses in no way reduced this responsibility, but merely led to its being concealed with an unconscious skill that rendered it all the more dangerous and damnable.

The following day, the third day of the trial, Deist kept the court waiting; the public, as well as the defendants, jurors, defense counsels, and Public Prosecutor had long been sitting in their places; in fact, a shy clapping, half admonishing, half amused, echoed from the audi-

torium, but still the Presiding Judge did not come. When the little
door in the background finally opened, he appeared (with everyone
rising in mute greeting), his hair fluttering as if in anger, obviously in
a bad temper, exasperated and harassed, climbed up to his chair, and
slumped into it like a man at the end of his tether, who has made up
his mind to comply with his formal duty, to keep up appearances and
leave it at that.

But even as they were sitting down and Deist was declaring the
session open (without even waiting for complete silence to fall on the
court), an extraordinary incident occurred. It was so extraordinary,
such a sudden, dramatic explosion, that it was all over before the
spectators had fully grasped what was going on. Even the reporters,
whose profession should have trained them to register the unexpected,
failed to grasp it, and this was the main reason why subsequent Press
reports of the incident were extremely cursory and either misleading
or downright inaccurate. The young man who broke through the
cordon of warders at the door, as Deist was coming in, and now staggered to the Bench with a strangely swaying gait, was taken for merely
a drunken rowdy who had perhaps come to the wrong room by mistake and in any event had nothing to do with the case being tried
here. In fact, however, it was someone who—though unknown to the
spectators by sight—had a very great deal to do with the case. It was
Jaquemar.

Why he had turned up at the eleventh hour, when the trial was
practically over, and moreover in an obviously feverish condition, no
one could tell, and he himself seemed to have difficulty in explaining
the reason to the Presiding Judge. Deist was dumbfounded and indignant and grew angrier every minute, because of the irregular
interruption of the proceedings and especially because this intrusion
threatened to prolong something he wanted to get over and have done
with.

Because he had not expected him, and therefore considered he had
no right to be there, Deist treated the new arrival as an unidentified
interloper, although he twice called up to him in a voice that was at
once shaky and impatient: "I am Jaquemar!" As he called out, he
clung to the Clerk of the Court's desk, relapsed immediately afterward into meditation, and answered Deist's angry declaration that it
was now too late, and the cross-examination of the witnesses was over,

with a harassed shake of the head and an unintelligible muttering in which the phrases "urgent charge" and "important evidence" could be distinguished, matters that seemed to concern him rather than anyone else and which the Presiding Judge neither understood nor wished to understand. He now banged the table furiously, so that the golden cross jumped, and bellowed: "Get out! You have no right to be here, I shall have you removed!" At this point Bompard, who had been shifting this way and that on her chair in something like lascivious excitement, shouted: "Let him talk if he wants to! Perhaps he has something to say that will save me from further ill-treatment and boredom!"

The impertinence of this intervention took Deist's breath away; he gulped and stared at her with an expression of incredulity on his balloon of a face; but this was nothing to the effect the interjection had on Jaquemar. All color was drained from the young man's face, which had been coppery and blotchy, an uncanny pallor spread across it and crept up to his eyes, around which it seemed to form white rings, his body stretched and tensed as though under the shock of a tetanus-inducing injection, in a way that was both relieved and agonized. Very slowly, with lowered lids, he turned toward the woman who had called out, but without moving from where he stood; he raised his lids and their eyes met, Bompard's confident and shining, Jaquemar's squinting and filled with hatred and disgust. His whole body quivered and he began to speak, at first slowly and with frozen lips, then louder and louder.

"Is the beast sitting in judgment," he said hesitantly, as though asking himself, "instead of being judged? Whence does a creature like that draw her arrogance? Why does it live? Why is the venomous serpent's head not struck off? Don't people see that she bites everyone in the heel and is after everyone's life? All the world knows that her accomplice is a murderer. But what is one murderer! How many will she turn into murderers, that is the question, with her ice-cold child's heart and accursed innocent smile? Every time, she will have just been a 'bystander'! She will serve up her Turkish violet cachous and other horrible sweetmeats to give her victims 'a treat,' she will put the rope around their necks 'unfortunately as a joke' and afterward she will purr her regrets and say it was 'nasty'! She doesn't even deserve a trial! Who would think of bringing the plague before a tribunal or passing judgment on syphilis? Such things exist to destroy so long as they exist—they must be destroyed. There she sits, with her wild-beast's nose and her impudent, merry eyes that are undisturbed by evil and unafraid of justice; betraying nothing but contempt for justice and scorn for its tribunals! But one thing she should know, and I solemnly promise her: justice shall be done to her! God grant it be done in this court. But if it be not here and now—let her not exult! As true as I am alive, and so long as I am alive, justice will seek her out and find her, will ferret her out of every hiding place, trample her to death, and render her harmless! Gouffé shall be avenged, upon my honor!"

A minute earlier Bompard had turned her head in a gesture of amusement, now her face assumed an expression of indignation and pity. She tapped Maître Rebattu, who was sitting benumbed in front of her, on the shoulder and cried: "He should be put to bed, he really is ill!"

At this, Jaquemar picked up an inkwell from the judges' table at his side and hurled it at her; it broke in pieces with a cracking noise on the rail of the dock, the red ink spurted like an exploding shell, spattering the woodwork and trickling down toward the floor. Too much had happened at once; Jaquemar began to stagger and sway, but he was caught by a gaunt, bird-eyed man who appeared unexpectedly, Lebigot, who, doubtless foreseeing trouble, had hurried after him to the court and now helped him from the room.

Only now did the people in the auditorium become aware of the scandal—though even now they did not understand what was happening; they jumped up and down on their chairs, trying to catch a glimpse of the scene out in front; Bompard had risen and was leaning over the wooden railing in front of her and looking down with interest at the dribbling ink; the gentlemen of the court exchanged astonished views on the incident with looks and gestures, and Deist, suddenly coming to life and a vigorous sense of his official duty, frenziedly rang his bell and shouted: "Silence! Silence! Disgraceful! I shall clear the court!"

As a matter of fact, the excitement died away almost instantaneously and the furious scowls which the Presiding Judge cast in all directions seemed pointless; only a barely audible whispering continued for a few minutes. Stranger than this, however, was the fact that, as though by general consent, nothing further was said about the incident, apart from a fleeting reference by Maître Rebattu, who made light of the occurrence and then dismissed it. It was as though everyone was resolved to forget it at once or pretend it had never happened; Deist once again declared the session open and called on the Public Prosecutor to speak.

Thenceforth silence fell on the courtroom and remained unbroken throughout the morning and afternoon (for the proceedings were protracted), except for comparatively mild expressions of displeasure or assent from the invisible audience outside the windows and the clatter caused by Deist twice dropping the cross, with which he was playing like a sulky child, during the speeches for the prosecution and defense.

Massicot's speech was monotonous—monotonous as even the most savage barking of a watchdog becomes monotonous after a while; and in this staccato monotony of snappish aggressiveness most people failed to notice that on several occasions he suddenly stopped, as though dragged back by a chain, gave vent to a strangled gurgle with twitching brows, then corrected himself and went on barking. "This act, gentlemen of the jury, this act of unimaginable brutality," he ranted with spittle flying, "this act was planned, as if it were the most natural thing in the world, by the infamous couple—er, was planned, I say, by Eyraudt, in cold blood, from a base desire for gain! From a depravity that shrinks from nothing, depravity that spits in the face of society, pollutes it, puts it in dire peril." This (as was easy to foresee) was what his hissing and barking were leading up to: Eyraudt's bloody deed perpetrated against an honest citizen, in itself a crime that merited death, was in addition and above all a brutal affront to civic order, to society, whose sense of justice and instinct of self-preservation were here represented by the jurors; society must protect itself, "for if anyone makes so bold as to defend the murderer by saying he was at the end of his tether, in despair, even his love for his accomplice, this disgraceful love, was one more reason for despair, he had lost all self-control—fie, I say, and woe! Woe to him and to all of us, if that is to serve as an excuse!

"On the contrary, the more abject, the more dangerous he is in these godless times! This despair is the sickness of our age! The despair of the godless! Cut off the diseased limb, I say! Or are we to let the poi-

sonous rot spread through the whole organism? Murder and robbery out of despair? And when there is nothing to steal, what then?
Murder for pleasure, running amok! The intoxication of destruction
and bloodshed out of despair! Gouffé for money, Perrier for a pastry,
the next victim for nothing! Murder as a pastime! That is what they
would be defending who tried to defend him!"

In simple words, his raging amounted to saying that he considered
the murderer "completely and utterly responsible for his actions," a
view which he advanced with little original argument and with unnecessary heat, since there was probably no one who did not consider
Eyraudt both guilty and responsible, "even admitting that the depraved young woman at his side confirmed him in his evil intent."
On this particular point the furious Public Prosecutor became worse
entangled than before, he was in full swing and hissed and barked:
"That this evil young woman influenced him, persistently, methodically, criminally—" Then the chain jerked him back, he choked and
continued feebly: "Criminal, I say. Eyraudt's deed remains criminal
and worthy of death, whatever we may think of Bompard. Her influence was bad, because she is bad, bad and irresponsible! Who will
believe her when she says she could not call for help? That after the
murder had been committed, she had no opportunity of reporting
what she saw—who will, who can, believe that, gentlemen of the
jury?"

Upon this he now hurled himself: the reasons the defendant had
given for not having reported the murder were untenable, totally in-
valid, in complete contrast to the "ice-cold resolution" of which she
had given such striking evidence even during the brief period of this
trial, evidence also of an obstinacy itself bordering on the criminal
and which, if she had acted in good faith, would positively have compelled her to find some means of breaking out and fulfilling her duty
to denounce the murder. "She could have gone to some police station
in America! At a pinch, she could have written, she could have conveyed her denunciation to Paris by letter, why not! Where there's a
will, there's a way—but she did not do so, she did nothing at all!
Only when her photograph had appeared in the papers, when there
was no longer any escape, only then did she give in! Only then did
she kiss the rod in her impudent prostitute's fashion! Fie, I say, fie
and woe to a society whose judges treat such a sin of omission with

leniency out of weakness for this despicable woman! Society is threatened! Protect it! Do not countenance this sinful concealment of a murder! Do not disavow society! Punish—punish the guilty!"

To put it briefly (a great deal more briefly than Massicot, for his speech lasted about two hours) the question the jury finally had to decide was, in the case of Eyraudt: Is he guilty of premeditated murder? But in the case of Bompard (and even this aroused a murmur of indignation outside the windows) it was: Is she guilty of failing to report the crime? Thus, after all the furious barking, the charge of instigation, complicity, and assistance was dropped entirely, and this unparalleled, not to say perfidious, partiality toward the co-defendant on the part of the mouthpiece of the State evoked a unanimous smirk of satisfaction among the public in the court, while the woman in question cried out in an indignant voice, not loudly, but so that everyone could hear: "How much longer is this farce going on?"

Then she shook her head with her everlasting, amazed smile. No doubt she actually found it as hard to understand why she was being treated in this way as Goron (though naturally in the opposite sense) did later. When he heard about it he sank back in his armchair and stared into space with his button eyes behind the crooked pince-nez, feeling as though a chasm had opened up before him, the unfathomable chasm of this world in which men trample underfoot the justice they have themselves created for the defense of their own dignity, trample on it again and again, and at times do so with a shameless ardor that suggests a thirst for self-destruction.

The Public Prosecutor was followed by Eyraudt's counsel, Chantegrei. He frequently rested both hands on the table and looked down with a meditative expression on his pure face with the slightly cleft chin, the silky lashes over doe's eyes, and the fine, grave mouth; he spoke with the candor of an absolutely clear conscience, only rarely uttering his interrogative and confirmatory "H'm" whenever he meant to introduce a new train of thought. He should have been given a client whose acquittal he could sincerely desire; but in this case, what was there he could do without violating his sensitive conscience? He could point to the luckless sexual thraldom of this man whom, like everyone else, he considered guilty, this bondage to lust that had torn him away from his wife and driven him to sordid adventures, fraud and the usurer—that had, above all, delivered him into the arms of

Gabrielle Bompard; he could appeal with genuine emotion to Madame Eyraudt's statement, could impress on the jurors that even at the time of the crime there was a core of goodness in the guilty man, an element of human tenderness, a timid shoot of genuine feeling, warmheartedness, which, if he had received the proper loving care, might have blossomed, might have smothered the other, weed-like impulses. He could and did say this, but to what purpose, since it is considered to be the responsibility and task of every mortal to make the best of the constitution with which he comes into the world? Was he to persuade the judges that it is pardonable to neglect the good one is given?

Chantegrei uttered no such blasphemous thought; but he called for justice to be tempered with mercy, he asked the jury to exercise a measure of humanitarian understanding because destiny had dealt the culprit, poor sinner that he was, the shattering blow of introducing Bompard into his life; "for this woman appeared to the morally unhinged man like destiny itself, a dark vampire of destiny that perhaps no one, and certainly not a morally enfeebled man like Eyraudt, could escape, an indulgence, which, once enjoyed, he could never again do without, a promising will-o'-the-wisp of the senses that lured him deeper into the morass with its cold, bobbing light and drew from him more and more heinous crimes."

Chantegrei the gentle, who, during all these days, had barely glanced at the co-defendant, held her guilty not of the murder, but of the fact that Eyraudt had become a murderer, attributing this to "her unparalleled power of seduction that has even succeeded in bewildering and bemusing the sound common sense of our people in all walks of life, and how much more, then, a man who was already on the slippery slope and needed only an occasional push to send him reeling into the abyss." No one would have credited the reserved Chantegrei with the language in which, gradually waxing fiery, he depicted the seductress; once he went so far as to call her "a radiant goddess of depravity, born of the foam of black sewage, as Venus was born of the silvery foam of the sea," he described her as "a unique manifestation of moral anaesthesia" and her love as "soul-polluting"; the people had sought to make a demon of her, and their instinct was not altogether wrong, for what she had radiated on the morbid element already present in Eyraudt's nature was demonically evil, a mental pestilence inseparably linked with attacks of ungovernable fury, a demoralizing character-rot. "I am utterly convinced, gentlemen of the jury, that this murder would never have been committed if she had not encouraged the culprit by her atrocious, corrupting influence—I do not say by direct instigation, perhaps not even by indirect promptings, although she undoubtedly created the opportunity and expressly informed Eyraudt of it—I say by her corrupting influence, by the poison of her boundless depravity, which was bound to rob a weak man like Eyraudt of the last vestige of moral consciousness, so that he acted, as Dr. Dubois explained to us earlier, only in a still more fundamental sense, in a state of frenzy and while his moral consciousness was severely curtailed. God preserve us all from being tempted as this poor guilt-laden man was tempted, upon whom you are to pass judgment. I would ask you to ponder deeply on this temptation, from which heaven preserve us, under which he was laboring when, in a state resembling delirium, he stumbled into the commission of his appalling crime; take it into account when you consider the question whether the defendant's act can be summarily characterized as 'premeditated,' since, in a strict sense, we can speak of premeditation only where we can also speak of freedom—but the defendant is not free, he is not within his own control. If you nevertheless term the defendant's crime 'premeditated,' this will be of terrible consequence, and it is you, gentlemen of the jury, who will have to bear this consequence, upon your own conscience and before God to whom we pray that he may forgive us our trespasses as we forgive them that trespass against us."

With this, Chantegrei closed his speech, and he had spoken with such purity of heart that his words reached what was pure in every heart; and though it is almost unbelievable, even the ghostly audience outside had not reacted to the severe attacks on their darling, had remained mute, and the dull muttering that now rose from below mingled indistinguishably with the emotion that had taken hold of the audience in the courtroom. The only one unmoved, apart from Bompard herself, who sat there with a dreamy smile, was the slit-eyed Deist; no sooner had Chantegrei's last word died away than he banged the cross down on the table in front of him, brusquely announced the midday recess, and made off with almost indecent haste, diving down from his high presidential chair and slamming the little door behind him.

But an hour later, when the sitting was reopened and silence had been established in the court, the speaker of the day, Maître Rebattu, rose with courteous negligence; he exchanged his gold-rimmed spectacles for another pair that looked exactly like the first and flashed every time a ray of sunshine caught the highly polished lenses; he spent a moment or two reading through some sheets of paper, which, unobserved, he must have covered with notes during the cross-examination and speeches for the prosecution and defense, and then put them away again—or rather, he was about to put them away, but could not refrain from first spreading out his hands just above the top of the desk, as though to say, "Well, now" and "what is there to say," a gesture of cheerful resignation that set the tone he was about to strike.

How naturally, how simply, he set about it! This *soigné* man with the crooked nose, the misplaced dark brows between which half-repressed laughter seemed still to be hovering—a forensic celebrity with the face of an intellectual gallows' bird whose great air of *bonhomie* cast an amiable veil over everything that might otherwise have aroused distrust (just as the flashing spectacles hid the tired look in the hazel eyes)—he thus invited his listeners to discard all formality and allow calm common sense to prevail. Indeed, it was as though unrestricted and unperturbed common sense itself were speaking—no wonder that long extracts from his speech were printed that same night in the evening papers, whereas only brief summaries of Massicot's and Chantegrei's appeared. The leading papers actually reproduced Rebattu's address *in toto*—which is more than we dare inflict on our readers.

Naturally enough, it was worth listening to from every standpoint, and moreover delivered in the most mellifluous, cultured, and pleasant French imaginable, accompanied only by rare and unemphatic gestures and embellished here and there with a frank and friendly laugh that seemed to well up from his heart—in short, a delightfully conversational rather than rhetorical discourse, which, even though in shortened form, demands to be imparted as well as we are able.

"Gentlemen of the jury," he began conversationally and with slightly furrowed brow, "I feel really quite ashamed at having to speak after such great orators, to pit my meager eloquence against the passionate outpourings of my learned friend, the Public Prosecutor, against the moving poetic fervor of my learned friend, the officially appointed Defense Counsel. The artistic quality of their speeches makes one feel almost morally obliged to agree with them, to assent with a wholehearted 'Thou hast spoken!' What a position I am in, a sober, uninspired man who unfortunately has to contradict them, because that is, after all, my task, and also because I am convinced that it is perfectly possible to see things in a different light. In the last analysis, they must be seen in a different light; in the last analysis, sober judgment has an essential, if modest, role to play, particularly in this court where truth is weighed in the scales of justice, with blindfold eyes as she is portrayed, eyes which, when I come to think of it, would perhaps see neither Monsieur Chantegrei's mythological visions nor my learned friend the Public Prosecutor's apocalyptic threat to society, to which my young client is supposed to have so damnably—though rather vaguely—contributed.

"Yes, gentlemen of the jury," he said, raising his brows and lifting his right hand in an unemphatic gesture, "those are great and weighty words: threat to society, goddess of depravity born of the foam of black sewage, carrier of demoralizing character-rot! It makes one shudder to think that anyone, whoever he may be, should be stoned with such verbal boulders. I ask myself how heavily they weigh in the scales of justice—if indeed there is any place for them there at all. There are stones which, though big, weigh little, porous fossil sponges, petrifacts of declamatory verbiage, whose magnificence falls to dust as soon as they are struck.

"I need hardly stress that I do not wish to ascribe any insincerity to my learned friends who preceded me: they were completely carried away by the certainty that they were right! But they were carried away, and it was not really clear to my uninspired mind why rhetorical fervor and poetic intuition should have reached such fever heat in their accusations against my client, accusations, incidentally, of little practical significance, inflate the mystic guilt of the accused to such proportions that no means of punishment at the law's disposal could ever be condign to such a monstrous crime; this crime, in fact, is not only beyond punishment, but actually unpunishable—since, regrettable as it may be, we cannot punish either the epoch or Destiny, except in that state of spiritual simplicity which leads certain inhabitants of the Central African bush to flog their domestic idols when they

have failed to come up to scratch. I do not entirely understand what
the monumental philippic was intended to achieve, I do not understand at all what it was based on—no, gentlemen of the jury, I do
not understand at all. Well, that's the way it is with people like us, the
magic power of orphic eloquence falls upon our ears and then we
ask: What's it all about?

"I will not bore you with a rehash of what you have heard with your
own ears. But now I ask you: can there be any doubt that, where
Mademoiselle Bompard is concerned, it contained more praise than detraction, indeed a positive hymn of praise, and yet admittedly there was
detraction too. The defendant Eyraudt hadn't a good word for her,
Monsieur Franquet found her extravagant, Monsieur Lévy inveighed
in Old Testament wrath against the 'woman of calamity'—and not to
forget Monsieur Goron, who is unfortunately not with us, yet we
know (and in any case, I can assure you) that this excellent man, to
whom we owe such an immense debt of gratitude for our civic protection, was angered by the young woman beyond all measure. On
the other hand, I would ask you to forget altogether the intervention
of Monsieur Jaquemar—anyone with eyes to see and ears to hear cannot fail to have noticed that he was delirious with fever and gave
utterance to words which, out of respect for this high court alone, he
would never have pronounced if he had been in his right mind.

"Now I cannot blame Eyraudt for being angry with the person by
whom he deems himself to have been betrayed and sold while he was
counting on her love and loyalty, I am not surprised that he accuses
her of having instigated the crime; who that has felt the thorn of
jealousy could fail to understand, who that is not destitute of all
imagination could fail to appreciate his desire to disclaim the ultimate
responsibility for his action? He would be killing two particularly large
and ill-omened birds with one stone if we were to accept his version
of events! Only for precisely that reason we cannot accept it.

"Monsieur Goron, chief of the Paris Sûreté, detests my client, he
was so much angered by her that, when I noticed it, I was genuinely
concerned for his health; in fact he allowed himself to be drawn into
the use of methods he would never have employed except under the
stress of profound anger; he explained to me, and these are his own
words, that it was impossible to imagine the obstinacy of this young
person, who willingly admitted the most hideous details, but reso-

lutely refused to make any confession of guilt. Supposing, I replied, she honestly cannot confess to what you want to hear? Gentlemen of the jury, Monsieur Goron is an eminent man, I admire him, his integrity is beyond all doubt—integrity? no, that is putting it too mildly, his passionate, almost obsessive desire to rid the world of evil, an obsession, which, in a humorous vein, might be called a heroic, masculine counterpart of the mania some women have for cleaning their houses.

"He is a great criminologist. Who would venture to assert that he understood the soul of a criminal better than Monsieur Goron? But suppose, for that very reason, he did not understand the soul of this young woman? In the face of unspeakable difficulties and obstacles, he had managed to cast a glimmer of light on this gruesome business, of which at the time it was impossible to say whether it was a crime or not, when a praiseworthy instinct led the attention of Monsieur Edmond Jaquemar, the brother-in-law and friend of the murdered man, to a photograph which the unfortunate victim had left in a book; in accordance with the traditional slogan cherchez la femme, the experienced criminologist knew that the woman in this photograph held the answer to the riddle, she was involved in the mystery, perhaps the motive and possibly the prize; she was the culprit behind the culprits; he became utterly convinced of this and that she must be found.

"But she came of her own accord. Not for one moment did she deny being involved, she confirmed that, in a sense, she had been the prize and the cause, yes, but she was innocent. This was incompatible with the criminal psychology in which he was an unchallenged master; either she was guilty and must be made to confess, or his psychology was wrong, and a career of unexampled triumphs had convinced him once and for all that his psychology was not wrong. Nevertheless, she stubbornly refused to confess to things of which, despite suspicious circumstances, she was not guilty, and meanwhile her mysterious and unaccountable popular appeal produced a situation in which not her reputation, but his began to suffer in the eyes of the public—a state of affairs for which there was, of course, no justification whatever, not even the young suspect's innocence. Now, would you not be angered if such a thing were to happen to you? And added to this was my client's curiously graphic way of expressing herself—

speaking to me (merely to give you an example of what I have in mind), she once described him as 'cheeky'; just imagine a girl of barely twenty describing the most eminent, the most famous criminologist in the world as 'cheeky'—what sort of things she must have said to his face when he vexed her (and he vexed her incessantly) as she was really not given to mincing her words! Whether she understood him, I don't know; but, in spite of an undiminished admiration for Monsieur Goron's genius, I say without hesitation that he did not understand her. He detests her; he cannot forgive Mademoiselle for refusing to confess herself a criminal. For my part, I cannot blame her—although, on the other hand, I can quite well understand Monsieur Goron's hostility.

"I wish I understood the prosecution and the official defense only half as well! But how can I, when they have not been able to produce a single witness worthy of being taken seriously who could give genuine and unprejudiced support to their furious denunciation? Just remember what happened. The defendant's wife, who could have been expected almost necessarily to have agreed with them and who could count on our sympathetic understanding whatever she said— what did she actually say, this good and upright woman, who did not wish to soil her grief with any dishonesty? 'I don't know the young woman. I can't judge how much influence she exercised over my husband.'

"But I myself, to be quite frank, was most strongly impressed by the evidence of Madame Montardon. It appears to me that during the period of my client's incarceration in the Cité a touching reversal of rôles gradually took place; first the jailer became a kind of attendant or nurse and finally the protégée became the protectress—without any bribery, please note, simply as a result of my young client's innate simplicity and fortitude and the power of her personality, which I for one cannot but admire. I am not generally inclined to sentimentality; but this account went straight to my heart; the idea, for instance, of the young girl showing the good woman how to celebrate Mass in that dripping wet dungeon (to call it a cell would really be too much of a euphemism)—I can't help it, the picture that comes to my mind has a bittersweet charm that moves me deeply, just as I was moved by the profound emotion that overcame Madame Montardon when Mademoiselle Bompard cautioned her, with a spontaneous little gesture of concern while she was giving evidence, against overstraining her asthmatic heart.

"I am not losing the thread, gentlemen of the jury, I am speaking with intent of Mademoiselle Bompard's personality; it is her personality that has been most savagely attacked here, and nothing but this blackening of her character could possibly inspire in you (which God forbid) any doubt as to your verdict on the curious charge with which the prosecution has seen fit to present you. I shall come back to this later and must therefore refrain, for the time being, from considering in any detail the vitally important statement made by Monsieur Carapin.

"For the present, I will say only this: no one who has ears to hear and eyes to see, no one, I say, who is in his right mind, can have failed to note that Monsieur Carapin spoke of his young friend in terms which, if he had not been as convinced of her spotless innocence as of his own knowledge of human nature, he must have feared would do the gravest harm to his own reputation. Monsieur Carapin is no youngster, he is a mature, experienced man; as a merchant engaged in a wide range of activities, he certainly knows better than we (but we, too, are not altogether ignorant of the fact) that nobody can afford to run such risks who, quite apart from his situation as a private citizen, also has an important business reputation to protect and cherish. And yet he did not merely defend Mademoiselle Bompard in the unfortunate situation that has made her a topic of conversation throughout the world, he was downright proud to defend her and to declare with the eyes of the whole world on him: I will stand surety for this young woman with all that I am and I have. What more can one ask, gentlemen of the jury? I can think of no more cogent testimony to my client's character, even if it had been given solely out of a sense of moral duty, an irresistible zeal for justice! But Monsieur Carapin did not think of trying to give this impression; on the contrary, with many charming details he stressed the *personal* nature of his relationship with Mademoiselle Bompard, his *intimate* knowledge of her character, and the unswerving esteem in which he held her character thereafter as when they first met; for you must bear in mind that he was not speaking in the first flush of a new love, but after experiences which might easily have shaken his trust, had his convictions been less strong. With emotion he called her, here in front of you, 'a little fanatic for the truth'; looking back on certain differences of opinion he declared that she was right and he wrong, indeed he cursed himself for not having listened more willingly to what she said; extolled her innocence in the most intimate as well as in the most everyday matters! This, then, is how she appears in the eyes of a highly respected man of the world who shared his whole life with her day and night for months—this is the officially appointed Defense Counsel's 'goddess of depravity born of the foam of black sewage.'

"No, gentlemen of the jury, I am not joking when I say this—nothing could be farther from my thoughts, I mean it quite literally —I turn to you for guidance, being at a loss myself I ask you: do you understand how Monsieur Chantegrei arrived at this awesome poetic vision? Was he thinking of somebody else? All this, and what other witnesses told us or accidentally and casually disclosed, is wholly incompatible with that gruesome if splendid picture; what we listened to were simple and sincere traits of character, all of which pointed without exception to Mademoiselle Bompard's profound *innocence*, innocence in the widest as well as in the narrowest sense. Can you see any sign of the 'demoralizing character-rot' with which the poor child is supposed to have infected those around her, as though by a kind of moral well-poisoning, if my understanding of the macabre poetic imagery is correct? She even stands accused of having poisoned the healthy common sense of our people in all walks of life, so that they now throng outside the windows of this house of justice and cry in the most unmistakable terms: 'Give us Barabbas!'

"When I paid my first visit to that horrible dungeon, I was prepared for anything, for any surprise of a pleasant or unpleasant nature; on my way through the underground corridor (in whose thick walls blue butterfly-flames were burning) I made the firm resolve not to let myself be duped, not to waver in my intention to take on this case only if the young woman corresponded to the mental image I had formed of her. Now, on this point I did not keep to my resolve. She did not correspond to the mental image I had formed of her, or to the mental image I had ever formed of *anyone*, she was bewilderingly different—bewilderingly in the first place, of course, because of her beauty, of which I shall spare you any tedious praise, since you have the irreplaceable original before your eyes. I shall not deny that I found her captivating, especially as, once more bewilderingly, she was totally unself-conscious, I mean devoid of all desire to please. So much beauty combined with so much naturalness—that is something almost impossible to find, however widely you search, it is almost, if you will forgive the paradox, unnatural, at all events very unusual in a beautiful woman, to whom a desire to please is as natural as a wild flower's scent of honey that arouses the appetite of its winged visitors and by this ticklish stimulation promotes fertilization. But such stimulation played no part here; in the most astonishing and captivating way it was absent, and I said to myself: if it were at all in keeping with my mature age, I would give anything to be able to pursue this fascinating absence to the point where these sublimely simple charms might be yielded up in the supreme surrender. Instead, since I know what I am entitled to, I simply rejoiced in the sight of her beauty and enjoyed it with the pleasurable appreciation appropiate to my advanced age. But this pleasure went hand in hand with an emotion that kept stirring at the back of my mind throughout our conversation. It had nothing to do with her wretched circumstances, with the tragic picture of youthful innocence immured in a noisome cell (for I am not naturally given to sentimentalizing), but it did have to do with her innocence. Had I a feeling of guilt toward her? Why? This indefinable emotion was by no means vague and generalized, but intensely personal; it brought with it an urge for decision, for action— and suddenly I realized with a shock that I had just addressed her as 'my dear child.' Now, I have no daughter and I am prevented from addressing strange young ladies as 'my dear child' not only by social convention, but also by a certain reserve which, frequently to my regret, I have found to be an innate characteristic of mine; but in this instance it came spontaneously to my tongue and sprang from my lips.

"I ask you, isn't it innocence for someone to be unshakably convinced that, because she is in the right, justice is bound to be done to her, that injustice cannot possibly be done to her—if that isn't innocence, what is? I call it innocence, and all the more so when this person displays, in every respect, the soundest imaginable common sense. I assure you that I have never met sounder common sense anywhere than in my client. Her arguments, her evidence are always down-to-earth, their logic is unerring, she assesses the people in her environment and their capacity to help her in her just cause with infallible accuracy. She sees the motherly good nature of honest

Madame Montardon and makes of her half a confidante, half a servant, in an intelligent spirit of 'live and let live'; she knows the value
of Monsieur Carapin's trustworthy devotion and calls upon his chivalrous services without a trace of hesitation or even humiliation; she
understands—God knows through what experience—the mentality of
the Press and foresees the reactions of the amorphous multitude.
Yes, gentlemen, if our ministers and other high officials understood it
half so well, we could heartily congratulate ourselves! But it is, of
course, a completely naïve, that is to say unprejudiced and therefore
innocent appraisal of persons she is exercising—hence her almost comical rage against an upright, if also fanatical, man like Monsieur Goron,
whom she rightly looks on as an enemy, and of whom she asserts, because he is unjust in his attitude to her, that he is trying to cheat the
world of the truth. Naturally, nothing is further from Monsieur
Goron; but in her own case she is quite right, and she does not mean
anything general by her assertion, she means: he is trying, by all the
means in his power, and not always the most pleasant means, to brand
me guilty; I am innocent, consequently he is trying to impose an un-
truth on the world—in other words, he is trying to cheat the world of
the truth.

"There can be no doubt that Gabrielle Bompard has a proclivity
for giving herself completely, with an orgiastic completeness, a total
absence of all restraint. I ask myself whether I have ever seen a more
impetuous willingness to submit to a man, any man, whatever he is
like, so long as he is man enough to give himself as completely as
she is willing to give herself—though 'willing' is scarcely the word; she
gives herself with a possessed exclusiveness that lasts as long as
she loves. 'He would have blossomed out in my arms—for as long as it
lasted,' she said; for she makes no secret of the fact that her love is un-
limited in every respect, apart from its duration; she does not look
back when the time is up and the man she loved yesterday does not
know what to do with his servitude and, as in Eyraudt's case, follows
the overwhelming pull of the void and leaps into the abyss of perdition.

"Yes, gentlemen of the jury, this too forms part of the picture—and
moreover, tragic as were its consequences, it is once again linked with
my client's essential innocence; you can feel that for yourselves, there
is no need for me to explain it. But by now you will understand that

I am not trying to delude you with paradoxes when I confess to you that, ever since I first visited her in the vaults of the Cité—when I saw her sitting in the light of the blue butterfly-flames with faint violet shadows under her eyes—I have felt the presence of this bound-less, perilous willingness to love, sanctioning every form of vice; while, at the same time, I was deeply moved to find that these very excesses proclaimed an essential and innate *virginity*. Virginity need not neces-sarily be understood in a physiological sense—although Monsieur Car-apin, who should know, explicitly extolled her 'most charming in-nocence' in their intimate relations and felt that what he delicately called her *joie de vivre* was to be explained by her innocence. Now, irrespective of whether he meant by this the lack of any desire to please, which I also touched upon, or whether he was referring to the pristine vigor of her will to love or the, so to speak, boyish temerity of her passion for dissipation, in any case he must have meant an un-dimmed capacity for enjoyment that made every act seem like the first, a chastity in the here and now, a fresh and innocent wonder, as if each act of love was the 'first,' no matter what has gone before, even if it was Eyraudt's filthy obscenity—in other words, an indestructible virginity.

"Her 'guilt' consists solely in the fact that, confronted by her, every-one *becomes* what he *is*. She is so completely innocent in every respect that it is logically impossible for her to be guilty in any respect. Since I cannot entirely avoid dealing with the prosecution's curious charge I shall do so in the briefest possible manner.

"I call the charge curious—and please don't think for a moment that I am covertly trying to cast ridicule upon it; I should never per-mit myself to adopt such an attitude toward this worshipful court. I can't help myself, it *is* curious that the Prosecutor should ask: 'Is she guilty of not denouncing the crime?' The question is no doubt worded in the form hallowed by custom, but as it is worded it cannot but be answered in the negative, since nobody, not even the Prosecutor him-self, doubts the fact that Mademoiselle did denounce the crime. He would have to have a very poor opinion of the abilities and conscien-tiousness of the jury to suppose that they could answer 'Yes' when the bare facts compel them to answer 'No.' Mademoiselle did denounce the crime—and whatever your free moral judgment of the young woman may be, gentlemen, as jurors, you are called on to pass judgment on one specific point only. In answering 'Guilty' or 'Not guilty,' you must keep strictly to the charge preferred by the prosecution, and under the circumstances you have no alternative but to bring in a verdict of 'Not guilty.'

"Are we to believe that such an experienced man of the law as my learned friend the Public Prosecutor did not foresee this? Of course not! It would be the height of impertinence to entertain such an idea. The Public Prosecutor has brought a charge which pure verbal logic alone condemns to rejection—why, since to prosecute is his right and duty, why has he done this if not because he has nothing to charge the defendant with?

"What could he really charge her with? As regards your verdict, gentlemen of the jury, it is unnecessary for me to discuss matters not raised by the charge; but since certain points were nevertheless raised in the speech for the prosecution and, so it seems to me, unjustifiably misconstrued, I shall also devote to them a few final words, which I recommend to your attention, not in the interests of an acquittal, which my friend the Public Prosecutor has already imposed on you, but in the personal interest of Gabrielle Bompard, who for the sake of justice must leave this court as spotless as when she surrendered herself to it.

"For she did surrender herself to it. She surrendered herself to the court, she denounced the crime because that was her purpose from the outset. Only ill will or blind stupidity can dispute that. She carefully preserved the vital clues, Gouffé's hat and Gouffé's sapphire, that were to give Eyraudt away when the time came. At the moment of the murder, she could not call for help without herself falling victim to her atrocious violator's blood-lust; she could not break out of the room of the murder for the same reason, she was all too familiar with his malignant character, which she wisely bore in mind after he had locked her in—very possibly with the intention of lying in wait to see if she would take a step that he would have punished with death as treachery; but at this same moment she slipped into his hands his victim's telltale hat: without delay, therefore, at the very first opportunity, she made the first moves in the plan which henceforth she was only waiting for a chance to bring to fruition.

"In America she joined forces with Monsieur Carapin and implored him to take her away to New York, expressly indicating that she had 'another bone to pick with Eyraudt.' Once in New York, she found out about steamship passages to France and kept her trunks packed until the moment came when her new friend, instead of following his business interests and going to Buffalo, would see that it was up to him to return with her to Paris. Then her photograph appeared in the Press, with such a grossly misleading caption that Monsieur Carapin was forced to come around to her point of view.

"So she traveled with him to France, reported at the Cité and, because she was there turned away, called on Monsieur Jaquemar. These, gentlemen of the jury, are the bare *facts* without comment. But my learned friend the Public Prosecutor did comment on them; to my regret, not very happily. 'Why did she not denounce the crime sooner; she could have written!' That, if I may say so, shows a complete lack of imagination! The young woman knew better, she knew that if she did not make her denunciation in person, it would throw the gravest suspicion on her, quite apart from the fact that, if it came to Eyraudt's knowledge through the Press, her life would not have been safe for another second. A written denunciation, which in the eyes of police and public would have meant no risk to her, would have led everyone to believe that she was actively involved in the crime; she would have been hunted down, arrested along with Eyraudt, and prosecuted as his accomplice. And if she had asked: 'In that case, why did I denounce him?' the authorities would have answered, with every appearance of justice: 'Because you had quarreled with him, because you wanted to be revenged on him for his brutalities, and above all because you hoped by your denunciation to win the clemency of the court!'

"On the other hand, if she came herself, this act of unparalleled audacity would prove that she must have a perfectly clear conscience —under the circumstances, a person to whom self-accusation, I mean morbid self-accusation, is utterly alien, could *only* have reported to the police if she was in fact innocent, and it was no more than a logical appeal to the facts when Mademoiselle repeated again and again during all the interrogations and in the course of the trial: 'Should I be here if I were not innocent?' No, of course she would not be here if she were not innocent! She denounced the crime at the earliest possible opportunity and in a way that proved both Eyraudt's guilt and her own innocence . . . so fully that not even the Public Prosecutor has ventured to accuse her of complicity.

"What more can anyone want? 'It is true she denounced the crime,' says the Public Prosecutor, 'but she *might* not have denounced it if the publication of her photograph had not compelled her to do so!' Now I really must protest! If that isn't hairsplitting! Might have, might have—what might she not have done! As though she, with her unshakable obstinacy, her irresistible charm, the power of her personality, especially over a man who was body and soul in love with her—as though, I say, she could not have persuaded Monsieur Carapin to take her somewhere else instead of New York, anywhere else in the measureless expanse of the American continent, to the Grand Canyon, or the picturesque deserts of the West, in a luxury liner to Hawaii or in a small sailing vessel on a voyage around the world, to the South Seas or heaven knows where, to some place where nobody cared a straw about Gabrielle Bompard and no newspaper gave news about her! Might have, might have! If we are going to talk about 'might have'—with the ladies' delightful capacity for transformation, she might have assumed any appearance she wished, she could have called wardrobe, coiffure, hair dye, make-up box, and lipstick to her aid, she might have fled—unrecognized, unrecognizable, and alone, for as long as she desired—anywhere she felt like fleeing to! Don't forget that over there not a single soul knew her from the past! Yes, she *might* have, she might have done this, that, and a hundred other things; as we know, there are no limits to poetic fancy; only she didn't do any of these things, that is the point. 'Perhaps she might not have denounced the crime'—but she *did* denounce it, and there I feel sorely tempted to let the matter rest.

"The publication of her photograph which is supposed to have compelled her to denounce the crime was, on the contrary—and this is amply proved—used by her to compel Monsieur Carapin to help her to denounce it. This is borne out by the evidence of Monsieur Carapin himself, who is better placed than anyone to judge the truth of this statement. The facts eloquently support Monsieur Carapin's testimony and no appeal to *ifs* and *might have beens* can avail against them.

"Gentlemen of the jury, that is all I have to say. Gabrielle Bompard is innocent. God forbid that in a country governed by truth and justice a person, whom even the charge brought by the prosecution labels guiltless, should be declared guilty by the legal representatives of the people. That will not happen. Your verdict, gentlemen of the jury, will be a true verdict in keeping with your high office, and it will be unanimous. It will be 'Not guilty.' "

Maître Rebattu nodded his thanks to the jury. With a sense of deliverance, Deist banged the gold cross down on the table in front of him and stuffed the handkerchief, with which he had been polishing it, back into his pocket. Maître Rebattu returned to his seat, crossed one leg over the other so that his narrow (and somehow youthful looking) patent-leather shoes were visible under his robe, and threw back his head with the flashing spectacles; he sat thus, lost in thought, his mouth shut tight and his arms folded over his chest, with the expression of one who has done his duty and now waits upon events. His speech still hovered palpably in the air and consciousness of the life around them returned only gradually to those who had been gripped by it: first the occasional twitter of a bird, from time to time a particularly loud sound from the traffic outside and a fainter hum from far away in the city, and while the chestnut candles swayed peacefully in the open windows, a thin burst of clapping rose very belatedly from the invisible audience in the street below, quickly died away, and was drowned by a dull murmur, a billowing mutter from which it was impossible to tell whether those down in the depths were approving, disapproving, or divided in their opinions. Meanwhile, Deist once more explained their duties to the jury in his booming voice (one could feel that he was carrying out a frequently repeated and tedious formality) and instructed them to retire. They rose to their feet, looked at one another as though to say "What do we do now?" and finally pushed their way in groups through a door in the background and disappeared.

Maître Rebattu remained as he was: his head leaning back, his arms crossed. Only once, while Deist sat there waiting with his face turned away and his chin resting in his hand, oblivious to the whispering that gradually spread through the courtroom—only once did Chantegrei lean over to the great man and pass a remark, with a shy smile, in response to which Rebattu bent his ear toward him kindly. Then he sat as before and had plenty of time to do so; for the deliberations of the jury took a long time, much longer than anyone would have foreseen; for some unknown reason, they took over two hours, though rumor claimed later that it was because the foreman, taking one of

Monsieur Rebattu's remarks too literally, absolutely insisted on a unanimous verdict, and there was unfortunately one voice that stubbornly contradicted the unanimity of the rest (out of pure self-importance, people said).

In spite of this grueling test of their patience, the public in the court and in the street remained quiet the whole time, contenting themselves with a whispered exchange of opinions, and would have continued to wait cheerfully until the end—with better manners than Deist, who was fidgeting in his chair like an ill-bred schoolboy—if all of a sudden, fortunately only just before the waiting came to an end, Bompard, who had been irritably shifting this way and that for some time, had not exclaimed indignantly in an undertone: "I'm going home!"—which she then made as if to do: she stood up, took the stole from Montardon's lap, and the latter, wringing her hands beseechingly, had the greatest difficulty in persuading her to sit down again. The little scene aroused great merriment, lively applause came from outside and within the court everyone laughed with amusement, while a few people began softly to stamp their feet, like a theater audience impatient for the curtain to go up. Deist turned his balloon of a face back to Bompard, unable to believe his ears—when the uproar died away, because the door in the background opened and the jury filed in.

They spread out along their double row of benches and stood with solemnly empty and stern faces as Deist asked whether they had reached a verdict. Their foreman replied that they had and that they were unanimous in finding Eyraudt guilty of premeditated murder, but Bompard not guilty of failing to report the crime. This verdict produced no reaction whatsoever in the courtroom, but the ghostly audience outside gave vent to powerful and sustained applause, the clapping of a thousand hands, reminiscent of the violent pelting of a sudden downpour of rain, which lasted a few minutes and then came rather abruptly to a complete stop.

Deathly silence reigned as Deist rose to his feet and waited with an expression of distaste in his slit eyes until those in the body of the court did the same. Once again a comical little scene was enacted by Bompard, who happened to be fussing with her shoe at this moment and continued to sit there bending down, oblivious to what was going on around her. Montardon first gave her a few urgent little nudges, which she ignored, then whispered to her to rise and took her obsequiously by the elbows; Bompard shook her shoulders irritably, finally looked with bent head at the public, who had long been standing, and jumped up exactly like a frolicsome child who is willing to take part in any sort of joke.

As Deist started to speak she kept her face with the clown's brows turned laughingly toward the people, and this was the last opportunity they had of studying the beauty of this unscrupulous young woman who had been dragged through the mire and lauded to the skies: the laughing face was white with a red mouth and black lashes, the enamel-blue hair flickered up like tongues of flame, as though blown aloft out of the fan-shaped collar.

The public paid almost more attention to her than to Deist, who read what he had to announce from a slip of paper, some of it in a thunderous roar, some of it in a monotonous drone, but all of it with utter contempt. The death sentence on Eyraudt, which had been universally expected, was greeted with icy silence, and even the condemned man stood mutely with hanging head; but he uttered a scream, as though the fateful decision had only just struck him, a high-pitched scream compounded of pain, hate, and nameless disillusion, as the Presiding Judge thundered on and read out the second part of the judgment, the acquittal of Gabrielle Bompard.

At this there arose such an ear-splitting din that Eyraudt's expiring shriek was drowned in the general uproar: an immense cacophony of raucous yells, jubilation, clapping, stamping, and whistling burst out inside the court; while with a sound that seemed to combine the rumble of bass drums with the rattle of kettle drums, the enthusiasm of the intoxicated populace poured in through the open windows, in which hats, sticks, flowers, handkerchiefs, and dancing shadows as well as glittering vortices of sand flung into the air appeared between the dreamy swaying of the chestnut blossom candles. Everyone, even the men in robes, seemed to be making their contribution to the pandemonium: Deist, who was waiting to give the reasons for the verdict (which he never managed to do), rang his bell and shouted inaudibly with his mouth wide open as though in ecstasy; Massicot, the Public Prosecutor, threw his books and papers one on top of the other as he disappointedly packed up; the jurymen laughed as they talked and nodded to one another, pleased that their verdict had been so well received; and only the seraphic Chantegrei kept his hands folded motionless over his flat abdomen and bit his lip sadly with downcast eyes.

But when Maître Rebattu turned around to congratulate his client on her acquittal, the dock was empty and only Montardon stood in front of the open door in the rear wall; she stood there all alone, holding out the white wool stole toward the gaping black emptiness of the doorway with hands that seemed to have been turned to stone in the attitude of one bringing an offering; and as a breath of wind from the window stirred the stole, it seemed as though the emptiness were sucking at it, only to lose interest and abandon the attempt as the draft died away.

Evening was already approaching; the street noises from the Rue de la Glacière and the rumbling, tinkling, and bustling from the Boulevard Arago entered, low but clear, through the open windows of Jaquemar's room, and the curtains swelled and rattled their rings on the brass rod as they were wafted by the tired breeze. The stillness of the hour reigned in the bare room, but not its relaxed peacefulness: instead an atmosphere of sullen brooding lay over the room and with the failing light seemed to grow in density as though a spirit was rising from the darkness already gathering in the corners.

The young people, Madame Chottin in the armchair, Jaquemar on the silk-upholstered stool facing her, sat in silence; the young woman was staring at the window unseeing, because she had to look somewhere and did not want to look at the young man's furrowed brow. After a while, she nevertheless felt compelled to do so; and she found the expression on his lowered forehead even more forbidding, more defensive, than if it had been angry, so that an urge to tears, which she immediately repressed, made her eyes wet and glistening; but her voice betrayed no trace of sorrow and scarcely any emotion at all. "Really, Monsieur," she said, trying courageously to be arch, "you don't make things easy for your friends. I ought to feel offended, for the last half hour you have barely opened your mouth."

She waited, and as he did not so much as blink an eyelid she continued in a jokingly plaintive voice: "What have I done wrong, that I should no longer succeed in winning your approbation? Do I deserve such sternness? Has anyone in the world worried about you more?"

But he did not move, and the "No" he uttered in reply (too promptly and almost mockingly, it seemed to her), without taking his eyes off the floor, startled her, and once more she had to fight back her tears. Forgetting to maintain her bold face, she cried out in an agonized voice and with a little sob: "Oh, it's true, when poor Monsieur Gouffé went, I lost more than one friend."

"I know I'm inadequate," growled Jaquemar, and whatever he meant by this remark, it calmed her emotion and gave a firm, sensible ring to her voice: "You have attempted too much! You have been staring too long at one point, you need a change. If only you had listened to me! But at least you will listen to me now, won't you? This evening it will all be over. Edmond, don't run your head against a brick wall, go away from here, think about something else."

"Of someone else, you mean, don't you?" put in Jaquemar, perhaps ironically, but so drily that it was not clear whether he was joking, especially as he went on in the same dry tone, without waiting for an answer: "Yes, you have been worried. More than that, you have tried not to let me see that you were worried. But your eyes keep on asking the same timid question, which I cannot answer. I don't want to speak ill of your anxiety, but you said yourself that what you fear is a loss . . . well, is a person ever thinking of anyone but himself?"

"I don't understand you," broke in Madame Chottin, with the trace of a smile that might have sprung from shame or pique, and a blank look came into her usually calm eyes. But Jaquemar took no notice of her interruption and went on with a certain stubborn persistence: "As far as I am concerned, this past year has been like a tidal wave that cast me on the beach of my own ego, no matter how I struggled. It is true that Gouffé was washed ashore with me, and I believed that it was him I had in mind when I fretted. Today I am no longer so sure. Is it he, is it I, whom I have in mind? Are we one? In any case, one dead man can place us under a greater obligation than all the living he leaves behind. I am under an obligation."

"Of course, Edmond, certainly!" she exclaimed. "Who is standing in your way?"

He looked up for an instant with his squinting eyes, lowered his head again, and replied: "I am not free to confide in you as you long for me to do. Don't think ill of me for this and just to please me, try not to torment yourself over it."

She gazed questioningly at his features; she tried to smile, but knowing that her smile would not be mirrored in his face, she abandoned the attempt and, with an effort of will, spoke with fresh firmness: "Must we talk about me? Very well, if you insist. What would I not do to please you? Have I not come here to send you away? Oh, I fear that for your sake I do more than my pride should permit me. Do you think I didn't know that you wanted to be alone today? I had to come. I was afraid, yes—for you, Edmond, for you! This accursed trial! Can anyone tell how it will end, who can say?"

"I can," retorted Jaquemar curtly.

"So I cannot console you," she cried, and now she really had tears in her eyes. "I cannot—"

"Why do you make things so difficult for us? Console? You have your portion of grief, I have mine."

"I ought to go," she rejoined, raising her head, not without dignity, and lowering her still tear-laden eyelids.

He rose and walked in his long gray dressing gown to the screen, which now, as originally, separated the bed corner from the rest of the room; he walked hurriedly with his rather too mincing gait, not hesitating till he came to the screen, where he stopped and said rather quickly and in a low voice, but without turning round: "Forgive my rudeness. You have deserved better of me, I know that very well. 'This evening it will all be over.' You know that is nonsense. This evening it will really begin! Yes, I want to be alone. Forgive me for that too."

No reply came from Madame Chottin; he disappeared behind the screen and reappeared with her costume jacket; but as he approached, she rose; she stepped back behind the armchair and began to speak in a frightened voice and staring into space: "No, no, you mustn't be alone now! I can already hear how they will shout out the evening papers: 'Bompard free! Bompard not guilty!' Unbearable! And there will be cheering in the streets, as though they had stormed the Bastille! They will carry that horrible woman on their shoulders! And the whispering will start again: 'Why didn't Jaquemar appear as a plaintiff? Why did she go to him in the first place?'"

"It no longer makes any difference," said Jaquemar briefly.

"Don't overestimate yourself, Edmond!"

"The mob has no memory; by tomorrow it will all be forgotten."

"But today, tonight?"

"What about tonight? Am I to run away from myself?"

"Let me stay."

He came up behind her, opened out her jacket, and watched as she felt about behind her reluctantly with her left hand. She turned her face to him once again to say something, but without returning her gaze he forestalled her: "What I have to do, I must do alone."

Again fear seized her. "You are so difficult to see through. What are you planning?"

"Am I planning something?" he growled.

Now she was standing facing him, strong, almost imperious. "Promise me! Nothing—nothing sudden! Nothing rash!"

"Come."

"Promise me one thing in particular—"

He put his hand over her mouth, and standing thus they looked one another in the eyes for a long time; but he was the stronger, she lowered her eyes and with her head bent she allowed him to lead her by the arm to the door. "Don't forget," he said as they moved across the room, "that I could swallow some of Lebigot's sleeping draughts if I wanted to. I shan't do that either, though."

On the landing, the darkness was already so complete that the little bit of dusk from Jaquemar's door made no impression on it; the only source of light was the small lamp burning on the bracket facing the well of the stairs; its flickering flame filled the narrow space with a dim and restless glimmer that made it look as though the captive darkness were silently seething.

Jaquemar looked around as though listening, and then put the young woman's right hand to his lips; but as she made a movement toward him, he took hold of her shoulders and kissed her on the ear. "Good night," he said and gazed after her as she strode bravely away toward the light.

Now she was gone; the well of the stairs had absorbed her and was already swallowing up the sound of her shoes tapping steadily down the cement steps and growing fainter with every instant. The young man stood lost in thought. He ran the back of his hand across his mouth; so now he was alone, and it was so quiet that he imagined he could hear the flickering of the dim light like the soft beating of wings, a suddenly very insistent aural hallucination from which he was awakened by a tiny sound, the beginning of a high-pitched grumbling or mumbling that faded away almost before it had begun. He looked over his shoulder: to his right the landing ended in an old-fashioned curtain that created the illusion of a way out, where in fact there was none.

In front of the dark, colorless curtain stood Gabrielle Bompard, in a very strange get-up—a long, ample black wrap that made her look rather like a monument, for it enveloped her compactly down to the feet, leaving nothing free but her head in the stiff fan-shaped collar with the short curls thrusting up like tongues of black flame above the shimmering whiteness of the face. But the flickering lamp was reflected in her large eyes with a dancing, merry light, entirely in keeping with her gesture, as she drew her hand from under the wrap and put her index finger to her lips in an admonition to secrecy that seemed somehow impish. Jaquemar turned on his heel and walked with a hurried but as usual mincing step into his room; he went over to the armchair, the high back of which he gripped with his right hand, and stood for a moment or two in this position before looking toward the door with a cold and icy expression.

But his eyes did not encounter the look of triumph he had expected: Gabrielle Bompard was standing attentively by the doorpost (he had not heard the footsteps that brought her there); she seemed to be waiting for him to beckon or speak to her, and when he growled contemptuously and as though to himself: "Has the creature really got the cheek?" she slipped around the doorpost in smiling embarrassment, soundlessly and on feet that remained invisible beneath the black drapery.

"I might have guessed it," he continued in the same tone, with the result that, just as on her first visit, she relapsed into a strangled mumbling and grumbling and began literally to writhe and wriggle as though struck dumb and struggling unsuccessfully to speak—and this set his blood boiling with rage, so that he snarled through his teeth, but nevertheless distinctly: "Either go out or come in, and stop that damned play-acting!" At this she laughed in her soundless way, watched him attentively for a second, and suddenly turned with the gay, dancing step she sometimes adopted, closed the door and stood there waiting again. But because he remained silent, startled for some reason that was not clear even to himself, she said, now without any impediment, but in a deep, husky whisper and very confidentially:

"I'm glad we're rid of that sentimental goose. You didn't tell her about this morning."

Jaquemar sat down abruptly in the armchair, raised his fist to his teeth and gnawed at the knuckle of the index finger, hypnotized by the suspicion that he might really have sent his friend away on account of this indecorous visit; he could neither believe nor disbelieve it. Bompard said: "The cowl suits you," and he, still in the grip of his suspicion, retorted impatiently and really involuntarily: "I've been ill."

"I know," she answered politely. "All in good time."

Jaquemar looked up. "In a minute she'll be sitting in my lap!" he cried, as though to himself, and he was quite right, for she had actually come over to him and was pressing herself against the back of his chair, though with an awkward expression on her face, in which the clown's brows were twisted into an anguished smile. Jaquemar sprang to his feet, and now they stood side by side facing in opposite directions.

"Montardon's uniform cape," she said, fingering the inside of her cloak. "Carapin was waiting with the carriage at the main entrance. I slipped away. There was a tremendous racket; you would have been amused."

"Oh, of course!" answered Jaquemar grimly. "It would have been music in my ears!"

"Don't worry about this morning," Bompard remarked with a slight shrug. "Nobody took offense at your agitation. Carapin wasn't even there yet, the naughty man."

With a contemptuous laugh, Jaquemar went over to the window and peered out and listened in the direction of the street below to see whether the news of her acquittal was already being shouted out, found that there was the same silent bustle as before except that the gaslamps were gleaming like dull stars among the foliage, and asked coolly and decidedly over his shoulder: "What can I do for you?"

Again she mumbled inarticulately, but this time it sounded less embarrassed than sulky. He turned around with a mixture of curiosity and scorn and saw her raise her yellow hands from under the black fabric, which slid down her back as a result. She tidied her hair and mumbled: "You know."

"I have no business with you," said Jaquemar distinctly. "Will you please remember that—none at all."

"But I must go away," she replied, shrugging her shoulders pertly;

she actually sat down in the armchair and began plucking at the upholstery of the arm. "We're going to spend the summer at Saratoga Springs, it's very boring."

"Not to me," commented Jaquemar through clenched teeth.

"Why should we leave Paris?" she went on, shaking her head. "Paris is a nice place, people are jolly. Montardon told me they are singing a new song:

> "Sweetheart, if you give me
> A little silver money,
> I will show you things
> You'll think very funny."

She looked across at Jaquemar and then gazed into space with her head on one side. They were silent for a while, until Jaquemar broke into a belated laugh and exclaimed: "How charming!" to which she nodded gaily.

"I am certainly grateful," he said, foaming with rage, "to be informed of the latest flowering of poetry, but I cannot imagine that you took the trouble to come here on that account—famous as you are. Time presses, your admirers are waiting impatiently. Once more then: what can I do for you?"

"Will you please settle accounts?" she answered in a businesslike tone.

"Settle accounts. . . . Do I owe money? To you?"

"Ten thousand francs, as you know," she said doggedly. "The formalities have been completed."

"Oh, the reward. . . ." said Jaquemar in a singsong voice, nodding his head and coming a step closer. "Payment for your services, that's why you're here."

"Of course," she replied in astonishment. "What did you think?"

"It's quite true," he blurted out. "Goron was right; she is the most hardened criminal in the world! No sooner has she slipped through the executioner's hands than she's here asking for ten thousand francs, please."

"No!" she cried indignantly. "Don't start that nonsense all over again! Do you think I let myself be bored and tormented for months on end for fun? I have done my part, now it's up to you."

"Haven't I heard that you are a—um, 'little fanatic for justice'?

I thought you had denounced Gouffé's murderer so that justice should be done?"

"Certainly, justice must be done. Denunciation is part of it: no denunciation, no trial; no trial, no verdict—ten thousand francs for Eyraudt's head, that was the offer. You've got what you wanted. The deal was worth a hundred thousand. Even apart from the rotten time I've had, the payment is mean enough. But now you make difficulties —no, that's going too far!"

"You make me shudder," whispered Jaquemar, and could not take his squinting eyes off her.

"That's your lookout," she retorted icily, and sat up straight in the chair. "There is no place for feelings in business. One expects an associate to pay his debts."

"The reward, Mademoiselle," he declared coldly and decidedly, "has been deposited at the Cité."

"But I'm leaving Paris tonight!" she objected, with an emphatic nod. "Heavens above! Why all these difficulties? It wouldn't cost you anything to be a bit helpful, nobody's going to steal your money from the police station! I should like mine in cash."

"You overestimate the opulence of my habits. I don't carry ten thousand francs around in my trouser pocket."

"A check then."

"A check then. . . ." he mimicked her, then remembered himself and inquired slyly: "In what name, if I may ask?"

She laughed soundlessly with her head on one side.

"In what name?" he reiterated intently, and took another step closer.

"We shall come to an understanding about that," she answered cunningly. "Why don't you sit down?"

He hooked the stool toward him with his foot and casually sat down on it.

"H'm, it's only a pity I haven't got a check book handy."

She clicked her tongue and stared sulkily into space.

"Yes," he remarked, "that's silly. Tomorrow perhaps?"

She peered attentively into his face, in which there was not much to be read, since it showed nothing but accumulated tension and in any case appeared in the dusk only as a shimmering brown patch.

"Can I trust you?"

"How can you ask?" he retorted with gentle irony.

"Do you know the little town of S—— N——? We're going there tonight. Make a note of the address: Hôtel Corbeau, S—— N——."

She had bent down to him confidentially, and Jaquemar, his eyes on hers, repeated in a sly tone: "Aha . . . Hôtel Corbeau, S—— N——."

"Tomorrow," she went on, her eyes still fixed on his, "and no nonsense! It's true I'm with Carapin, but a woman like myself must be independent, you never know . . . and here's another thing, just in case: when we get to Saratoga Springs, we shall take rooms in the Grand Union."

"I shan't forget," he said slowly, as she raised her crooked index finger in a childlike threat: "I get angry when I'm let down. People must pay their debts."

He suddenly moved away from her on his stool. She sighed sullenly: "You've never seen so many boring people all at once as at Saratoga Springs. Some of them stand all day long in the brooks fishing for trout; it makes a disgusting noise when the hook is torn out of their mouths, the fish lash about with their tails and their eyes pop out of their heads with the pain."

"You're so confiding," commented Jaquemar, once more sarcastic. "There's just one thing you haven't confided in me yet."

"Yes, the name!" she broke in, laughed and stared into space with her head on one side.

"Labodère, Bompard, Carapin or . . . ?"

She gave him a quick glance full of interest, he smacked his lips in mocking amusement, and she answered questioningly: "Madame Carapin perhaps?"

"H'm," he said meditatively, "we mustn't lose sight of the technical difficulties; after all, you aren't Madame Carapin. Of course, you're not Mademoiselle Labodère either, you're Mademoiselle Bompard—that's right, isn't it, you are Mademoiselle Bompard?"

"No, let's stick to Madame Carapin," she decided in a detached tone. "Bompard isn't practical at the moment."

"Oh, why not?"

She looked into his eyes and motioned with her head toward the open window. Yes, now the cries that Madame Chottin had feared on his behalf were drawing closer, they seemed to be converging from all sides on this point in the street below, it was as though he could hear the running feet and the cries themselves, although in reality the latter were quite indistinguishable: "Bompard free! Bompard not guilty!" He sprang to his feet, hurried with his mincing gait first to one window, then to the other, slammed them shut, leaned against the frames, quivering with hate and rage, and turned halfway round toward the dark room. "Get out!"

"It would be better if you hid me," she commented, with her eyebrows very much raised. "If people see me coming out of your hotel door . . ."

He turned right around, stamped his foot, and yelled: "Get out, get out!"

She shrugged her shoulders and rose with a captious little growl.

"Will you call me a cab," she said sulkily.

"No! Get out, will you!"

She bent down to the wrap lying on the floor, with her arms dangling, took hold of it, and straightened up. She shifted about where she stood, passed the cape from one hand to the other, pulled and plucked at the piece of gold jewelry incrusted with beryls, and mumbled to Jaquemar, looking up at him: "Carapin gave it to me."

Jaquemar rushed toward her, seized her hand, and dragged her to the door; she followed with resisting, tottering steps and let the black cloak drag along the floor. Jaquemar pushed open the door, she held tight to his hand, so that he shook it with a groan, and she cried out in a clear, anguished voice: "How can we fail to dream of one another? Oh, let go of me, Jaquemar—take care of yourself, adieu!"

She let go of his hand. He stared at her breathlessly and did not know whether this was a detestable farce intended for some listener in the darkness, or whether for some unknown reason she meant it, since her face, with its raised and anguished brows and a woeful smile around the mouth and little tiger's nose, was so frankly offered, almost surrendered, in the flicker of the dim light. She turned, took a few hesitant steps, came to a stop and looked back over her shoulder with a slight shrug; then he stepped quickly back into his room and shut the door. He leaned his head against the doorpost, rapidly came to himself, opened the door a fraction and listened. There was nothing more to be heard, she was gone; the black cloth of the cape wriggled along the stone floor around the corner of the wall at the bottom of the stairs and disappeared.

Meanwhile outside, through the narrow Rue de la Glacière to the Boulevard Arago and at the same time in all the boulevards of this dreamy city where Gouffé had been happy and unhappy and had met his death, the running and shouting began that announced to the world the final apotheosis of the tragedy, the news was called out to attract purchasers beneath the light of gaslamps, the cries rang hoarse amid the soughing of the tender spring foliage as though uttered by people in agonized flight: a sou for the crooked truth of Gabrielle Bompard's innocence and acquittal.

Naturally this sensation in black and white sold like hot cakes, and those who were carrying it among the people, holding the fluttering sheets above their heads, really had no need to run themselves into a sweat. But no one could say there was jubilation as if, in Madame Chottin's words, "they had stormed the Bastille." People bought the papers, they laughed, on the café terraces and in the bistros they read and studied Maître Rebattu's forensic *tour de force*, they chatted about it with a snigger, waxed enthusiastic or shook their heads—and all the time, life went on undisturbed in its simple seeking after pleasure: the venturesome strolling along the pavements, with shining eyes and titillated nerves, the furtive bargaining at dark street corners, pocketpicking and love in hotel rooms let by the hour, in a word— life, the way it is on a beautiful summer night in Paris.

All suspense plays itself out in the end. When, next day, Le Jour, a newspaper close to the Cité, reopened the whole case in a fiery article in support of Goron, the public treated it almost with indifference, dismissing the article as a helpless outburst. It was a last-minute attempt that could do Goron nothing but harm, because whatever it had to say in defense of the Sûreté was simultaneously a ruthless attack on other departments.

Goron drove and hustled everybody as before, ran grimly up and down the corridors, slammed the doors, berated his subordinates, and as regards the article, which was signed with an X and could only have originated in the Cité, he turned a blind eye and pretended to know nothing about it. Heavens above, how stupid did he think people were? The startling fact was that he really did know nothing about it, he had never thought of writing an article, he had neither read it nor heard of its existence. He himself *wanted* to be blind at the time, and the only member of his entourage who meant well by him, Guillaume, initially shared the general opinion and, as if offended by his chief's lack of finesse, withdrew into pained silence, and when he at last began to see through the plot it was too late.

For events followed one another in quick succession: on May 15 the last word was spoken in the Eyraudt-Bompard trial, on May 16 the article incorrectly attributed to Goron appeared, on the morning of May 18 he received notification that he had been "appointed" head of "all" the police forces of French Morocco. He turned down the invitation by return of post, on the grounds that his heart, "weakened by the excitement of the last few months," would not stand up to the tropical climate. In a communication bearing the same date as his own, the Ministry of the Interior replied that, in view of the state of his health and with great regret, his resignation had been accepted— the proposal that he should be made a knight of the Legion of Honor, in recognition of his outstanding services, had already been completed and dispatched.

Notification of the Press took place the same hour, along with the appointment of the former Chief Inspector Jaumes as head of the Moroccan police and of Latrille as chief of the Paris Sûreté. As a result of this, Jaumes, half sick with rage, saw the promotion he had been hoping for go to a subordinate and even his own old position taken over by the latter's friend; for he was replaced in the Sûreté by the oval-skulled Delattre from the Prefecture Secretariat, henceforth the right-hand man of the comrade whose secret maneuvers he had so faithfully assisted, without, however, having any active part in the final coup, for the article in Le Jour, having been inspired by Lozé, was for the rest entirely Latrille's work.

But neither Latrille (according to Guillaume's report, he laughed, showing his white teeth for the first time, when Goron took his bowler hat from the rack in his office for the last time)—neither Latrille nor the fish-eyed Lozé was reckless enough to regard what had happened as secure, merely because it had happened. They did all they could, shrinking from no sacrifice, to disclose and hammer into the public the straits in which the Paris police force had been and how urgently it required reorganization. To be sure, Goron had been fighting desperately for years for every improvement that was now announced with a fanfare of trumpets, but he had made no headway, stuck fast as though in the clay of a country lane in the tenacious opposition offered by the Prefecture and the Ministry; but this hopeless wrangle had gone on in secret, behind the scenes, an internal matter known only to a few initiates, especially Latrille, who had exploited these very difficulties in his intrigue against his chief, while demanding their removal as the price of final victory.

Now the time had come, once again people could see how splendidly clean a new broom sweeps, the windows were thrown open, fresh air poured in! The public heard that the Cité personnel had been considerably increased, its appropriation doubled, a special appropriation established for emergencies—in short, that an end had been made of the niggardliness that had taken root there with the passing of time, to the detriment of the underpaid and overworked officials, to the detriment of the public, whose security was endangered by these false economies. As a matter of fact, they had reached positively grotesque proportions; thus, believe it or not, it had not been deemed necessary to furnish the country's foremost security organization with a telephone or a regular subscription to the most important publications of the international or even the national Press, which supplied free copies only in return for inside information, the disclosure of which was often prejudicial to investigations in progress! These, first tacitly accepted and then bluntly denounced, were scandalous conditions, and people were grateful to the new chief (who was not from Brittany) for eliminating them one after the other. An end to them! An end, also, to the long-since outmoded, long-since pointless regulations that limited the Sûreté's range of action as though walled in and kept on a chain by a misplaced democracy, according to which the country's central police authority had been denied a status higher than that enjoyed by the police of any provincial département and had no right to carry its investigations into the territory of any other local authority, let alone to intervene in any investigation of theirs, no matter how urgently necessary it appeared. The Paris chief—once more almost incredibly—was not allowed to leave the city, either privately or officially, be it noted, without express leave of absence to be granted by other branches of the administration. The new man possessed the self-assurance, intelligence, and vigor required to break down the old walls and wrest for his organization the independence he needed in order to do his work undisturbed; he had authority.

Latrille really did have authority: in relation to Lozé and Sallier, because they were his accomplices; in the Cité, because the salary increases had won him popularity, and also because he was quite capable of asserting himself when necessary. The boor Soudrais rubbed his hairy paws with the ingrown wedding ring, under the illusion that his time had come, and sauntered into the chief's offices; he was out again in the twinkling of an eye, having been unsmilingly informed that a detective sergeant had no right to visit the chief unless sent for.

Guillaume, whose potential hostility he could feel and was unable to overcome by a persistently friendly attitude during his first few weeks in office, was appointed to the post at the Prefecture vacated by Delattre, a transfer that amounted to promotion, especially as it was accompanied by a fresh and not inconsiderable increase of salary. But Latrille, with his temperate and amiable demeanor (he concealed his malice in the interests of his new post and withdrew it from his face into his thinking)—Latrille also possessed authority in the eyes of the world, and with some justice. For he was a first-rate policeman, who had learned a great deal from the master he had betrayed and had avoided taking over the recklessness that sprang from the latter's fanaticism. Of course, he was no Goron; but what he lacked in originality he made up for by his worldly wisdom and by systematically developing the methods which his predecessor had adumbrated but been prevented from putting into full effect by lack of means.

He was determined to eliminate both excessive familiarity and secret enmity, outside as well as in his own headquarters; and in pursuit of this aim he took one step too far, for which he could have kicked himself. In the desire to remove any "resentment," as he called it in his own mind, he paid a visit to Goron, believing that he could dupe the man who had been sacked with a display of unshakably loyal regret—and was not received, was turned away with the offensive reply: "Monsieur Goron does not wish to see you."

No, Goron no longer suffered from psychological blindness; it was as though the scales had fallen from his eyes—now, after the disaster had run its course and struck him down. But it was already too late in every sense, since immediately after the verdict in the Eyraudt-Bompard case he had suffered a heart attack, and the subsequent vexations had provoked a second and far more severe one from which he was only gradually recovering, making a slow return to a life that in any case could not last long. He must have felt this; at all events, he was a changed man, he was almost wise, and what an impetuous progress from success to success had not been able to teach him, the last, final, and irreparable failure had taught him: to smile. He saw right through the motives of those who had worked for his downfall: Sallier's exasperated slothfulness, Lozé's knavish fear of an accessory, Carnot's offended pedantry, and above all the ice-cold, scheming ambition of Latrille, the slippery eel, who was willing to employ any intrigue and any accomplice, even the boneheaded Soudrais, as a means to his end; he contemplated the whole spectacle of malice, hatred, and intrigue, in which he had stormed across the stage in the role of a simpleton, or a clown in the circus, until he caught his foot in the noose and went down slap! flat on his face, to the merriment of the crowd. No doubt about it, the play had its funny side; looked at from a distance, it was amusing, and he smiled, even if it was a disdainful smile and not entirely free from bitterness.

Only when he thought of Gabrielle Bompard, her white face with the brows raised in anguish and her brazen impudence, was the smile missing—but so was the bitterness. He did not understand her, not even today; his heart beat a little faster, the thought of her did not force any more definite emotions from him, no anger, no hate: his feeling for her had become a question mark after a question that was never asked. He read Maître Rebattu's speech for the defense and admitted to himself that the lawyer might be right in claiming that in her presence everyone became what he really was; but was that the solution to the riddle, did it not become, on the contrary, all the more enigmatic? But over this, too, he shrugged his shoulders; he had felt her power, let it rest at that.

This was what had happened to Goron, the fanatic. At times he felt quietly surprised that the "too late" had no further sting for him; for he was simply too innocent to see that the innocence of the fervor with which he had set out on his course had outlived this fervor and that this very innocence protected him from extreme disappointment. He merely knew, in a general way, that he had staked his life, in vain perhaps, but not wrongly, and he no longer desired justice but merely to tell the world what he had been striving after. He wanted to answer for his conduct. Unfortunately, he had no skill as a writer; but he had to make the best of it, and he sat down to write his memoirs. He had retired once and for all from the field of action; his vision of the past fascinated him and made him insensitive to the present. He wished no one either good or ill, and if the "Monsieur Goron does not wish to see you" had stung Latrille like a whiplash when he called to see him, it had really been meant quite literally and without any particular animosity.

When Guillaume visited him, Goron told him he "wanted to write up a few things" and asked if he would help him to get hold of some of the Cité files on cases he, Goron, had "collaborated on." Was he on good terms with the new chief, Latrille? Oh, yes, replied Guillaume ironically and hastened to assure him there would certainly be no difficulty about satisfying this request. He was right in this; for Latrille found it expedient to put both of them in his debt, Guillaume as a potential adversary whose future career was unpredictable, the chief he had betrayed so that he should not make any more serious trouble for him than the whiplash at the door. As a matter of fact, however, one does not propitiate enemies by giving way to them. Where Guillaume was concerned, Latrille was to find this out later (but this does not concern us here); he did not find it out from Goron, who, in his disinterestedness, had outgrown all desire for vengeance.

Guillaume, who now paid more frequent visits to his former chief, carrying thick bundles of files under his arm, noted with secret amazement the constancy and extent of this withdrawal. Even the meager supplementary details of the case over which he had broken his neck were merely of literary and historical interest to him; they stirred no personal emotion in him, nothing perturbed him. Eyraudt had appealed to the President of the Republic for clemency through his defense counsel— "It won't be granted," commented Goron, shaking his head and thrusting the copy of the text back into the folder he had prepared as a receptacle for the papers and labeled "The Gouffé Case."

Guillaume had spied out and copied the order in which Latrille had called off attempts to trace the anonymous author of the libelous pamphlet J'accuse. "Well, what good would it do, anyhow?" said Goron. It was easy to understand that, for his part, Latrille wanted the Gouffé case buried and forgotten; only once did he come to speak of it in the Press louder than was absolutely necessary, in a tone of moral indignation.

It was not enough that Gabrielle Bompard's hair style had become
the rage of the ladies of the boulevard of every price level and that the
artists in hair were advertising it as the latest specialty under the
slogan *coiffure à la belle Gabrielle* at a fee of from five to fifty francs,
according to its closeness to the original; no, the crime itself—the
setting, the circumstances, the white dressing gown with the cord, not
forgetting the trunk and the Turkish violet cachous—had become an
article of commerce in the Paris erotic market. Mr. Grattan in London
was surprised by the number of orders for trunks he received from
Paris—and always for the same cumbersome model! Miss Evergreen,
in her Villa des Fleurs, had for a long time no inkling why such preposterous rents were offered for the little room in the annex, or why
the particular beauty who happened to be living there at any given
moment enjoyed such an influx of gentlemen visitors. Reconstructions
of the crime grew daily more popular; customers were too numerous
for the demand to be met by the one genuine room, and ten or twenty
imitations of it, down to the crooked mirror over the fireplace and the
minutest knickknack, were to be found in every *arrondissement* in the
city and served for nightly performances of the intimate scene between *l'huissier galant* and "our little demon," with the addition,
naturally, of a happy ending designed to please the public.

Against all this, Latrille inveighed in the Press, declaring to the
world at large that the Cité would not tolerate this abomination, but
would stamp it out with the utmost severity—or did people imagine
that the police could stand by and watch one of the most regrettable
and atrocious crimes of the age being publicized and peddled around
to stimulate and delight heaven knows what illicit impulses? "Well,
everyone has got something out of it," commented Goron, slipping
the newspaper page, as the final item, into the folder marked "The
Gouffé Case."

But to return to the chronological order of our narrative: weeks
before this satirical epitome of the Gouffé tragedy opened (to be more
exact, three days after her visit described earlier), it happened that
Madame Chottin called at the Hôtel des Mines again and found in
room 12a, the door of which was open, not Jaquemar, but Lebigot, the
eternal medical student, standing by the window reading a book, for
which purpose he had pushed his glasses up on to his thick-skinned
forehead above his now blind-looking eyes. Nevertheless, as she

stopped in the doorway, with a spasm of foreboding, he looked over to her almost immediately and remarked drily: "No further market for soporifics and narcotics, however sweet they be, young woman." He turned back to his book with his lips pursed like an old woman's; she drew nearer, wide-eyed, and asked: "Where is Jaquemar, in heaven's name?"

He shrugged his shoulders and answered, still turning the pages: "Up and away. After the lovely trollop, I should guess." "No!" she cried. "He would have told me!" "Would he? I bet he didn't know himself, even when he was already on the station platform." She lowered her eyes, which filled with tears, she pressed her lips together in pain and burst into tears. "Stop that damned blubbering!" yelled Lebigot furiously, hurling his book down on the floor. "That's the last straw!" "Lebigot," she sobbed, "oh, Lebigot, how could he do that to me?" "To you? Blessed innocence!" he retorted, and came toward her blinking his parrot's lids.

Like a child seeking protection, she leaned against his chest, clasped his shoulders, and blurted out in the midst of her sobs: "You are his friend—it's bad, isn't it?" He stood there as though made of wood, his long arms dangling, raised his right hand and tapped her cheek briefly with his big, red sadist's fingers, and asked half-mocking and half-compassionately: "Tell me, what did you expect?" "Oh, it *is* bad, Lebigot," she sobbed and nodded with her head on his chest. "That terrible woman will ruin him, she will destroy him."

He gazed at her hair with his round, hard eyes, his arms now dangling again, and finally answered, pulling his glasses down onto his nose: "The Lord looks after his own, dear child. Do you know the story of the boy who set out to learn what horror was? Perhaps he will come back having won a kingdom."

BOOK TWO
THE FINAL STRUGGLE

~~~~~~~~~~~~~~~~

"A bitter God to follow,
a beautiful God to behold."
SWINBURNE

1

JAQUEMAR'S DEPARTURE
AND CROSSING

We are what we experience. Were this not so, both the chronicler and the reader could very well dispense with a detailed account of Jaquemar's departure and rather tedious crossing (it took thirteen days); for little out of the ordinary happened, and the few events that did occur were so vague and insignificant that possibly no one but this young man would even have noticed them.

But Jaquemar did notice them; he perceived them as indications of something above and beyond themselves, as pregnant with secret meaning . . . and is this not how we all perceive our own lives and experiences? Without this hidden meaning, would the events we encounter really deserve to be honored with the names *life* and *experience?* No, we experience only with the depth, the distance, and the nearness with which we live, we experience only what we are. For this reason we have no need to rack our brains and guess at the significance of events; we perceive whatever tallies with the question or the answer that is within us. This also applies to Jaquemar. What happened to him on his trip was, heaven knows, not worth talking

about; only his sensibility is worth talking about, and his sensibility
was acute, it attempted to defend itself against the sinister, engulfing
quality latent in these insignificant events and met with little success
in its endeavor; for something in his nature that was stronger than his
acute sensibility allied itself with the forces outside him. Or was it
not something in his nature; was it his condition?

Jaquemar's condition was shaky, the sickness was still present in all
his limbs. Otherwise he would not have allowed more than twenty-
four hours to elapse before setting out in pursuit of Bompard. Why
did he? And why, the morning after Gabrielle's evening call at the
Hôtel des Mines, did he pay a fruitless visit to Goron, who was unable
to receive him because of his illness? What did he hope for from this
visit? Encouragement or dissuasion, confirmation of his decision or
clarification that would lead him in another direction?

The only certain thing is that the day after his conversation with
Bompard his fever, which he had believed over, suddenly rose again.
He ought to have been in bed, and at least he lay on the bed. Morning
turned to noon and afternoon, and evening came in through the open
window with its darkness, with early summer breezes and faint sounds
of the street, and he still lay on his bed. Yesterday this had been
Bompard's hour; but it, too, passed, and now it was night, ten or
eleven o'clock; and in Jaquemar's ears what had been one and indi-
visible separated and split up: the world outside with its faint bustle,
hum, confused turmoil, and occasional distinct sounds that fell like
drops of water into the general hubbub. And the world inside the
Hôtel des Mines with its deep silence—was it holding its breath, was
it waiting? All of a sudden it spoke into Jaquemar's ear, and the voice
was the voice of Bompard. As the previous day when she left him she
cried loudly and plaintively: "Leave me alone, Jaquemar—good luck
and good-by!" Something seemed to tear in Jaquemar's brain. Hell
and damnation! he thought, jumping up with clenched teeth. That
would just suit you, you bloodstained whore!

He was fully awake now and saw from his watch that he must hurry
if he wanted to catch the night train to the coast, and he did want to
catch it. Untidily, but not missing much, he threw his small stock of
clothes—underwear, shoes, and anything else that happened to come
to hand—into his bag, refusing to be put off by the fact that tiny beads
of sweat immediately broke out on his brow with a tickling sensation.

He was so vigorously impelled by the sudden access of will power that he did not even trouble to shut the door of his room 12a, let alone allow himself to be held back by his weakness. But it had its effect on him; he staggered and stumbled under the weight of his bag, which contained very little; the darkness of the corridor and the flickering of the oil lamp at the head of the stairs irritated and depressed him, as though the gloom itself were beckoning to him in this melancholy and insulting manner. This was nothing but the oversensitivity due to a slight fever and was forgotten even as he descended the spiral stairs, and even more once he emerged into the fresh air below. The May night was beautiful with the dreamy whisper of the still, dark air in the leaves of the trees like a child murmuring every now and then in its sleep, and the friendly life, laughter, and pleasure-seeking on all sides. By good fortune an open cab was standing waiting at the corner of the Boulevard Arago; the driver happened to be looking in his direction, noticed that he was dragging a case, and raised his whip in questioning invitation. Jaquemar nodded.

With a feeling of relief he sank back into the rear seat, the cabby clicked his tongue, the tired horse moved off and quickly fell into a comfortable trot. So he was on his way. If only the upholstery of the cab seat had not been so musty, had not smelled so unappetizing! And the fever continued to play its pranks on the young traveler. A moment ago he had been sweating with the heat; now he felt an icy shiver between his shoulder blades and turned up his jacket collar to keep out the cold. Nevertheless, the journey did him good. His bag stood in front on the little bench; he enjoyed the sensation of throwing back his head and gazing at the roof of delicate foliage, yellow in the light of the gas lamps as it passed slowly over him into the background.

The regular echo of the horse's trotting hooves in the narrower streets delighted his ears, and the signs of the bakeries, dairies, and butcher shops, the brown wood with the bronze lettering—a childhood landscape and the present moment at one and the same time—moved him to melancholy, as though he were never coming back, a feeling of "once more and perhaps never again," to which he surrendered himself with pleasure. He felt angry—or rather, in his overwrought state, exasperated—that the cab was halted as it bore him along and forced to make a detour, because shortly before their destination the street was blocked by a barrier of ropes stretched between crossed iron bars; smoking paraffin lamps with dim cores of light hung from it in warning but did not explain why the barrier had to extend across the whole width of the street; for behind it there was only a small excavation, at most ten feet long and six across, in the middle of the road, in front of which, with his back to Jaquemar, stood a workman in a smock looking down and scratching the back of his neck in perplexity, as though the little pit presented him with an insoluble puzzle.

In the station entrance there was still considerable activity, though it was really not clear why; for when Jaquemar went through onto the platforms, he found them strikingly quiet and almost deserted, even the one at which his westbound train stood waiting; there was no bustle around it, and the asthmatic snuffling with which the engine was puffing away at the front suggested that it had already done its stint. At regular intervals it ejected against the track a thick, watery steam permeated with particles of coal that rose up in a gray and black cloud around the carriages.

Jaquemar entered his carriage through the middle of this cloud and was glad to find an empty compartment. The porter, also wearing a smock, put the bag in the luggage rack; the conductor was on the spot and, eager for a tip, volunteered to keep other passengers out of the compartment. He told Jaquemar to pull down the curtains between himself and the corridor, push the basket-shaped blue shade over the ceiling light, and leave the rest to him. Jaquemar rewarded the ministering spirits and did as he was bid. The deep red velvet seats were very comfortable. He snuggled up in the darkness of the window corner and through the pane watched without much interest a lady in widow's weeds who was standing outside and every now and then spoke to someone in the next compartment. But as the train moved off without whistling or hooting, she suddenly flung both hands into the air as though to grasp something that was being torn away from her, opened her mouth to weep, and the same instant disappeared amidst a cloud of steam from the engine.

The train rocked unhurriedly along through the outskirts of Paris to the accompaniment of creaking and groaning noises, most of the time on a raised embankment; these districts were virtually unknown to Jaquemar and held little interest for him, being bleak and miserable

like the outskirts of all towns. But the comfort of the deep velvet seat
and the pleasant swaying, which yet did not conceal the mighty force
driving the train ceaselessly forward, the indifferent gaze which he
turned on the lights outside that glided up and down and past—in
short, the cosiness of the journey, which gave the traveler a sense of
being, so to speak, on leave from life, gradually lulled the solitary
young man into a pleasant doze. Unresisting, he allowed himself to be
visited by half thoughts, fleeting sensations, and mental pictures, a
mild inner turmoil in which this hour of parting mingled now with
dreams and now with memories. At one moment he seemed to see
Gabrielle Bompard again, or what he had seen of her on the last
occasion: she walked hesitantly along the gloomy, flickering corridor
in the Hôtel des Mines and set off down the spiral stairs, letting the
fabric of her long wrap drag behind her; it writhed like a black snake
and disappeared into the depths.

Jaquemar arrived at the little seaport in a thoroughly dejected state,
and staggered out into the open carrying his own case because there
was no porter in sight. Thank heaven there was a cab standing outside. The cabby on the box was asleep, tightly wrapped up in his black
coachman's overcoat with its multiple black shoulder capes, a battered
patent-leather top hat on his bowed head, and his chin resting on his
chest. Jaquemar threw his bag into the cab, sat down himself, and
cried out, exhausted: "Corbeau. Hôtel Corbeau." The cab moved
quietly away, without the man on the box having answered, taken up
his whip, or visibly changed the position in which he was sleeping;
he was slumped in the high seat like a huge black sack, and the horse
seemed to be doing its job without him. In reality, no doubt, it was
still very early, morning had barely begun, and though the mist had
now lifted, an icy, bleak, and pallid dawn prevailed, and the sky lay
over land and sea like an endless ceiling of dirty wool. The sea could
be seen and felt on all sides, and the fine drizzle that filled the air and
compelled Jaquemar to turn up his coat collar was laden with the
smell of rotting seaweed and fish, so that the young man, whose lips
it struck and condensed into drops, imagined he was tasting a slime
composed of fish and salt.

The main street, along which they drove, ran straight down to the
sea, and by comparison with the infinitude of its gray-green, heaving
surface the little human settlement on the ground looked pinched

and miserable: the trees stripped of their leaves, the asphalt burst open in long cracks, the low-roofed, seemingly abandoned houses with their rusty window bars and lowered sliding shutters, from which the paint was peeling, looking like scurf.

Close to the sea the street broadened out into a square; an awning of striped tarpaulin, which someone had forgotten to raise, cast a shadow on a pane of glass at ground level bearing, diagonally, the word *Café*; in the semidarkness within stood iron furniture, little tables and chairs with splayed legs, piled one on top of the other. But the strangest thing that met the newcomer's eye was a black metal figure standing out in the water, with long hair and dressed in what looked like a nightshirt, an angel or patron saint of seafarers, who stood with his back to Jaquemar holding a palm frond attentively in his sinewy right hand as though on the watch for flies or ready to whip the sea if it should become unruly. Immediately after the square, the street forked and ran in both directions along the sea front; they took the left-hand fork and stopped, where the street turned back inland, by a reef projecting far out into the sea on which towered the Hôtel Corbeau, taller than all the other houses but just as scurfy and pallid because of the white window curtains, a canine tooth of civilization pointing at the malignant and formless chaos of the watery waste.

There was no obstacle to his entry; the door was open, and inside, at a rough wooden table in front of pigeonholes for keys and post, the proprietress was already awake. She was a thin but big-bosomed woman with a tightly laced-in waist, and she sat writing in a thick book, her head bent, a wide taffeta ribbon dangling from the crooked pince-nez on her long, pointed nose and the sickly yellow skin of her face, whose cheeks looked as though they were being sucked in, positively shimmering with an unhealthy gleam. But what a fright Jaquemar had when she looked up; the two pupils, shiny black like sloes, lay close to the root of the nose on either side and stared at Jaquemar malevolently with a squint compared with which his own was a mere nothing. The Carapins? Yes, the lady and gentleman were in room 14 on the first floor, room 13 next to theirs was free—"if you're not superstitious!" she added, with a laugh that sounded like a cough, and returned to her book.

Jaquemar lay down to rest in the uncomfortable room, for two or three hours, as he thought, but in reality until it was already afternoon. He just managed to reach the travel agency, which stood in the square next door to the café, before the shops shut. Here he elicited rather discouraging information: this was a port for the South Seas, not the North Atlantic; and there was only one ship bound for New York at the jetty, the *Orphée*, which was sold out. She was due to sail the following afternoon, and Jaquemar was requested to call again shortly before she left, in case there might have been a cancellation.

During this conversation a man in a black oilskin mackintosh and blue knitted cap, which in spite of the warm weather he wore pulled right down over both ears, was leaning against the counter beside him. Jaquemar noticed him only casually; he was a tall, muscular man with a trim red toothbrush moustache, whitish eyebrows and lashes, and skin which, though weather-beaten, was milky-white like that of most red-haired people. As Jaquemar went out, lost in thought, he turned on his elbow and gazed after him, scratching the corner of his mouth with his right index finger.

Jaquemar did not notice this; he was preoccupied by the bad news he had just heard, and as he sat down under the awning of the café to drink a brandy and soda he unwillingly remembered that in his sleep, or just before he woke up, he had heard through the wall of the room next to his something like singing, singing in such a high, thin little voice that it sounded almost like chirping. For some reason he would have preferred to regard it as an illusion. It was a song he had been told about: "I will show you things / you'll think very funny." But he went on listening (and surely no one had told him what he heard next?): "When the sun rises into the sky / out of my room you will have to fly, / but what I showed you while you were inside / you will never forget, what e'er betide." Without any clear connection, it occurred to him that shortly after Bompard's arrest in his room at the Hôtel des Mines, he had received a brief note from her, which someone had slipped under his door at dusk. There was nothing on the envelope but "Jaquemar!" and on the sheet of paper inside was the following, in the same vertical, penciled handwriting: "Dear Jaquemar, the fat horror has actually locked me up in the cellars, where it is unpleasant. I'm starving, set me free! Yours, Gabrielle B."—a piece of impertinence that he had wisely kept to himself and since forgotten. Just wait, you bitch, he thought, and resolved to sail with the *Orphée* even if he had to slip aboard through the coal hatch as a stowaway.

As it happened, nothing of the kind was necessary. Perhaps it was his resolution that helped him, for circumstances remained unfavorable. After an evening with brandy and soda outside the café and a night's sleep that lasted until midday the following day and refreshed him wonderfully, he received in the early afternoon the same negative reply from the travel agency: no, there was nothing to be done, no bunk had become free, there was no prospect of an early passage on a different ship—this was not a port for the North Atlantic.

As on the previous day, the tall, muscular man in the black oilskin mackintosh and blue knitted cap was leaning against the counter beside him, gazing indifferently into space and poking at a back tooth with his tongue. Jaquemar turned away, brooding on his problem; as he walked off, his dainty step grew firmer, and when he had come out into the square he stopped and, with fists clenched, looked with unseeing eyes out to sea, where the figure with the palm frond stood attentively in the splashing water.

Someone cleared his throat close behind him; he whipped around. "Dieudonné," said the man in the oilskin mackintosh, who must have soundlessly followed him, for Jaquemar had heard nothing; but there he stood, with both hands in his overcoat pockets. "What do you want?" Jaquemar asked in irritation. "I'm Dieudonné," replied the man with a smile, "captain of the *Orphée*. You're looking for a passage." "Yes!" cried Jaquemar, and in his eagerness seized the man's forearm. "Yes . . . ?" "My ship is full," Dieudonné replied unhelpfully. "The shipping company won't be able to find a berth for you." Jaquemar let go of his arm. "What can you do for me?" he asked straight out. Dieudonné slowly turned his head and looked calmly and carefully behind him, then he turned back to Jaquemar with his smile and said: "I'm the skipper. On board *I* give the orders." Jaquemar scrutinized his face through puckered lids. "Well, you know how it is," commented Dieudonné, and gnawed for a while at his upper lip with the red toothbrush moustache. "One good turn deserves another, and one hand washes the other—that's an old saying."

The young man suddenly understood. He reached for the pocketbook in his jacket, but the captain immediately drew out his great red-haired hand and checked him. "No!" he whispered, without moving his lips. "Not here. Later!" "Five hundred francs," Jaquemar whispered back, looking straight into the other man's eyes. Captain Dieudonné jerked his head toward the café. "I'll wait for you. Pack your stuff and tell the old cow at the Corbeau to have it taken aboard the *Orphée*, but make it snappy." Without smiling, he winked at Jaquemar and set off toward the café, both hands in his pockets; he had a springy, easy walk that bespoke great self-confidence.

Jaquemar hurried into the hotel. As every time he had passed through, the big-bosomed, sickly-looking woman with the taffeta ribbon on her pince-nez was sitting at the rough wooden table in front of the pigeonholes for post and keys, scribbling with bony fingers in her thick book. "My bill!" said Jaquemar. She nodded, looked into the book, and muttered as though to herself: "One room with view of the sea . . ." ". . . and of the angel with the fly swatter!" added Jaquemar with a laugh, and continued in a matter-of-fact tone: "Be ready to have my little bit of luggage taken across to the *Orphée*." He bent down to her and inquired confidentially: "The Carapins, tell me . . . which ship are the Carapins sailing on?" The woman stuck out her chin. "We are not in the habit of divulging information of that kind in this hotel, Monsieur," she answered loudly and tartly. "Which ship could they be sailing on, you goose?" retorted Jaquemar drily, and he was amazed to see how badly the woman squinted. "There's only one!"

Then he noticed that her squinting eyes were not looking at him at all, but past him into the little entrance hall, which was really only the wide end of a passage. He glanced around. In a shabby red-silk armchair, under a shaky wooden stand bearing a dusty potted plant and surrounded by a great many trunks, bags, and hatboxes, sat Gabrielle Bompard. She was wearing a smart traveling costume, and her feet with their powerful ankles were shod in high laced boots of white leather; one leg was crossed over the other and she was moving her free foot to and fro laughing with head thrown back from under the veil that covered her face down to the tip of her nose. Jaquemar's expression turned sullen and heavy with contempt; he straightened up, walked through the hall with a rather stiff, self-contained step like an army officer's, and mounted the stairs, now almost at a run.

When he reached the first-floor landing he saw someone coming toward him: a gentleman with curly hair streaked with gray and vivaciously sparkling black eyes. At this moment, however, the stranger stopped in front of a tarnished mirror in a flaking gilt frame that was hanging on the wall and examined himself, not without satisfaction, while he put on his hat with some ceremony, pulling it down over his forehead and tilting it slightly to one side at a becoming angle. He suddenly looked back, clapped his beringed hands gracefully but distinctly and cried: "Come along, my friend, hurry up! Madame doesn't like to be kept waiting!" Thereupon the shiny black back of the hotel porter's waistcoat appeared in the doorway of the room next to Jaquemar's; then the green-aproned porter emerged carrying one end of a heavy trunk, which swayed out through the doorway, carried at the other end by a second panting porter.

Jaquemar caught his breath. "Gouffé's trunk!" he thought, and stood as though paralyzed while the ill-omened transport passed him. The dandified stranger had long since disappeared without noticing him by the time he walked hesitantly on down the corridor, passed his room, and came to a stop outside the open door of room 14, which was in the state of desolate untidiness that follows a departure. The white curtains were drawn across the windows, the colorless room had a sickly, stale, even slightly rancid smell. As though drawn in by a magic spell, Jaquemar advanced into the room with constrained steps, walked past the foot of the tumbled bed, completely at a loss as to why he did so—until with his face turned to one side he noticed that something pink, diaphanous, and alluring was peeping out from under the pillow. He stepped quickly over to it and pulled it out: it was an intimate garment, a pair of knickers of the finest muslin that could be crumpled up inside a clenched fist. He wiped the back of his hand across his lips, crushed the undergarment in a fist that was trembling with rage, and then mastered his feelings as a fresh thought struck him. "Thanks for the greeting, Madame!" he said in an undertone, and thrust the ball of muslin into his trouser pocket and quickly left the room.

Jaquemar had to walk a considerable distance beside the comfortably striding Dieudonné through the almost empty streets of the bleak little town and into the harbor, which lay inland and in fact seemed to be the only thing in this dismal coastal settlement that did not belong to the sea. It appeared beneath the gray, drizzling sky in the shape of a vast, hilly fallow field of yellow clay, and only after climbing an eminence with shoes sticking in the mud could Jaquemar see a few stretches of milky water here and there, which sank out of sight again as he descended, so that even the distant Orphée, whose thin black funnel was sending up a thread of brownish smoke, looked as if it were stuck fast in the mud. There was indeed a customhouse; but it had gaping and for the most part broken windowpanes, and there was no customs officer to be seen anywhere around; there were also a few dredgers, but they were leaning inactive against the edge of deep mud pits; and at one moment Jaquemar saw in the background a cab driving slowly away from the Orphée with the cabby slumped on the box.

Jaquemar pointed with his chin. "That must be the Carapins," he remarked half questioningly, adding rather angrily, because his companion did not reply: "Monsieur and Madame Carapin are your passengers, aren't they?" "Don't know," replied Dieudonné unperturbed. "I don't know the people by name." Furious, Jaquemar (who was also put out by the hard, compact appearance of the man's skull in his blue knitted cap) said: "When you gave me the order just now to have my baggage taken on board . . . whom were you referring to with your 'make it snappy'? Me, or the woman in the hotel?" The captain glanced at him sideways with a little laugh. "Oh, the woman in the hotel, of course, the woman in the hotel," he answered. "Yes, and suppose we settle our little bit of business, eh? The sooner we start, the sooner we'll finish."

They stood still in the mud and the drizzling rain. Dieudonné, with both hands in his overcoat pockets, watched the young man take the money from his wallet. He withdrew his hands from his pockets and took the notes, licked his thumb, and counted them carefully. "Correct, thank you," he said, pulled up his overcoat, slipped the money into his trouser pocket, and moved off again. "Carapin?" he continued, after they had been walking for some time, now in a friendly tone. "No, never heard the name."

Looking almost like a buoy, the Orphée lay deeply embedded in a hummock of sludge. She was short, massive, in fact her hull was almost round, and she had a disproportionately high superstructure, comprising three or four decks, out of which the smoking, narrow funnel projected like a stovepipe. The silence surrounding the ship and the smoke rising from the funnel created the impression that they were just waiting for the captain. In rows, one above the other, idle passengers were leaning with their elbows on the rails watching the new arrivals, shadowed by the deck above them and pale in the dull light of this rainy day reflected from the yellow mud. Walking ahead of Jaquemar, his hands in his pockets, Dieudonné strode with his easy, long-legged gait up the ribbed gangplank with the rope handrail on either side into the interior of the ship.

No sooner was he inside, where it was dark, than Jaquemar heard a burring signal bell ring somewhere in the engine room, which he saw gaping beside him through a doorlike opening in the black iron wall as he walked past. No doubt this bell that rang out dully and impatiently through the hiss of steam and the sound of coal being shoveled up and thrown into the boilers was a sign that the vessel was ready to put to sea. Meanwhile, he was led through oily, fusty, and otherwise evil-smelling gangways, past galleys and narrow messrooms with empty benches and tables, up stairways, and finally up a steep iron ladder to the top deck. Here stood the bridge with the steering wheel, the ship's bell, and tackle racks still covered with tarpaulins. The bridge extended on either side slightly beyond the edge of the deck itself, the whole central section of which was occupied by a poop of brown wood. This contained, in the forepart, the chartroom and the captain's living quarters, and at the rear Jaquemar's cabin, the doors of which were open and hooked back against the outer wall, a spacious room with thinly barred square windows instead of portholes, which let in plenty of light; it was a modest but pleasant room, apart from the fact that it was pervaded by an acrid smell of strong disinfectant.

To his astonishment, Jaquemar found that his bag had already been delivered; it lay on the narrow bunk. As he entered Jaquemar could see through the window above it far out across the muddy expanse of the harbor, over the town crouching on the land and out to the sea in which the angel with the palm frond stood close to the shore, like a watchman forever at his post ready to deal with the element which might occasionally require disciplining, but which at the moment was merely bobbing up and down and splashing a little. Over the sea the drizzle was falling, denser and paler than on land, but still gray on gray—a dismal sight, which the spectator could equally well turn away from or plunge himself into, according to his taste and frame of mind. Jaquemar turned away.

He unpacked and discovered that most of the numerous drawers in

his cabin were locked. He climbed down the iron ladder and wandered
around the ship; he hunted through companionways, strolled along
decks, and peered into public rooms; there were passengers everywhere, sauntering or scurrying about in the state of aimless excitement
usual when a ship puts to sea, though fewer than he had thought
when he saw them from the land standing in rows along the decks;
but there was not a trace of the notorious beauty he was looking for,
nor of Carapin, her companion. It was perhaps not surprising that he
allowed this to put him in an ill-humor, but the way in which this
ill-humor showed itself was sheer stupidity: he took an immediate
dislike to all his fellow passengers, from whose company he now
anticipated not the slightest pleasure; he considered them petty,
bourgeois, dull, colorless people, insignificant individuals, not fit
society for him, Jaquemar—he would leave them to the company of
one another! Just at this moment the ship began to shake from stem
to stern, evidently as a result of the effort of hooting, if that word
could be applied to the sound it was making: a watery hissing and
whistling that gradually turned into a doleful, long-drawn-out drone.
And now Jaquemar also noticed that the engine had started up with a
beautifully muted thudding.

Savoring the noise and vibration, he stood with bowed head outside
a dimly-lit room of medium size whose side walls were lined with
plush benches and small tables and which a brass plate by Jaquemar's
head proclaimed to be the "Smoking Room and Bar." Jaquemar could
also discern the bar, an insignificant little counter to the left against
the rear wall; lost in thought, he strolled across to it and ordered a
pernod, his habitual and favorite poison, from the steward, who had
suddenly popped up from behind the counter as though out of a trap
door on the stage, and now pushed across to him a whole bottle
together with a blue siphon and a glass. Holding the glass with the
milky green fluid in his left hand, he turned toward the window on
his right elbow and saw directly in his line of vision the low yellow
hillocks in the thin rain, through which they were slowly plowing
their way with a low thudding and grinding. Drinking to himself, he
raised his glass of pernod and murmured: "*Bon voyage,* Jaquemar, and
good hunting!"

The following morning, a day full of sunshine, no further sense of
the land remained. The open sea stretched to the horizon, rocking

gaily and peacefully and taking an unexpectedly vigorous grip on the keel, so that the *Orphée*, utterly alone in the measureless expanse of water, was caught up in a rolling motion. The thudding and grinding of the engine had given place to a kind of roaring or blowing, and even this was fainter than the whistling high overhead in the empty shrouds of the two masts. It was a beautiful voyage, with dolphins as an escort and the smoke from the funnels curving into short, brown, decorative feathers on the blue of the waves.

This, then, was for a time Jaquemar's world, a world in which he had no sense of destiny, especially as he felt himself lulled into a condition of mild intoxication by the perpetual pitching and rolling; but this intoxication, like the most lucid soberness, seemed to render him clairvoyant. He was no longer troubled by disappointment over the fact that Gabrielle Bompard had fooled and eluded him . . . for how long? He was far too determined for her to stand any chance of escaping for good! At mealtimes he treated his obnoxious fellow passengers, of whom there were some forty or fifty, as flies or rather noisy shadows, they meant no more to him than that; and apart from a daily chat over cocktails with a gray-haired lady in the smoking room, where she was always sitting, he kept to himself. The aft section of the bridge deck, on which his cabin opened, was very rarely visited by anyone else; he would sit dreaming in his deck chair, occasionally hearing in the distance the ship's bell, a melancholy admonition that rather amused him: did they hope in this way to divide up or measure eternity? Vanity and illusion! Eternity stood still, no clock knew its duration, even though its hands followed one another sagaciously around in an everlasting circle.

Jaquemar no longer had any trace of fever, and the only thing that betrayed a certain residue of hypersensitivity was the fact that he allowed two unimportant details to annoy him. The first was the smell of disinfectant in his cabin, of which not a grain or a breath escaped through the open door—which now remained open even at night. This acrid vapor stood so dense and solid in the confined space that Jaquemar gradually gained the impression that it would stand there in a block even if the four walls were suddenly drawn up into the air. Captain Dieudonné, to whom he could have complained, was almost impossible to get hold of. He was either on duty on the bridge, or he lay on the side bench in the smoking room, one leg pulled up at a right angle, the other resting with the foot on the floor in readiness to jump up, and slept, insofar as one can describe as sleep a state from which he darted like a trout at the slightest unfamiliar sound in the ship's hull and hurried off to see what was wrong.

The second source of annoyance was if anything even less important. After the third day out, two enormous carcasses hung to left and right on the corners of the wheelhouse on the bridge deck, oxen suspended on silver hooks, red and blue and with bones and ribs that shimmered gray through the flesh, the four stumps of the legs sticking out into space and an empty circle where head and neck had once been. Jaquemar could not avoid passing them; the sight of them revolted him and took his appetite away more and more every day, particularly since the progressive diminution in the size of the carcasses served as an indication of the hunger and consumption of the useless party of travelers, and also because it was impossible to overlook the extent to which the meat was growing continually harder and blacker.

One day Jaquemar was seized with positive rage about these carcasses; the captain happened to be leaning over the rail of the bridge with his feet crossed behind him just at that moment; the young man —disregarding the fact that access to the bridge was forbidden—approached him angrily and cried: "Monsieur Dieudonné, does that carcass have to dangle there like that! It's enough to make one sick!" Dieudonné slowly turned his head in the taut knitted cap toward him. "Well, well," he said calmly, allowing an unpleasant grin to appear at one corner of the mouth in his leathery, white, weather-beaten face, "are you that squeamish? Have you joined the vegetarians?" "And the stink in my room!" continued Jaquemar. "It's unbearable!" "There's nothing more wholesome in the world," replied Dieudonné cheerfully. "I rig you up a private nursing home on the cheap—you'd have been glad of a place in the coal bunker—and now . . . These landlubbers, they're never satisfied." He shook his head, turned it to the front again, and continued to stare straight before him; he had not shifted his comfortable position.

The days passed and so did the nights—who could say how many there were and whether they went quickly or slowly? For what is time, when we are in an apparently limitless expanse without signposts and are not visibly moving forward, the situation in which Jaquemar found himself, what does time mean to us? It no longer counts, and all in all, apart from the carcasses and the reek of disinfectant, this time that did not count was lovely. Since he had once ventured onto it in defiance of official orders, Jaquemar now visited the bridge quite frequently, particularly at night. He was always ready with the excuse that he could not sleep because of the stench in his room. But perhaps the blue knitted cap Captain Dieudonné wore around his leathery white face and pulled down over his ears made him deaf; leaning negligently against the rail, he did not notice his visitor and never spoke to him.

Jaquemar stood unperturbed at the end of the bridge with both hands on the rails, looking gravely out into space. More mysterious than the foam gliding away on either side of the ship was the spray plowed up by the bows, into which the *Orphée* plunged with an appearance of self-surrender in her smoke-belching onward thrust and a creaking of timber sounding through her round hull, only to rise out of it again with a slight twist and a dripping nose. The young man enjoyed this, as when the night was clear and still he enjoyed the limitless dull silver mirror of the sea and the black smoke which the *Orphée* released with a low, regular puffing from her stovepipe funnel and trailed out behind her like long mourning weepers. But more beautiful than all else in Jaquemar's eyes was the shimmer of moonlight that brought a glow to the card of the compass on the bridge.

One morning Jaquemar emerged from his cabin; he had already packed and here outside there was still dusk, dusk and mist. It was a dense, damp, whitish mist that was trying to swallow up everything, at times even the bow and stern of the ship and even the masts, which then quivered and swelled in the midst of it like ghostly fat shadows, dissolved into nothing and reappeared again. The screeching of the convoy of birds at the stern was ceaselessly audible and sounded like ill-tempered quarreling. But the *Orphée* churned her way forward at quarter-speed with unerring caution and frequent blowing of the siren, barely raising a bow wave in the exceptionally calm, milky-blue water that occasionally became visible through the mist and glowed with a dull-red reflected light.

Jaquemar went up on the bridge. The man at the wheel was a specter, and so was Dieudonné, who, as usual, was leaning on the rail, his feet crossed behind him, his head covered by the taut woolen cap.

In front of them, at some height, there was now a hint of sky, and the red glow of the rising sun sank into it as though into blood-soaked cottonwool, producing a pale incandescent nucleus in the center and jagged edges, which gradually spread. Jaquemar too now leaned on the rail, not far from the captain; but he was looking overhead and a feeling of nostalgic melancholy began to invade him. "Beautiful," slipped from his lips—he didn't know why. "Yes, beautiful," responded Dieudonné expansively, and slowly turned his leathery white face toward him. "I suppose you know the old saying?

> "Red sun at night—
> Sailor's delight.
> Red sun in the morning—
> Sailor, take warning."

All of a sudden the scene broke into movement. There was a rending noise like torn metal, the ringing of a bell in the interior of the ship, the shouting of orders, and Dieudonné was gone. Out of the swirling white mist on the starboard bow loomed a shadow that gradually emerged as the bows, funnel, and tilted mast of a sturdy little pilot cutter.

The *Orphée* was soon chugging ahead again. She changed course and the water splashed and gurgled softly. The sky overhead grew lighter, patches of blue appeared from time to time as though through thin, swirling steam, and now they were out in the open. The calm, bluish water stretched out in front of them, shimmering gently. On the starboard bow it was limited by a thick white cloud that seemed to have been piled up on the water with a shovel; it lay there motionless, apart from a delighted flickering at the top, and all of a sudden shapes appeared to Jaquemar's eyes out of this quivering haze. They lit up as though by magic: roofs, tall buildings, church towers, some dome or other; all of them floated flower-hued and shell-gray without foundations above the bank of mist, towering out of it as though out of snow, a fata morgana, aglow from within, alluring, more beautiful than anything real could possibly be.

2

AMERICA. FIRST STOP:
SARATOGA SPRINGS

Behind Jaquemar lay "the largest natural harbor in the world," with New York towering pink and shimmering on the right and New Jersey's steep clay shore topped by a scurfy-looking rim of scrub on the left. Most remarkable of all to Jaquemar had been the Hudson ferryboats, paddle steamers equally rounded fore and aft that glided along, leaving a double track from their paddle wheels, like giant water boatmen and with their two thin funnels side by side conjured up Mississippi boats, jungle rivers, tangled lianas, and other romantic visions of the tropics. The train journey up the Hudson also nearly lay behind him. The brown curtains were tapping with their rings and flapping against the open windows; every now and then streamers of smoke and a whirl of black soot poured in through them; the hurried puffing and panting of the engine were ceaselessly audible from out in front, along with its frequent shrill hooting that echoed in the narrow river valley like cries of anguish and lament, a sound that a transoceanic liner might have been expected to make, but not a railway engine.

In the long carriage without compartments the air was hot and dusty, and the light, because of the ravines through which they were passing, traversed by shadow. Passengers on the seats were sleeping with their feet on the seat opposite and their hats on their heads. They carried their tickets stuck in their hatbands, from which the ticket inspector took them without a word, punched them, and imperturbably replaced them without a movement from the sleeping passengers—that is to say, without a voluntary movement, for the screeching train shook violently as it tore through the winding gorges, and rocked and swayed the sleepers so that their heads were bounced to and fro as though on rubber necks and their upright boots on the opposite seat were twisted from side to side, both of which made a pitiful impression on our young traveler. A wagonload of corpses! thought Jaquemar.

At midday the train reached Poughkeepsie, and it was afternoon when with shrill cries and the clanging of bells it steamed into Saratoga Springs. And this, in spite of the town's worldwide renown, must have been an important event; for the engine's exhausted puffing and blowing and its continual clanging mingled with that of another bell that rang in the little timber turret of the wooden station building, excitedly and incessantly, as though fire had broken out.

The platform ran out, at the same level and without railing or step, into the square that fronted and flanked the station, and here, alongside the rows of servants and porters, a crowd of idlers had gathered —men, girls, women, a multitude of children, and even babes in arms with their fingers in their mouths, all of them watching the arrival of the visitors with intense and staring curiosity. The background was formed by hoof-scraping, mane-shaking horses and the multifarious vehicles to which they were harnessed: cabs, phaetons, dogcarts, tandems, and in among these the heavier shapes of the red and yellow shuttle buses of the big hotels—United States, Clarendon, Peace of the Elms, and all the rest of them. And while lightfooted gentlemen jumped out of the railway carriages to assist their ladies, who clambered down the steps with great to-do in their ankle-length skirts and bustles, carrying umbrellas, reticules, and hatboxes on their arms gloved to the elbow—while all this was going on, Jaquemar had already strode across the square, forced a passage through the sightseers, who gaped on undisturbed, and climbed into the Grand Union Hotel omnibus.

A quarter of an hour later, when a few more guests had climbed in, they moved off, left the puffing and clanging behind them, and drove at a leisurely pace through a pleasant district of detached suburban houses. These houses, some of them built of brick with stained-glass windows, oriel towers, and antiquated woodcarvings on the verandahs and roofs, others painted white with wooden pillars in the Doric style under broad, pointed gables, stood snugly ensconced in the leafy shade of small gardens or looked down from the heights of close-cropped undulating lawns, which shimmered a fresh, juicy green, although everything was enveloped in a heat haze that seemed to be clinging to the crowns of the mighty elms in the visible, tangible shape of a gauzy fabric woven of mist. It was a well-kept, elegant neighborhood; and an old lady walking sedately along, followed by a liveried Negro servant, half a pace behind and bent respectfully forward as he held a parasol over her face and hat, fitted into the picture beautifully.

They soon turned into the central district of shops and hotels and finally into the main street, the Broadway of Saratoga Springs. It was modeled on the Paris boulevards. The towering house-fronts displayed the same high, narrow windows flanked by wooden shutters and preceded by tiny balconies with low balustrades; the lanterns, like giant plants with dangling blossoms, bent their white domes high above the sidewalk, and even the circular iron railings around the elms—whose foliage was here more meager, however—were not missing. What was missing was the life; for it was the hour of the afternoon nap, and the street looked deserted, all the more so because of the dreary appearance and enormous dimensions of the hotels, especially the Grand Union, which was a positively colossal building—disproportionately huge, impressive but grotesque.

It was actually shaped like a horseshoe, with three wings of equal length enclosing a garden forecourt, but what was visible, the façade facing Broadway—gray with countless black window frames—stretched from one side street to the next, with a rather higher, square central section on the roof of which stood a short, thick flagpole with no flag. Broad stone steps led up to the entresol of this central section, and to the right and left of the ornate entrance an open terrace, the so-called piazza, extended along the whole length of the building, bordered by boxes of flowering petunias and geraniums and set with three rows of green-painted rocking chairs in which a whole crowd of people were swaying to and fro in silence and as though keeping time. The picture was rendered still more fantastic by the singular columns that ornamented or framed it, the enormously long, yet barely nine-inch-thick, iron pillars that rose from this piazza to the floor level of the fourth or fifth story and, in spite of their gaunt and spindly shape, cast a certain amount of cool shade on the gray-black surface of the wall; they did not carry a roof, but merged up above with cast-iron creepers, and were therefore nothing but a decorative scaffolding intended to break the monotony of the vast façade.

When the omnibus stopped and Jaquemar climbed the entrance steps with his few fellow passengers, the universal rocking to and fro on the piazza came to a halt. All eyes followed the new arrivals, full of unbelieving astonishment, until they had vanished into the hall, whereupon the rocking began again, as though agreeably resumed after a brief attack of paralysis. Oh, what a picture of peace! Perhaps it was the orderly rows in which the multitudinous gathering was arranged, perhaps its silence and the uniform rhythm of its uninterrupted movement—it looked as though, unless frightened to a stop by some fresh disturbance, it could continue unchecked through all eternity.

In the hall Jaquemar allowed his fellow arrivals to precede him and gazed for a while into the spacious lounge to the right. The floor was covered by a thick red carpet and the ceiling was of gilded stucco; this, combined with the fact that the velvet door curtains were three-quarters drawn, produced an atmosphere of blood-red, bronze-brown gloom and snugly alluring plushy warmth in which the milky glass of the many-branched chandeliers shimmered palely, like the clusters of bleached skulls in a headhunters' kraal. The rows of yellow-silk chairs and sofas around the walls had their counterpart in an excessively long seat with the same upholstery extending along the center; people sitting on it would be back to back, separated by a shoulder-high ebony panel, and faced by long, low ebony tables with liver-colored marble tops on which silver containers for iced water flashed. But there was no one sitting on it.

Indoor plants with leaves the shape of paws, and enormous showy vases, whose gilt ornamentation glittered dully, stood about in lonely state; the repeated warning "For Ladies Only" in indecently ostentatious lacquer letters hung to no purpose on the Japanese folding screen concealing a door in the corner of the room. And the gigantic Venus in the mural painting that occupied the whole of the wall facing the entrance smiled into the empty gloom, her chin resting with a look of expectancy on her hand and bare forearm; painted with mannered smoothness in misconstrued imitation of the antique, the Cyclopean beauty lay back on the cushions of a marble ottoman, a comb in her coquettishly lifted golden hair, her body naked and pink but with a cloudy veil draped for decency's sake around hips and abdomen and her opulent breasts encircled by a garland of roses, staring with a smile in her azure cow's eyes into the silent dusk, in which only a muffled shout or the sound of moving carriages occasionally echoed from Broadway.

Jaquemar crossed the hall and found the chief receptionist no longer occupied. He was a melancholy, liverish individual with black rings under his black eyes and heavy lids that seemed unwilling to open, and did so only to reveal eyes in which sadness and disgust with life were mingled. Yes, yes, the Carapins were occupying an apartment on the third floor, and there was a "nice" room free on the same floor, though not in the same wing, with a view of Broadway and at an exorbitant price which the dejected receptionist named laconically.

A liveried Negro boy carried Jaquemar's bag and conducted him to the elevator, which moved upward with an oily crinkling and crackling in the barred shaft, a soaring cage. The bleakness of the endlessly long corridors above was in positively offensive contrast to the sumptuousness of the public rooms below. They were not even carpeted and were furnished on the walls with thick, white-painted, perforated pipes, and on the ceilings with a series of drum-shaped, perforated lids, all of which were parts of an extensive sprinkler system for fire extinction, which had obviously been given priority at the expense of any other luxury. Jaquemar's room was equally wretched, more of a cell than a room, in fact, and not even separated by a curtain from the cavelike little bathroom with the tiny bathtub. It contained an iron bedstead, spittoon, wooden chair, a single armchair with a shabby, torn cover by the window, and on the wall beside it, suspended from an iron hook, a coil of thick rope bearing a cardboard notice with the words "Fire Escape" painted on it—fire, it seemed, was an obsession at Saratoga Springs.

In this little room then, the young man installed himself. The fact that in spite of the drawn curtains it was filled with the broiling afternoon heat and all in all was thoroughly wretched upset him little; for a tremendous, fierce joy had run through him when the melancholy receptionist below confirmed the Carapins' presence in the hotel. Whatever the place was like, for him it was the right one, he was where he wished to be, and he ground his teeth with pleasure at the thought of what lay in store for Gabrielle Bompard! And in the early evening of that same day he caught sight of her.

The square at this time of day was empty. Jaquemar sat down in the front row, in the rocking chair in the corner formed by the balustrade, which stood on top of a deep wall and separated the terrace from the entrance steps and the street in front. As though from a grandstand, he looked out over Broadway, with its few pedestrians and carriages, and toward the billowing greenery of bushes and trees which the spa park introduced into the urban scene. Paths and gravel drives opened out underneath the foliage and ran out into Broadway like shady little rivers and canals.

On one of these something fiery white suddenly glowed in the dusk of early evening, a pair of white horses drawing an exceptionally light vehicle with only two very high wheels, whose thin metal spokes flashed blue and made a thin, needly, crackling sound, like the works of a watch, as it sped across to the other side of the street.

Jaquemar, who had unthinkingly been rocking himself to and fro, kept still; the white-clad gentleman holding the white reins of the little carriage on the other side of the street was the dandy from the Hôtel Corbeau, in other words Carapin, and beside him sat Bompard, also in white and wearing a top hat of white felt, under the brim of which her long blue-black curls blazed out and backward like flames. The modish vehicle, generally known as a spider phaeton, was no sooner sighted than past; but after a few minutes it returned, this time on Jaquemar's side of the street, and came to a stop directly under Jaquemar's grandstand. The thoroughbred horses tossed their heads, snorted, and pawed the ground. Carapin laughed, but Bompard shrugged her shoulders and commented sulkily: "I don't know what the hurry is." She clambered down to the street before Carapin's astonished eyes. "Gabrielle," he stammered, "Gabrielle . . ."

She was deaf; and she did not see Jaquemar, who felt his heart throbbing in his throat and watched as she mounted the stone steps, lifting the skirt of her white costume, her clown's brows as agonized as ever, and around her cheeks, kissable mouth, and little tiger's nose the everlasting smile which, as he knew, meant nothing, but was merely an illusion and enticement, an imposture of the flesh and totally unconnected with her pitiless heart.

How radiantly beautiful she was, and how he hated her! Hated her also for having walked past him and up the steps and disappeared into the hall without noticing him. Poor Carapin! he thought, as his eyes strayed back to the latter. What will she make of you! And sure enough, as he sat there in the little carriage with his curly head bare, staring despondently into space in spite of his innate vivacity, he seemed to have grown grayer and older even in the short period since their last meeting in the Hôtel Corbeau. Clicking his tongue faintly, he shook the reins and drove slowly away.

The Carapins did not put in an appearance at dinner. This was taken in a room like a hall, and consisted of a long series of equally insipid, milky dishes that were further spoiled by the seasoning, since the salt had a smell of rusty iron and a medicinal taste of iodine that offended nose and palate; perhaps this was why Jaquemar noticed the people around him drinking astonishing quantities of iced water from glasses that were perpetually refilled. Before the end of the meal, and unobserved by anyone, he left the dining room, rose up in the soaring cage to his little room, and went to bed.

Early the next morning, while the light was still feathered with pink but the warmth of day already quite considerable, Jaquemar went for a stroll in the park, which he found to be extensive and pleasant, in some parts laid out like a garden, in others left in its natural state, with wooded hillocks, hedged paths, well-kept flowerbeds and plashing fountains, but at this hour of the day totally deserted. Pieces of sculpture shimmered among the bushes—fauns and nymphs grinning into the greenery. They looked as though they were naughty versions of Philemon and Baucis who had been turned into stone instead of trees on account of their dissolute amatory enjoyments; for their heads, curly-haired and horned or with greedy-looking mouths and snub noses, were intact, whereas their bodies immediately below the chest narrowed into stelae around which, at the point where their sex had been, they folded their hands, which were also left to them. This image of sexuality magically conjured away was apparently much esteemed in Saratoga. It peeped and smiled in a kind of perplexed self-satisfaction from among bushes and foliage, and even stood out in the open, insignificantly naked, in thwarted recklessness. In a powerfully scented grove of jasmine there was a granite pool, and at the narrow end of the pool, like mirrored reflections, stood the same faun stelae, but with conch horns to their mouths, each blowing water into the lined and grinning face of the other, whence it flowed and rained with a splash into the pool below.

Here, because the moving wetness breathed a touch of cool into the scented warmth, Jaquemar sat down on a little marble bench. For in spite of his fathoms-deep sleep during the night he was tired, and he pricked up his ears as though suddenly waking when the sound of a potpourri of popular songs and operatic music played with a wealth of sentimentality reached him.

He rose and set off in the direction of the sound. Now there were already a few scattered walkers on the paths, and further on people were strolling around the circular court ringing a pumproom with stained-glass windows, and tables and chairs outside; they were all carrying beakers that had been dipped into the spring on the end of a long pipe and filled with its healing waters. The movement of the strollers, as they circled to the sickly-sweet tones of the orchestra dressed in white jackets and playing their instruments in a pavilion higher up on the grassy hillside, seemed enchanted in its charming aimlessness, and only the approach of a new group of guests brought life or something like startled attention into the dreamy round dance.

Once more, as yesterday, Jaquemar felt the same wild joy run through him, together with a feeling of repugnance that hung around his lips in the shape of a contemptuous smile. Of course, he had been expecting it—who else but *She!*

This morning she was wearing a small round straw hat on the flickering enamel-blue of her curly hair, a simple little silk blouse, and a long black skirt held with a black patent-leather belt, like a boarding-school girl. She was smiling in imperturbable innocence with her clown's brows and beaming eyes into the early-morning brightness of the warm summer's morning, while Carapin—no question now of dejection—chattered at her side, laughing and gesticulating with his beringed juggler's hands. But it was altogether an animated group that surrounded her, a pack of young and older men obviously of varying social status: a lanky red-haired fellow who crowed and croaked in a high-pitched eunuch's voice; a hefty chap, with bushy eyebrows, smoking a pipe and giving vent to jolly bass laughter that came from the heart; a refined, somewhat clerically garbed gentleman with gray hair smoothed down with water and a rosy, boyish face; and a few others, among whom one in particular caught Jaquemar's attention, a very grave, bony young man with deep vertical lines in his face, a wide torn-looking mouth, and altogether of a touchingly beautiful ugliness that it was for the moment impossible to define more exactly. He followed the pack at a slight distance, as though hesitantly, and yet inseparably bound to it. It was he who went with quiet but long strides to the pumphouse and fetched the center of this throng her silver beaker of medicinal water, just as Jaquemar, squinting straight ahead, half barred her path—which she, however, did not notice, as at that moment she took the beaker with a polite, boyish little bow and gave her thanks with beaming eyes and yet not looking at anyone in particular: "It's very sweet of you. Anyone can see that you look after me."

Jaquemar had left the group behind him as, keenly watched by the other visitors to the spa, it vanished with talk and laughter in the depths of the park. He couldn't very well run after her, so he made his way grim-faced back to the pool with the spitting fauns' heads, there to sit down on the little marble bench in the cool, jasmine-scented air in a state of incomprehension that he could not understand, because it lay on his heart like a mild attack of cramp. The impudent woman's failure to recognize him annoyed—indeed, offended—him, just as though, either by chance or by design, she were scorning some prearranged engagement.

But it was by design. In the evening after dinner, at which she had once more not appeared, Jaquemar returned to the park on an aimless search. Here darkness, solitude, and a myriad-toned but voiceless insect concert reigned, a concert that was simply part and parcel of the warm night air, a ceaseless chirruping, sawing, croaking, grating, and drumming. The flowers had grown colorless and the fountains fallen silent, the paths were untrodden, and the bushes and trees were huge masses of foliage that stood there mutely imploring, and only here and there dully lit by the reflection from a lamp globe. On a low hillock Jaquemar discerned an old-fashioned villa with a narrow, though double-winged front door, in whose frosted-glass panes engraved stars glittered like real frost, and windows that were pitch-black.

Nevertheless, he mounted the rotten wooden steps to the veranda, after a moment's hesitation opened the door, and found inside a Negro servant in a tail coat and silk knee breeches snoring loudly on his chair. Jaquemar sauntered through the rooms; the walls were covered with age-darkened leather hangings and the floors with thick, colorless carpets, the curtains over windows and doors were of heavy velvet, and black and white enamel spittoons stood about all over the floor. On some of the many leather armchairs men sprawled rather than sat, their feet on stools in front of them, their shoulders pushed up, staring blankly into space.

There was no conversation, nothing but the almost inaudible ticking of a clock broke the silence, and Jaquemar was on the point of leaving this Catalaunian spot when the noise of new arrivals came in through the door and drew nearer, a gay and eager uproar of male voices in which the eunuch's crowing and croaking and Carapin's tartly commanding tones were soon distinguishable.

Now they appeared in the room, the same group as in the morning with the addition of an old man who towered above them all with a fiery red face, pale eyes, and snow-white hair that fell in beautiful waves over his small ears. He walked along with head bent, looking in front of him from under his lowered brows and stepping softly, as though the fragile length of his legs compelled him to walk with care, waving his hands about and whispering down from his great height to the bushy-browed pipe-smoker, who smiled knowingly, although he could not possibly have understood the whisper from above. They were in dress clothes, the gesticulating Carapin with pearls in his stiff shirt front and the ribbon of an order in his black silk lapel, and only the beautifully ugly youth with the torn mouth and pensive eyes, who followed slightly behind the others as in the park, was wearing crumpled trousers and an old-fashioned swallow-tailed coat with very short sleeves that did not cover his wrists and a threadbare black tie on his soft white shirt, the sloppy fit of which gave him the appearance of a country lawyer's clerk.

What so gripped Jaquemar that he sat motionless in his chair by the wall as though paralyzed was the costume in which Gabrielle Bompard, who incidentally was shorter than anyone in her entourage, rustled along in the midst of this throng of vassals. No doubt about it, in this country she was a great lady and moved with regal self-

confidence in her evening dress of plain red taffeta, which was embellished with flashing diamonds on the huge red bow over her bosom and
had a train overlaid with diaphanous black lace. Under the shadow
of this lacy web the train was iridescent in the light and so long that
the whole figure, topped by the thrown-back curly head and smiling
face, described a curve bent vigorously back on itself, like a scorpion
in attack.

Notwithstanding her smile, she was in fact really angry and demonstratively sought to disregard the Negro servant, who, probably because
ladies were not admitted here, ran protesting after the cortège, until
the whispering old man stopped him and he allowed himself, with
gradually slackening gestures of desperation in the direction of the
party that continued on its way, to be partially pacified. The old man
whispered gravely down to him from on high, fished a coin out of his
waistcoat pocket, and let it disappear into the coal-black hand, whereupon the Negro, though without a word of thanks and with his underlip hanging sulkily, stepped aside and allowed matters to take their
course.

Jaquemar slipped through the closely drawn, heavy door curtains,
immediately behind the old man, into the next room, in which, to his
surprise, people were gambling at a number of tables in complete silence. The gang had already sat down at one of the tables. With clown's
brows and beaming eyes, Bompard was joyfully watching the soundless circling of the roulette wheel, the hopping of the softly tapping
ivory ball, and the actions of the croupier, who, when the wheel
stopped, scraped counters, bank notes, and coins across to himself or
pushed a smaller quantity over to the winners, cold and businesslike,
an official of the unpredictable goddess Fortune.

The youth with the deeply lined cheeks had taken up a position
directly behind Bompard, his head bowed and his underlip protruding; he was standing directly opposite Jaquemar, and all at once
Bompard looked up with her head on one side. She gazed straight
into Jaquemar's face with her imperturbable smile; he started, and
was all the more determined to catch her eye—but quite in vain, it
was like trying to catch and hold a dog's eye and meeting nothing but
glitter and glimmer with no substance behind it. She didn't see him.

"Let's try his luck," she said, stretching her hand out to Carapin,
who was sitting beside her. "I'm putting three thousand dollars on

number 13—for Carapin." "But beloved," he whispered, twisting his head to one side as though his collar had grown too tight for him, "three thousand . . ." But when she made an impatient movement with her fingers, as if paying out money, he drew out his pocketbook with a gulp and handed her three brown notes. Tensely watched by all, the little ball clattered and hopped once more and, after circling around, finally came to rest in the compartment for number 27. Carapin tried to smile, the pipe-smoker remarked with a jolly, bass laugh: "Lucky in love, unlucky at gambling."

But Bompard sat sulking, notwithstanding her smile, like a punished schoolgirl, and growled disappointedly: "He's not lucky." She tilted her head to one side and for the second time gazed unseeingly into Jaquemar's face; she raised her anguished brows a fraction higher and stated with precocious wisdom: "A lesson worth what it cost. He hesitated. Every child knows you must take fortune by the forelock."

Before the blind radiance of her eyes—out of aversion, hate, rage, or whatever it was—Jaquemar staggered a step backward into the darkness. Only the young man standing opposite with the grave face looked at him as he did so with deep, calm, sad eyes. Jaquemar turned abruptly on his heel and left the room—and anyone acquainted with him from the past would have noticed that the daintiness of his gait had given place to a certain stiffness or stubbornness; for he held himself, and strode along, like an army officer in a corset.

Outside in the voiceless, myriad-toned insect concert, he came upon a sight he had never seen before in such splendor and power: the black, tower-shaped shadows of the treetops were alive with the spurting and sparking of fat little jets of fire, of stars now silvery blue, now golden, that flew up in flashing swarms and went out, like those Christmas-tree decorations known as Bengal lights that spit out their spray of stars in every direction except downward as they burn away with a sizzle. As it was repeated from tree to tree, this sparkling and flashing lent the great garden the solemnly festive look of a garden in a fairy tale; and the fact that it was an entirely natural phenomenon, namely the swarming of innumerable fireflies, in no way detracted from the atmosphere of fantasy.

Jaquemar slept badly that night. One of the firefly tribe had wandered by mistake into his cell in the Grand Union and flitted questingly from one corner to another with a brilliant cold blue light and thereby

illumined the darkness of the whole room as though with the flashing
of mysterious signals. Moreover, it was warm within these four walls;
the flat, hard, uneven bed had no bolster, only a planklike, inflexible
little pillow, so that the would-be sleeper lay stretched out like a
corpse, with no possibility of finding a comfortable position; the
drumming, sawing, croaking, the monotonously wordless insistence
of a world that seemed successfully to have silenced the world of men,
poured incessantly in through the window; only the long-drawn wails
of the locomotives, which now rang out more frequently, or at least
more distinctly, than by day, and broke through the unrelenting
pounding of natural sounds as though in bitter distress, only this
hooting like the sirens of ocean liners echoing across the nocturnal
landscape contained a reminder of human existence. But the animal
croaking and throbbing, through which there ran from time to time a
dull vibration, as if the same string were being continuously plucked
without a sound-box, was overwhelmingly powerful and swallowed up
everything. And it seemed to Jaquemar as though the tireless rhythm,
growing more and more repulsive, was beating its way into his skull
and forcing his brain to function in time with it, like the pulse of some
infinitely larger creature that was taking possession of him in this
mysteriously agonizing way, absorbing and digesting him. His temples
were throbbing feverishly; he felt as if he had been reduced to tiny
proportions, as if he were the last remaining speck of human life
abandoned in this monstrous nonhuman realm; he was nothing but an
unanswerable interrogation, a martyred grain of questioning consciousness, and he projected a senseless hatred on the enormous country
that was submitting him, already so sorely tried in spirit, to this
absolutely unendurable trial.

   With daybreak, the firefly's light went out and it settled in the
form of an insignificant beetle somewhere on the faded wallpaper.
The drumming had ceased, and a threadbare, violet shimmer gleamed
through the window. Jaquemar lay on his uncomfortable bed with
open eyes; being tucked tightly in under the mattress at the foot and
sides of the bed, the wafer-thin blanket molded his body in every
detail, making it look exactly like a youthful corpse; it held his feet
fast and left him little freedom of movement. Yet he did feel free after
successfully enduring the trial of the night that lay behind him, free
and clearheaded. With a laugh, he quoted to himself Bompard's sulky

remark, "I don't know what the hurry is." And he answered it with "No, Madame, there's no hurry; you'll be surprised at Jaquemar's patience!"

He resolved to wait and watch; he wanted to get used to the place; and in so doing he involuntarily adopted the ways of the other visitors to the spa. At all times of the day he drank quantities of iced water, because this produced a sensation of inner coolness, though it was really no more than an illusion and only lasted a few minutes. Like all the rest, he sat on the piazza of the Grand Union, on the rocking chair in the front row nearest the entrance steps, which was left free, and even reserved, for him with silent good nature, because he had taken a fancy to it; and here he rocked himself or was rocked— for whether it was an active or a passive state he was unable to tell. With the rest he sauntered in the morning, afternoon, and evening around the pumproom and through the bush-lined paths in the park; he saw the furrowed fauns' heads grinning through the foliage with their little horns and their curly hair, content in their emasculated lechery; he let himself be lulled by the scent of lilacs in the heat and the sentimental and dashing tones of the orchestra on the raised pavilion . . . until Gabrielle Bompard popped up somewhere or other, gay if, as was usually the case, she was encircled by a dense throng of admirers, sullen if she was accompanied only by the severely aged Carapin, but terrifyingly beautiful in either case, a triumph of beauty that made the fierce fire of hatred blaze up in Jaquemar. What a prey! No wonder the beast hypnotized every man's eyes and senses: her innocently radiant promise displayed a readiness and capacity for love that were denied by destiny to the women of this country.

In spite of their natural prettiness they were devoid of fragrance like immortelles, coarsened into mannishness by some deep disappointment, deaf and blind to allusive tenderness, and hostile to the male. Not that they were lacking in elegance; on the contrary, they overdid things in this direction. Age and discretion constituted no bar to them: stiff-necked old women with mouths like a sergeant-major's appeared in schoolgirl frocks and coquettish little flowered hats, and schoolgirls in costumes unsuited to their undeveloped figures. What for? Jaquemar asked himself. What is the purpose of all this ostentatious finery, which makes them look almost like members of the demimonde, when they obviously have no wish to seduce? For it did not seem as if the most feminine of all activities, seduction, meant anything to them. Nor did they need to practice it, they were on top anyhow, they looked down with vapid, hard eyes in cold appraisal on possible suitors and full of contempt on the husbands who followed, bowed, submissive, and spiritless, at their sides.

They were the masters in this strange land that Eros had fled or never trodden, Eros, the god who bestows joy and creates culture—and who wants to live without joy? But that is how it was. At best a man came away empty-handed after moving among these women, he did not receive the tenderly piquant emanation of the other sex, the partner of his destiny on earth. Jaquemar felt it through every pore: the subtle, gentle effervescence in the air which back at home had played on and—although without thanks—caressed him was missing on this continent; although it was heavy and sweet with the scent of flowers, the atmosphere was empty and insipid, and the young man's secret thirst was not stimulated here, let alone satisfied. The fauns in the greenery, with their idiotic grins and their hands clasped around the sex that had been spirited away as a punishment, seemed to him the mawkish sculptural tables of the law of this matriarchate given to a rule of terror, in which She alone, the one he hated and would destroy, was feminine in his sense; but her femininity, too, was voracious, cannibalistic—which perhaps made her the supreme representative and embodiment, the uncrowned queen of this man-murdering women's state.

He watched what went on around him. The pipe-smoker was standing with his fusty, flat-chested, and embittered wife by the pumphouse; Bompard swept past with her retinue, changed her mind, stopped, and called back: "Carapin is offended, Doctor. Why do you cut him . . . and me?" He took the pipe out of his mouth and gazed after Gabrielle, as she swept away with a shrug of her shoulders; his wife hissed at him with the venomous jealousy of the unattractive. Wait till you get home! thought Jaquemar, involuntarily amused. You'll laugh on the other side of your face!

The tall old man who looked up from under the eyebrows of his bent head was frequently absent from the throng of admirers; and gossip in the hotel lounge, which Jaquemar now visited often, had it that his participation in the youthful wooing was making his gout grow worse every day, although he regularly poured into himself—

without ever tipping the Negro boy who ladled it out—many times the dose of Empire water prescribed here for his complaint, a quantity that was probably in correct proportion to his excessive height.

Bompard's favorite, however, was unquestionably the grave young man with the deeply lined face, who alone, apart from the sulkily tolerated Carapin, seemed to be allowed the favor of accompanying her on his own, and always followed a little behind his passion, with sad eyes and clumsily shortened steps, in huge boots that were smeared with blacking and tied with coarse gray laces. Bending submissively forward, he held an enormous cotton umbrella outspread above her head to protect her from the summer's heat or rare falls of rain; Gabrielle Bompard marched gaily on ahead, and he suffered with torn mouth and introverted gaze from his desire, which he was doubtless prevented from gratifying by lack of experience and courage and failure to snatch his opportunity. But what were his troubles and those of all the other suitors beside Carapin's!

Carapin was in a bad way, whether from unrequited love, physical indisposition, or business worries, in a very bad way indeed; his appearance left no doubt about that. True, he continued to swagger with gesticulating hands in the lilac-scented park, in the role of Bompard's owner; his laugh rang out, full of self-satisfaction, even above the eunuch's crowing and croaking, and his dark eyes sparkled vivaciously. But looked at closely, his face, framed by iron-gray curls, was vivacious out of desperation, livid and emaciated, so that the furrows grew deeper on his brow and more harshly incised around his mouth, so that his nose projected sharp-pointed and short. And when he was left to himself and strolled through the rooms of the hotel as though searching for something, he looked lifeless and embittered and, above all, pitiably shrunken in his all too smart linen and silk suits, which now hung about him loosely, as though made to grow into. Jaquemar had been a bare fourteen days in Saratoga Springs; a kind of fraternal sympathy for Carapin was gradually taking possession of him, and he was shocked when at a certain point (later, he was completely unable to remember what time of day it was) he witnessed a scene which suggested that his, Jaquemar's, person might secretly be contributing to the gallant gentleman's ruin.

He was sitting in the bloody-red, bronze-brown gloom beneath the skull-like glimmer of the chandelier domes in the hotel lounge, dream-

ing away on the yellow-upholstered central seat and looking straight
into the eyes of the Cyclopean Venus in the mural painting, who lay
stretched out on the marble ottoman, her chin on her hand, naked
yet decent, waiting with a foolish smile for something or other that
never happened. There were only a few mute guests in the room, of
no interest to Jaquemar, when the Carapins, who were sitting on the
same seat but back to back with Jaquemar and separated from him by
the central back rest, began a brief conversation in an undertone.

"My dear Edmond," began Gabrielle Bompard in her didactic
fashion, but was immediately interrupted by the piqued Carapin:
"My name is Edouard, my dear—Edouard, not Edmond!" "There you
are, you see!" she retorted angrily. "I try to show my kindness and
forgiveness by addressing you by a Christian name, instead of calling
you Carapin as I usually do—and that's the thanks I get! You take
offense." "You could keep to my Christian name," said Carapin, with
stifled anger. "I beg your pardon, but you could stop making this everlasting mistake." "Will you please leave me to decide what I could do?
What can you do? You are far too vain in relation to your scanty
potency. You bore me."

With that she rose to her feet; the listening Jaquemar thought he
heard Carapin draw a snarling breath, but he controlled himself and
stayed where he was, while she made for the door, first sweeping out,
then hesitating, and finally disappearing with a shrug of the shoulders.

Why does she call her lover by my name? Jaquemar asked himself.
Has the wicked creature a presentiment somewhere at the back of her
mind that, for all her efforts, she cannot escape me? Is she, despite
all her beaming and smiling, afraid? Take comfort, Gouffé: the day is
not far distant when she will get her deserts, my word on it.

One afternoon soon after this, the broiling heat in his little room
had plunged him into a heavy sleep, so that he appeared later than
usual on the piazza. All the rocking chairs were occupied except his
own, and when he sat down he found himself next to the young man
from Bompard's retinue. He was such a hulking fellow that his bony
knees were far higher than the chair he was sitting on, and between
them he held the great colorless cotton umbrella with both his hands
on the rough wooden handle.

He turned his face to Jaquemar with the trace of a smile in one
corner of his torn lips and remarked: "I was told this was your chair.
That's why I sat here." "Very kind of you," Jaquemar answered

formally. "I haven't a chair," the other went on calmly. "I'm not staying here." "But," Jaquemar let slip half involuntarily, "you have certain interests here. You are often to be seen in the company of the charming Madame . . . What is her name? Carapin?" "Oh—her," said the young American, shaking his head as he stared in front of him and adding after a while: "She's a great woman. I'm merely tolerated." "H'm, a great woman . . . she doesn't seem to be very good for her husband, he looks old and haggard." "That's true," said the young man, nodding deliberately. "Poor fellow. He must have lost a fortune at the races. She's crazy about betting, and her tips are always wrong." "A rather expensive passion," commented Jaquemar. The other almost imperceptibly shrugged his shoulders and said again in explanation: "Why, she's a great woman . . . she gets what she wants, the price is no object." He turned toward his new acquaintance and said with a smile in his sorrowful eyes: "You know what women are like. They regard it as a proof of love. Of course, in this case poor Carapin doesn't take it too well. Every other night he has an attack of colic. I know that, because she jokes about it. 'Gentlemen,' she says to her friends, but completely in public and in his presence, 'Carapin had his gripes again. Would you believe it? Men are so lacking in passion. It makes a peculiar impression on a comparatively young woman when her husband is perpetually prevented.' Because she's very outspoken. You understand what she means, don't you?" "I understand," said Jaquemar. "Yes," said the young American, "that's the way she is."

Jaquemar gave him a searching sidelong glance. "You're quite full of her. Take care or you'll end up by falling in love with her." "I'm afraid I'm already in love with her—oh, I love her," he replied, thoughtfully and frankly. "But she's married." "If that's the only obstacle . . ." drawled Jaquemar. "Don't say that; she's a good wife," answered the American in a high, singsong voice that sounded gently reprimanding. "She fools around a bit, sure, we've played forfeits once or twice and so on, but that has nothing to do with it—all the same, I once got a kiss from her. Of course, I drew conclusions from it. 'I'm nothing,' I said. 'We should have to start from scratch,' and the sort of thing one does say. But she wouldn't hear of a divorce. 'He's still alive,' she retorted, meaning Carapin, 'and besides, you're not the right man for me at all.' And that was that."

"Is she so faithful?" queried Jaquemar sarcastically. "Yes," said the other simply. "Since then I've often asked her what she has against me." He couldn't help laughing himself at the memory. "Do you know what she answered? 'You want to butt, and yet your horns still have the velvet on them.' But I'm twenty-three! Listen, I can't think of anything but her. It's like an obsession, a mental illness." "You'll get over it," said Jaquemar dourly. "No," replied the other, shaking his head sadly. "A man like me only loves once, and then it's for always." "Oh," replied Jaquemar irritably, "there are other women, thank heaven, and more wholesome ones." But the young man shook his head with gentle obstinacy. "Believe me, I know what I'm talking about." "Let us hope not," remarked Jaquemar dryly.

The young American laid his hand on Jaquemar's knee. "Forgive me. I'm behaving like a savage, burdening you with my affairs; it's impertinent of me. But as you see, I can't talk about anything but her. You're very patient. I thank you for your forbearance."

"There's nothing to thank me for," replied Jaquemar in an indefinite tone. "You've no idea how much it interests me." "My name is Gaunt," said the other unexpectedly, "Chester Gaunt. What's yours?" "I'm Edmond Jaquemar," answered Jaquemar, unable to dodge the question. "No!" exclaimed the young man in amazement. "Edmond? But that's the name with which she often addresses Carapin, and then he gets angry." "A coincidence," replied Jaquemar briefly. "What else could it be?" said the young man thoughtfully. "She also asked me whether any of us knew you. But nobody knew you. That's to say, Carapin thought he must have seen you somewhere before. And Mr. Tulipan (that's the tall old gentleman, he's an anthropologist), Tulipan said: 'Judging by his physiognomy, the young man is a member of the well-to-do French middle class.' Whereupon she laughed and answered 'Well-to-do, eh? Well, that's something.' I hope you don't mind my telling you all this? It's indiscreet . . ." "On the contrary," said Jaquemar with an impassive face, "it's very kind of you. Who wouldn't be flattered by the interest of such a great lady?"

To this, young Chester Gaunt nodded pensively. He seemed, however, to have some appointment elsewhere; it was almost dinnertime, and he drew from his waistcoat pocket a watch shaped like a fat Idaho potato and remarked with a furrowed brow: "Well, I think it's time . . ." "You're not going already?" inquired Jaquemar, as though startled; but the other, having already risen to his great height, did not hear him.

"Nice to meet you," he said, touching the brim of the hat he was wearing tilted back on his head, and pushed clumsily past Jaquemar. He descended the steps and disappeared to the right along Broadway, with long, calmly stalking strides, using the cumbersome umbrella as a walking stick.

Jaquemar continued his leisurely way of life, sauntering at intervals around the pumphouse, meeting her every now and then by chance, when he could not restrain an ironic smile, rocking to and fro on the piazza, and swallowing endless meals that discouraged his palate; and in addition to all this, he carried out certain experiments in listening, which anyone else would have thought foolish. Night after night he would sit for hours in the park listening in a mood of surrender to the insect concert, for surrender was what the unviolent might of this natural clangor seemed to demand . . . and that was all that could be gathered from it. What else? Well, of course, the obvious fact that when man's hubbub ceases, this other noise takes over, a noise which, because of its less refined organization, will probably end by outliving the din of mankind: croaking, throbbing, drumming, sawing, chirping, grating, grinding, whistling, the monotonously insistent, voiceless voice of the night.

In order at least to have a clear picture of the authors of this monotonous rhythm, Jaquemar looked it up and found in all the books he consulted exactly the answer he had expected: it was made by crickets, tree frogs, red-bellied toads, common toads, gnats, cicadas, owls and other species of night bird, and also by small quadrupeds with high-pitched squeaks—rats, mice, woodchucks, and so on, who were out in the darkness searching for prey and love.

Banal information! As banal as the festive spray of glittering stars in the dark towers of the trees, around the shadowy globes of the bushes, around the hedges and thickets—nature, nothing more, forever concerned with its own affairs and deaf to the cries of distress with which the locomotives howled their way across the country and which brought such strange pain to Jaquemar's heart.

One afternoon he once more found Chester Gaunt, the young American, sitting in the chair next to his, the only empty one, with knees projecting high above the chair, his cotton umbrella between them, and both hands on the handle. He raised his right hand in greeting and said quietly: "Hello, Edmond. I was just going." "Have you been waiting for me?" asked Jaquemar in surprise. "No, no," replied the young man, and continued without any manifest connection: "I think she's leaving." Jaquemar stared at him with his squinting eyes, recollected himself, and remarked with a laugh: "You're an optimist." The other ignored this and stared into space. It seemed Carapin had insisted he must go to Buffalo, his "cure" demanded it; Madame (he pronounced it "Ma'am") asked in laughing protest what she was expected to do in Buffalo or whether he intended to leave her in the lurch; but Carapin, who generally kept matters like that to himself, brought it up again day after day in front of everyone, and now Bompard merely shrugged her shoulders about it.

"And you think that means she has given way?" inquired Jaquemar sarcastically. The American nodded. "She said to me: 'I shan't be here much longer. You hear what Carapin says.' Well . . . I must be going. Glad to have seen you. So long." He lumbered up from the chair and pushed past Jaquemar, who was staring at the flagstones and geranium boxes at his feet. He knew this was the moment to act. He got up quickly and hurried down the steps, to the left along Broadway, and up the first side street.

Next day after lunch Jaquemar sauntered into the lounge; in the corner, on a low marble table, opposite the sign "For Ladies Only," lay a pile of daily papers with the *Saratoga Chronicle* on top. He turned the pages and found, in thick black type under the heading "Social Titbits," the following notice:

The striking beauty who moved into the Grand Union Hotel some weeks ago with a certain Monsieur C. as his wife is in fact a world-famous and much-discussed personality incognito. Further information will be released later.   Ja-.

Not exactly brilliant, thought Jaquemar, running his hand across his lips as though to wipe away a smirk, but it will serve its purpose! He tore out the page and folded it, slipped it into his pocket, and went out of the room across the hall to the elevator, whose doors the Negro boy was on the point of shutting from inside. "Just a minute!"

cried Jaquemar. The boy leaned out, opened the gates again, and stood aside for the guest to enter. Inside stood Bompard, laughing, with her head on one side. Jaquemar remained grimly silent; in silence all three rose to the third floor. When they had reached it, Bompard hesitated, and Jaquemar thrust the torn-out sheet of newspaper toward her, but she did not take it.

"You'll laugh on the other side of your face!" he hissed, although she was not laughing at all.

"You're behaving in a silly and thoughtless way," she said tartly, but had to laugh before she went on: "Yes, do you think I don't know who's behind it? All the same, I'm warning you. I'm warning you for the last time! Don't tease me any more."

"I see: 'Teasing the animals is forbidden.'"

"You're as fragile as a hen's egg, you'd crack in pieces the moment a hard finger tapped you. And you are trying to annoy me? Heavens above. Out of inborn kindliness and for the last time: leave me in peace!"

"No, not 'annoy,'" said Jaquemar through clenched teeth, and again she had to laugh.

"What little plans have you got? Such a young man—one could almost feel sorry for him. What do you think you can do against me—even if I am alone?"

Even if I am alone? thought Jaquemar, pricking up his ears but lowering his head; he looked up again in a moment and found her gone. He walked slowly to his cell.

In the evening, when Jaquemar was about to leave the lounge and go over to the dining room, he had to wait in the doorway to avoid running into the hated woman, who had just emerged from the hall and was making for the exit amid the rustle of her garments. All the other guests who were looking forward to swallowing their food and drinking their iced water did the same, the dolled-up women with their hard expressions, the men with their drained and hypnotized look—all of them, whether they were sitting, standing, or just finishing off a chat, fell silent and stared at the enchanting vision who took no notice of them whatsoever.

She was accompanied only by Mr. Tulipan and Chester Gaunt. The young man with the beautiful, ravaged face and introverted eyes was dressed, as before, in his short-tailed, short-sleeved swallow-tail jacket and wore under the loose, soft collar of his soft shirt a thread-bare black tie. The old man looking up from under his eyebrows was in rather shiny evening dress, which gave him the appearance of an old café musician.

Where is Carapin? shot through Jaquemar's head as he watched Bompard draw near, and for the moment could think of nothing else. Good God, yes, she was a great lady in this country! What a bearing, the smile that was directed toward no one, the shining eyes that looked at no one, the forward-thrusting walk, whose rustling suddenly sounded in Jaquemar's ears like the beating of wings! And her whole figure, small and firm between her tall escorts, curved like an attacking scorpion in the exquisitely simple dress: black Lyons silk almost as thick as velvet, nothing but a flashing diamond between the naïvely gathered fabric covering the two breasts; and standing up with jaunty little corners a brocade collar with a golden ground, the sumptuous material of which also broke out through the full train in a long wedge-shaped panel that grew wider at the bottom—it wriggled sinuously along behind the vanishing wearer like the mating tail of a fantastic tropical bird.

Carapin isn't there! thought Jaquemar again. Where is Carapin? Has she taken care that the milk does not dry up in the cow when I flirt with her at night? Is the unwelcome witness out of the way?

For he knew that the time had come. He now stood before the goal, the either-or from which there was no turning back. He had no leisure for a meal, and left the clatter of dishes in the dining hall immediately after the hors-d'oeuvre (insipid seafood in salad without vinegar), went up to his room via the elevator, and there wandered up and down for a long time, always from one narrow end to the other, completely pervaded by his future plans. After a while, he leaned out of the high, narrow window and looked down unseeing on the pedestrians and carriages on Broadway, as they went unhurriedly on their way beneath the gentle light from the bending flowers of the street lamps to and from the distant point at which these two convergent rows of "candelabra" finally met. The movement of the vehicles was accompanied by a muffled rumble, above which hung a dreamy net woven of the softer sounds of human voices and footsteps. This peaceful picture gradually faded away, like ink soaked up by blotting paper, the sweet clamor gradually fell silent and was drowned in the greater

clamor, the croaking, chirping, sawing, and whistling whose everlasting rhythmic rise and fall pulsated through the warm night air to its
very limits. That's right, thought Jaquemar with a cruel laugh. Sing,
go on, sing, you voiceless ones! We need music; for I have come to
take her home—to the block in the yard of La Roquette, or, if she
won't confess . . . well, God have mercy on her! *It must be tonight!*

The great street below was almost deserted; eleven o'clock was
striking from every tower, an hour before midnight, when out of the
narrow space between the "candelabra" in the background a black
lacquered coach with a coachman and a servant in black livery on the
box approached almost at a gallop and drew up with a sliding of
horses' hoofs in front of the Grand Union Hotel entrance. Even
before the lackey had clambered down, the door was thrown open
and out stepped Bompard, laughing. Only after that did young
Chester Gaunt step down onto the sidewalk, stretching limbs that
were far too long, as though he had been folded up in the little box
of the carriage. But Jaquemar was looking inside himself and did not
see him. "Have patience!" he said, thinking only of her. "The next
hour that strikes will strike you!"

The clocks outside set up their midnight clangor. Jaquemar stepped
out of his door, walked quickly along the bare corridor with his head
down, as though he knew the way by heart, and where it forked in
several directions he unhesitatingly took the fork leading to the side
wing. He came to a stop outside Carapin's apartment, knocked, and
watched the latch, listening intently. It was very quiet in this extensive
building (people go to bed early in Saratoga), and it seemed to
Jaquemar that he could hear in this silence a low spluttering and
giggling followed by a faint clatter. He knocked harder and, receiving
no reply, simply pushed open the door.

He shut it behind him and was enveloped by the darkness. He was
astonished by the dense, sticky heat that prevailed in this room; it
was suffocatingly stuffy and smelled of old age in every sense, of
moldy fabrics, even of stored vegetables, of worm-eaten timber, carpet
dust, bugs, and old camphor; and all this was mingled with a slightly
unpleasant odor of femaleness, of armpit sweat and stale lavender, the
fustiness of a bedroom after a consummated wedding night—although
the room in which he found himself was not a bedroom. He could

see this; his eyes grew accustomed to the darkness a good deal sooner than he had expected; he was in the Carapins' living room, and even though the door curtains, transfixed diagonally at the top by halberds, were completely drawn, he could distinguish the shadowy shapes of one or two pieces of furniture—tables, easy chairs, whatnots—and above all, throughout the whole room, a ghastly untidiness that suggested an early departure. Everywhere, even on the thick carpet, lay clothes, umbrellas, underclothing, capes, and toilet articles; and as he groped his way forward he stumbled and bumped into an open fitted trunk the size of a clothespress. He grazed his shinbone and clutched at the edge of the trunk with a groan; the enormous lid fell and struck him painfully on the fingers. Perhaps it was the shock; anyhow, he felt a sudden indescribable, anguished sensation, as though a spring wound around his heart had been jerked violently downward. He immediately pulled himself together, cleared his throat, and on looking up noticed a very pale glimmer of light gleaming through a crack in a door in the wall in front of him. He groped his way over to it and and felt blindly for the handle.

"Come right in!" said Bompard's voice, rather gruffly and without surprise.

He found the knob, opened the door, and as a greeting asked curtly and in a low voice: "You're alone?"

"Whom did you expect to find?" she asked back.

"But you were expecting me!" he observed, saw her shrug her shoulders, closed the door behind him, and was now inside.

This room, too, was rather dark. As in the one outside, the curtains were drawn tight, and only a small oil lamp, with a flower-painted spherical container of opaque glass at the foot of the glass chimney, spread a faint, flickering, shadowy light. It stood on a platelike extension of the dressing table, in front of whose damp-stained mirror Bompard was seated on a stool powdering her face. She looked in the mirror at the man who had just entered, and again he had the feeling of a spring around his heart; she was in a negligee—what shameless impudence!

"You were expecting me!" he hissed between his teeth, adding derisively: "I suppose you thought I had come to bring you the ten thousand francs."

"I never thought of it," she retorted indifferently.

"Oh, didn't you?" he said, involuntarily surprised and staring broodingly at the tips of his shoes. "Then . . . what did you think?"

With a leather cloth between the tips of her fingers she wiped the septum that divided her bold nostrils, which were of a charming pink; as she used both her hands for the purpose, she looked like a cat cleaning itself.

"I didn't think much at all," she answered at last with a shrug. "Have you come to apologize for your indiscretion in the *Chronicle*? What did you expect to gain by that? Did you hope to attract my attention to you by that piece of tomfoolery? I have sent you my greetings several times and that's that. I'm leaving."

"Aha," he ejaculated, with a derisive smirk.

"Yes," she replied, laughing and looking up at him again in the mirror as he came hesitantly nearer. "I'm slinging my hook. I've had enough of Saratoga Springs. As I told you, the people are unendurably tedious, not one of them has any staying power." She began to mumble in her old way as she added: "Other people want to have something of me too."

"So it has nothing to do with me, eh. . . . But don't forget that you have a business interest in me," he remarked, keeping his eyes on her as he sat down casually on the silk stool standing close to hers at an angle. "Don't I owe you ten thousand francs?"

"But, good heavens, I had those long ago! I should have been a pretty simpleton to rely on you! I simply wanted you to be out of Paris when Papa Rebattu went to the Cité and collected them for me, in case you made difficulties. Thank you for obliging me. We're even."

She stood up. Her negligee was very lovely, of white lace with a wide lace collar around the shoulders and a lace belt that dangled down beside her in a series of golden tassels. It was designed to emphasize the wearer's femininity, with padding at the back surmounted, Japanese-fashion, by a bow, which made her boyish behavior seem all the more comical as she bent quickly down to a chest of drawers against the opposite wall, tore open a drawer, and hunted recklessly through it. The drawer hung out of the chest of drawers, which stood next to the bedside table beside the low, wide double bed; and without his paying any particular attention to it, Jaquemar's eye was caught in the semidarkness by a small, bright object lying in the drawer between crepe de Chine and lace underclothes.

"Ye-e-s . . ." he drawled, "quits. . . . Do you know that a procedural error was committed in your trial?"

"The whole trial was an error," she said sulkily, without interrupting her hunt through the drawer. "*I* can't be accused. The farce was a waste of time."

"All the same, since a procedural error was committed the farce could be repeated, especially if you were first persuaded to make a confession," he replied, slyly following her figure with his squinting eyes as she came up to and past him and disappeared into the bathroom next door, to reappear immediately with a large bottle of Eau de Cologne. "Madame is preparing herself for the night—a lonely night, as I regret to note. Surely Monsieur Carapin hasn't also—'slung his hook'?"

"What's Carapin to you?" she retorted obstinately.

With a rustling of her robe that reached to the floor and beneath which only the tips of gold-embroidered slippers were visible, she strode across to the bedside table, placed the Eau de Cologne bottle on it, together with an ashtray, which she took from the chest of drawers, and a bowl full of brownish-yellow Russian cigarettes. She arranged all this with a certain pensiveness, pushing the things this way and that, and finally said with a shrug of the shoulders: "Carapin is my affair. You needn't worry about him."

"Oh, no," he said with a laugh, as she turned to her stool and sat down again. "Now, about the trial. . . . Your name is Bompard, I suppose, or isn't it?"

"Are you still on about that rubbish?" she cried indignantly. "Of course I'm of unknown parentage. The Bompards bought me a place in the Angoulême convent boarding school for a sum that was far too high, and it was only because they passed away too soon that they didn't adopt me."

"So you're not Bompard!"

"Why not? One name's as good as another as far as I'm concerned. I hear you're paying a pettifogging lawyer to pump the Angoulême nuns. I don't mind. They don't know anything, and if they did they would take care to keep their mouths shut. That's an old story there. . . . Anyhow, a young man as fond of traveling as you are, and who is as deeply in love as a cat that has smelled valerian, should keep his money in the safe till he can put it to better use."

All at once she broke out laughing and twisted around toward him on her stool. She did not look at him, however, but beamed down into her lap, in which her fingers like twisted roots were playing; she grew serious again and continued in a thoughtful and confidential tone: "You want me to confess? All right, if it interests you. But it's a romantic story, I'll tell you that straightaway. You wouldn't think such things could happen in our enlightened times. . . . Michi, who was always strutting around with his comb up, like an old cock in the chicken run, flattered himself he was the first to have his fun with me."

She looked up at Jaquemar with a smile and continued: "It was a man of God who first laid hands on me, and no good came to him of it; but what did I have to suffer! I was a young girl when I entered the convent, and I can't deny that I felt abandoned and also bored, with the everlasting clanging of bells and the ringing for Mass and the pious mutterings of the priest and the nuns, who at all times of the day and wherever they happened to be standing or walking, immediately fell on their knees the moment the bell started ringing.

"One day I found a fledgling in the convent garden that couldn't fly yet and was hopping about cheeping, because it had fallen out of its nest. I saved its life. I took it up to my cell, made it a bed with cottonwool in a cardboard box, and fed and cared for it, in response to the maternal instincts that were already fully alive in me then, at the age of seven. But the little bird was ungrateful and made a mess. After a few days, I took it downstairs, to get rid of it, and the poor creature trembled with cold in my hand. I was feeling very sorry for it as I went through the big kitchen, which was empty at this time of the day—it was early evening. The iron top of the huge oven was glowing invitingly. In my compassion I thought, I'll make him nice and warm before getting rid of him, and in a trice I had put him on the oven top. Would you believe it, he positively screamed with delight and got furrows on his forehead from pleasure, tiny as he was? He hopped gaily from one foot to the other, screeching and flapping his little wings, until he fell over.

"Now, we had a lay brother in the convent called Baptiste, a lad with a forehead two fingers high whom the holy women saddled with all the heavy work. And as bad luck would have it, when I looked up from my game he was standing in the doorway with his mouth open. I could see at once that he misunderstood the situation. I quickly seized hold of the little bird and as he came toward me threateningly I shouted: 'If you touch me, I'll wring his neck!' He clouted me so hard in the mouth that I nearly fell over, but I kept my senses just enough to twist the little bird's neck, as I had promised. I threw it down at the boy's feet and cried: 'Shame on you! That's on your conscience!' But without seeing the crime he had committed and with no consideration for my tender years, the hulking oaf went for me with his fists, and he beat me so savagely that some dim memory of it remained in his dull mind.

"I did not complain about him, but swallowed my distress and consoled myself in my childish innocence with the conviction that heaven would one day punish him for his brutality—I had no thought of vengeance, as you can see. Nevertheless, I often felt Baptiste's eyes on me, especially as I grew up. Note that I am patient by nature, time makes no odds to me. I lived in peace for many years and soon had little breasts that stood out most gaily and attractively in the wretched frocks we were forced to wear to teach us humility.

"Despite his everlasting signs of the cross and his womanish gown, Brother Baptiste was a man like other men, pious on the outside but very different inside; his lustful eyes were glued to my breasts, and this confused my virginal mind. He was also quite a handsome young man, and the fact that he had once given me a drubbing naturally bound me to him, and it was only reasonable that I should allow him several assignations as a sign of my forgiveness, first in snug hideouts among the bushes in the convent garden and finally, when he could contain himself no longer, in my cell, where I promised to give myself to him in love. I let him undress and, because the smell upset me, I stuffed the whole bundle of clothes into my cupboard, which I locked, so that nothing should get lost.

"Then I gave him what I had promised, for one must keep one's word; only he was so big-built that it hurt me; so when I thought he had enjoyed himself enough on me, and I could stand it no longer, I began to yell my head off with pain. He jumped out of bed and, being such a stupid fellow, couldn't find his clothes, so he hopped with his long, bare legs straight out of the window, which was rather high, as high as our room here in fact, that is to say on the third floor. This was unfortunate for him, because he had a nasty fall, and as it was winter and bitterly cold outside he lay in the ice and snow with his legs broken. Great God, how the man whimpered! It might have softened a heart of a stone. But what could I do? My shouts had died away unheard, nobody stirred in the great building; so I shut the window and regretfully went to sleep. And when the bell rang for matins, the brides of Jesus saw the naked man lying there in the snow as they made their way through the cloisters.

"I went to the Mother Superior, who came toward me gesticulating angrily, as though to rebuke me—would you believe it, she was going to rebuke me! I looked at her sternly and said: 'Reverend Mother! What is the use of all this piety? What is the use of our having to wear chemises even when we bathe? Last night Brother Baptiste slipped into my cell and raped me. It can be proved by medical evidence, and the clothes I tore away from the libertine are locked in my cupboard. A house in which such things can happen is no place for me. But if you let me go in peace after I have suffered this disillusionment I shall not compromise you.'

"What could the fat woman do? It would have caused an unparalleled scandal, especially as Brother Baptiste fell ill with septic pneumonia a few days later and, after a repentant confession and receiving absolution and the holy sacrament, gave up the ghost.

"So I shook the dust of Angoulême from my feet, went out into the world, and made my way to Paris—where I unfortunately fell straight into Michi's filthy fingers. . . .

"Yes, those are memories of my girlhood. Things have never been easy for me."

With these last words she sighed through her nose, continuing to play with her yellow fingers in her lap.

"What are you thinking of!" Jaquemar spat out in disgust, his anger making him shout louder with every word. "What are you thinking of, plaguing me with your dirty little stories! You haven't grasped the purpose of my visit, it seems! You will grasp it!"

"Ssh!" exclaimed Bompard, raising her crooked yellow index finger and listening. "Don't shout! Walls have ears, believe me."

"Are you worried about your reputation, you?"

She gave him an indefinable smile, lowered her finger, and said in a not unfriendly tone: "You should remember that if I scream you will be in an awkward situation. I'm wearing nothing but this nightdress, it's easy to tear, all Frenchmen are libertines. . . . Who wouldn't take my side? In this country? But don't get cold feet on that account. I hate scenes. You're in an awkward situation in any case. You are compromised."

"When I leave this room," said Jaquemar through his teeth, "that won't matter any more."

"That's what men say before they've had their fun," she commented noncommittally. "I shouldn't have any objection, only today I'm in a melancholy mood. A friend of mine is ill, perhaps he's already dead."

"Oh, Carapin?" inquired Jaquemar with derisive sympathy.

She gave him the same indefinable smile again and shook her head. "Not Carapin at all," she answered belatedly and in icy tones.

"When will it be his turn?" he asked offhandedly.

"You mean because he is losing weight and looks like rancid drippings? You can't go by that, he has probably got a tapeworm; constitutionally he's wiry, tough, and full of life; on the other hand, of course, nobody lives forever. At bottom they're all fragile, the whole slimy brood born of women."

"These aren't the confessions I came to hear," Jaquemar interrupted irritably. "Let's come to the point! You're not a Bompard. The case was against Bompard. It will be reopened because the accused was wrongly described, so that the case was not made out against the right person."

"What do you mean, 'not the right person'?" she asked, shaking her head slightly and turning back to her damp-spotted mirror. "I've never heard that anyone doubted my identity. Bompard, Labodère, Carapin . . . and suppose I decided tomorrow to call myself Jaquemar: it was I, it is I!"

In sudden gloom, Jaquemar looked down at the carpet and said, but as though he were thinking of something quite different: "I am speaking of your person in a legal sense."

"In a legal sense?" She laughed.

"You think it's funny," he murmured from out of his gloomy meditation.

She was now running a comb in each hand through her upswept curly locks, with vigorous movements as though throwing a ball; the combs crackled in the wiry hair and little golden sparks spurted from the blue-black mass. She was obviously in a good mood and asked conversationally: "Do you know the song: 'Sweetheart, if you give me / a little silver money / I will show you things / you'll think very funny'?"

"You acquainted me with it in Paris," he murmured, without even attempting to assume an ironic tone. "You gave me that pleasure in Paris."

"Yes, Paris . . ." she drawled. "That was different, there we had common interests. But you don't like talking about it and you're my guest. The second verse is also very beautiful: 'When the sun rises into the sky / out of my room you will have to fly, / but what I showed you while you were inside / you'll never forget, what e'er betide.' "

"My interests," said Jaquemar, looking up at her slowly and malevolently, "will not change until I have brought you to destruction."

"I'll give you a piece of advice: turn back, and consume your inheritance in riotous living while there is still time! What do you seek here? Things are different for me, I have to earn my living. But you? This country is no use to a young bon vivant like you. People either drink Adam's ale or pure firewater that knocks down the strongest man. Women are only here to destroy their bedfellows, French love is forbidden by law, the fruit is watery and the climate inhuman. Go home."

"After tonight, when I have settled with you."

"I really don't know what you're after."

"Even if I have to break every single limb one by one," he ground out between his teeth, "you will make a confession tonight, or I shall crush you as one crushes a poisonous insect with one's thumbnail."

"Oh, as to crushing . . ." she replied, with a dismissive gesture. "Look, in Paris it was different, in Paris I might have quite liked to start something with you. There we had a common interest. But here? I've more or less fallen on my feet. I don't see what use you could be to me."

"A common interest? You forget the trial!"

"Good God!" she cried furiously, flinging the combs down on the dressing table so violently that they bounced off the glass top and onto the carpet, and jumped up from her stool. "Are you really going to start that nonsense all over again? How long am I to let myself be plagued by that silly business, in which I just about covered my expenses and no more? You snatched the lion's share, you glutton, you grasping miser! I've had enough of it, once and for all! What do I care about your hairsplitting fiddle-faddle? So much fuss about such a petty, dreary bagatelle! There were times when a man fighting a duel would apologize to his opponent for dirtying his clothes after running him through the belly with his sword!"

He too had risen to his feet; they were now standing face to face, and Jaquemar was quivering with rage and hate.

"Dreary bagatelle, hairsplitting—it will cost you your head; Monsieur de Paris is already waiting for you in the courtyard of La Roquette."

"It is a bagatelle," she insisted. But now in a sulky tone. Turning a little, she raised one shoulder, tilted her head to one side, and beamed into space with her anguished brows raised. "These are things that just happen. Who can help them? Who can be held responsible for them?"

"Who indeed!"

She looked at him attentively and said casually: "You're hot. Your face is all patchy. Take off your jacket, I've only got this rag on."

"Who indeed!" repeated Jaquemar.

She went on looking at him and all of a sudden, as though an idea had struck her, she raised the crooked index finger of her right hand.

"That would be a possibility. So far, no one has thought of accusing me of the murder. . . ."

He squinted at her in astonishment. It was quite true, she had never been accused of her true crime; somehow he had forgotten that, and coming from her it sounded absurd. How could he have forgotten, when for months he had thought of nothing else?

"But there's just one thing you must remember," she remarked gruffly. "You won't get away with a measly ten thousand this time. This time you'll have to put your hand deep down into your purse, I'm warning you. Otherwise you'll find yourself on the dust heap, like your friend Goron, who wanted everything for nothing. Mind you, I can't see what's in it for you, but that's your lookout."

"What an unspeakable wretch," Jaquemar burst out through frozen lips. "To think a creature like that is allowed to go on living!"

"You must take a broad view for once," she urged him, speaking like someone who is gradually waxing enthusiastic. "Granted, you would have a pretty shaky case, but if you tackled it the right way . . ." She raised her left hand and as she enumerated the following names she counted on her fingers: "First, we have Brother Baptiste, who forgot his vows and exercised neither Christian gentleness nor chastity, and as a result jumped out of the window and died of septic pneumonia. Second, Michi, the ox, who overreached himself and thought he could thrash me with impunity, and therefore had to bite the dust. Then with Carapin it's only a question of time; although he was excessively lecherous, he loved his vanity more than me, and between ourselves he's now on his last legs. A friend of mine is in a thoroughly bad way, it's all over with him if you ask me, people say it's because on my account he didn't stick to the diet the doctors prescribed him. And of course we mustn't forget the bailiff, who did Michi out of the money he had to swindle so hard to get, the *huissier* or whatever he was. . . . What was his name? Oh, yes. Gouffé!"

"Don't utter his name!" yelled Jaquemar.

"Ssh!" she exclaimed angrily. "I told you, walls have ears! Why do you shout? We could dig that old rubbish up again, if it means so much to you. I'm game. If there's anything to be got out of it, why not? He paid the penalty, too. He thought he could use me as a substitute for that spoiled goose Chottin; as a result he had to go naked into my trunk, which he dirtied with his excrement, and was tipped out along with the filth down the hillside at Millery. Gouffé—"

"Hold your tongue, you scum!"

"To my regret," she added.

Quivering with rage, he seized hold of both her ears; he was standing right up against her, tearing at her ears and shaking her head.

"Stop," she mumbled. "You're hurting me."

"How was it planned?" he shouted. "Come on, out with it—or by God . . ."

With a growl, half-struggling against his maltreatment, half-surrendering herself to it, she tilted her head slightly back; her eyes closed, so that only a slit of pupil remained visible, shimmering like mother-of-pearl in the flickering darkness, and her arm snaked up around Jaquemar's neck. Grinding his teeth, he plunged his left hand into her hair and gripped her upswept curls; he threw back his right hand in preparation for a terrible blow—and staggered forward, dragged by her unexpectedly powerful embrace, so that his lips entered her mouth, which was half open to receive them. But the kiss she gave him was such as he had never been given before; not that it was sophisticated or unnatural; on the contrary, it was nothing but nature and seemed like the activity of some creature lower than the human species: it sucked at his lips in short jerks like the sphincter muscle of the mouth of some horrible shellfish or snail. He fought against it desperately, with all his strength; he jerked and tugged himself back, groaning, and was all the more inescapably delivered to it; the tongue, serpentine, hard, and sharp, thrust itself between his lips and played lasciviously in the corners of his mouth. Oh, it was a loathsome kiss, slobbery and wet; it took his senses away and grew wilder and wilder the more he struggled against it; a kiss that suddenly turned into a razor-sharp, brief bite, so that his blood mingled with all the saliva; then the slobbering and sucking began again, as though the kisser were striving completely to absorb and consume the head of the kissed; it was the kiss of a praying mantis, who swallows her mate in the ecstasy of the orgasm.

Jaquemar's senses were gone, and only for the fraction of a second did he take fright again, as though burned by ice, but with a pleasure that he had neither the strength nor the presence of mind to resist, as her hand burst through his clothing and touched him with cold, gentle firmness and cut him with its fingernails, so that shivering thrills ran up and down his spine and shook him to the marrow and brain. They were both out of their minds; Bompard was breathing with snorting sounds through her little tiger's nose; she stumbled and staggered backward, without her grip on Jaquemar relaxing by a fraction of an inch.

Once again she groaned and mumbled plaintively: "Jaquemar, Jaquemar, sweetest . . . you are violating me."

Jaquemar made love to her on the bed; he felt himself enveloped by something hot and tight and his whole being consisted in nothing but the urge to release an overfullness in his body into this unspeakably thrilling, twitching, milking grasp; for out of the womb we come, into the womb we thrust, and have no other home for our woes; we would make a pilgrimage all the way around the earth for this one inexpressible fulfilment in which, as in a magic arc, ego and world shoot together—making for a few moments into One that which is otherwise two, which to our anguish is otherwise separate and mutually repugnant. Never in his life had Jaquemar felt his own ego more intimately, never more voluptuously lost it to the night: for it was the night, darkness and the void, to which he lost himself.

Only gradually, as he lay open-eyed beside her after his fall, did the more homely darkness of the room grow accustomed to his eyes, modestly return into them, and once more take possession of his senses. An almost impenetrable black twilight reigned, in which there was a flickering as of shaken waves of gray dust. The little flame in the cylinder of the lamp with the bowl of opaque glass beside the mirror was crackling and spluttering in an attempt to suck the last drop out of the wick, giving the gloomy dusk a fluttering movement like the flaccid beating of wings; in the semidarkness Jaquemar could see a pale glimmer through the door that Bompard had not quite shut earlier. This was the zinc lining to the headpiece of the bathtub, which was boxed in and glistened with a spectral gleam in the angular black wooden frame.

Jaquemar found the sight offensive; he closed his eyes, opened them again, and turned them toward his companion. Her flesh was glowing with the gentle pallor of a flower in the darkness. Her lids remained lowered and the fine lashes cast a faint, corpselike shadow on the lighter part of her face, which created an impression of feline, hypocritical innocence and gratification. She was naked in her negligee, and the darker nipples stood out full and lascivious under the drapery, like little nuts, on the two beautiful hemispheres of her breasts. Taut, a shadowy cone only sparsely grown with black moss, the mountain of Venus rose between the resting thighs; this sight, too, disgusted Jaquemar, so that he let his eyes move on, till they came to rest in the drawer hanging at an angle from the chest of drawers and on the object that had attracted his attention before, as it lay between underclothes of crêpe de Chine and lace.

The heavy little object seemed to be winking at him in the twitching gloom; it was of polished nickel and mother-of-pearl and barely the size of a child's fist—now the nature of the object penetrated deep and emphatically into his consciousness. He rose on both elbows and was looking more closely, when he jumped with fright and whipped his head around, thinking he heard a noise, a creaking sound, nearby. But he neither looked nor listened; for at this instant recognition of his degradation shot through him and he groaned: "God, my God. . . ."

"Why have you left me?" Bompard's voice grumbled sleepily. "Come back."

As though gathering up a sheaf, her hand and arm drew him back into the depths of the bed and in spite of his resistance brought him to rest on her breast.

"It's your nerves," she mumbled lazily. "Take some Eau de Cologne or a cigarette. . . ."

Now he lay on her breast, which was naked and cold, with hard, granular buds, and stared into the flickering gloom. Anguish of conscience tormented him unendurably, and to breathe the dense clammy heat of this room was also almost unendurable. The heavy curtains cut it off like a cube of hot night from the greater night of nature, a block of gloom unbroken save for the glimmer of the zinc bathtub that gleamed alluringly when the dying light of the wick filtered through the darkness. An impertinent odor of sweat and the consummated act of love clung poisonously to the walls like leaking gas and made his temples pound agonizingly with veins that were turned to wood.

Bompard mumbled sulkily: "A fine how-d'ye-do."

The breast beneath him bounced up and down and Bompard commented with a dreamy, soundless laugh: "So you had to come all the way across the ocean just to rape me."

But her eyes still did not open, not even when Jaquemar freed himself from the hand that had all the time been scratching his ear as one scratches a dog's ear and raised himself on his elbows again. Something inside him compelled him to stare at the object in the open drawer. Yes, it was a revolver, a small, shiny, handy weapon.

But although her eyes did not open, she remarked above a half-repressed yawn: "Carapin gave it to me."

"Yes, Carapin. . . ." said Jaquemar, lost sight of the revolver although his eyes did not move, and wiped the back of his hand across his lips—they were aching and burning, especially one spot on the lower lip, which was swollen; yet he felt this to be only a fraction of the horrible disorder, depravity, and degradation to which he had fallen victim in the seduction of this accursed hour.

"Take some Eau de Cologne," she said indifferently and with no evident train of thought. "I put it there specially for you; it's refreshing."

But the sense of his abasement went on growing in Jaquemar, only it came out of him in a distorted, almost petty-bourgeois form.

"Yes, Carapin," he said hollowly. "What will Carapin say?"

"He'll be good and angry," she answered briefly.

"Where has he gone?" asked Jaquemar, turning his eyes slowly toward her.

"He's away," she said, shrugging her bare shoulders and adding, with pouting lips and eyelashes that formed lovely, hypocritical shadows: "At noon today I read the *Chronicle*, and because you couldn't wait I sent him away. And he was very unhappy. What is Carapin to you?"

"But to you!" gritted Jaquemar.

"I'm leaving here," she rejoined, drawing her clown's brows down over the muscles of her eyelids. "I'm not interested in bankrupt men."

"I must go," murmured Jaquemar, more to himself than to her, and slid over to the edge of the bed on his elbows.

"Why are you in such a hurry all at once?" she grumbled. "You had time to rape me."

"I must straighten things out with myself," he said, staring down at the floor.

"How on earth are you going to do that?" she retorted with a laugh.

"I don't know," he replied gloomily.

She was now swinging the golden slipper on her bare foot to and fro; she lethargically raised her eyelids slightly and pointed with her bent-back thumb at the little revolver.

"I saw that pretty toy in the window of a shop on Broadway, sparkling in the sunshine. And since in his recklessness he had had bad luck and suffered considerable losses and was forever pestering me about having to go to Buffalo to 'restore his finances,' I said: 'Give me that little weapon, darling, in case anyone tries to violate me; then go to Buffalo, you can take a holiday.' So he went to Buffalo, as he wished."

"I must go," reiterated Jaquemar dully.

"Must you keep on harping on the same old string?" she exploded angrily.

She pulled herself up into a sitting position, and although the nocturnal gloom had now become really impenetrable (for the dusty flicker of the lamp was growing dimmer and dimmer, and the ghostly glimmer of the zinc bathtub in the next room was almost extinguished), he nevertheless believed he could see her eyes spurting cold fire and her blue-black locks rising like tongues of flame; he could clearly distinguish the gentle curve of her cheek and the bold form of her little wild beast's nose. She really looked comical, for she was waving her hands about, shaking them with her rootlike fingers outspread as she went on angrily scolding.

"It's always the same. In your credulity you expect something new from every new man, and what you get in flagrante is always the same spineless insult! First they swagger and show off with heaven knows what lure and weapon and can't get their way quickly enough; then in a trice they're backing out with their tails between their legs. They've no perseverance—not one of them has any staying power!"

He rose and began to leave, groping his way with both hands.

"Take care," she grumbled after him ill-humoredly. "Don't bang into my trunk again. I'm fond of it, it's a souvenir I value highly. Carapin had it specially sent from London for me."

Meanwhile, with hands outstretched and the certainty of a somnambulist, he found his way to the door and through the chaos of departure that filled the next room. He had completely forgotten her; he strode forward as though rendered mysteriously light and carried by some unknown force toward a goal that he both feared and yearned for—his destiny, which he knew to be a somber one.

He opened the door of her apartment, shut it behind him, and was conscious of a feeling of weakness induced by the different, rather cooler and chalky air in the corridor. He leaned back against the door with his eyes closed, opening them only when he heard someone creeping cautiously along not very far from him. The man approaching from the end of the corridor, casting shy yet venturesome glances behind him, now turned his face toward him, revealing a pipe gripped between large teeth and rather tight lips. He caught sight of Jaquemar, came to a stop, took the pipe out of his mouth, positively gaped at him—and turned on his heel and disappeared. With a shock, Jaquemar looked down at himself: his clothes were disordered, he must look disheveled, and licentious, like a stage character caught in the middle of an orgy. *Disgrace!* he thought, but he instantly forgot the pipe-smoker, because the thought of his horrible ignominy surged into his brain.

He did not tidy his suit. Just as he was, he felt his way along by the perforated pipes on the wall, under the ceiling sprinklers, quite oblivious of the fact that he might meet someone else and give himself away again. He met no one else, however, and remained unaware that the pipe-smoker was standing on watch in the entrance to another corridor, openmouthed and with his pipe in his hand, staring at him as he came toward and then past him.

He entered his room, went to the high, narrow window which, as usual, was open, and leaned out. The insect concert outside was raging with unparalleled vigor and vitality, and it seemed to Jaquemar as though for the first time he heard amid this ceaseless croaking, chirring, and throbbing, certain high-pitched individual voices, in the dull pounding rhythm a silvery trilling and warbling that bespoke joy and triumph. The pulses in his temples refused to adapt themselves to the mighty, jubilant drumming of the night, and with a groan he turned his head to the mirror on the wall. Sufficient light from the glimmer on Broadway came in through the window to show him the ravages visible in his face above the half-torn-open shirt collar, the swelling on the right side of his lower lip, the mouth all disfigured by her sucking kisses. It was remorse, disgust, and contrition that looked out at him from the mirror, and a vertiginous hatred rose in him, hatred of his own dishonored reflection and an even more bitter hatred that itched for action, for violence and revenge.

He walked quickly over to his bed, lay down, and stared at the ceiling. His hatred rendered clear thought impossible; but he felt as though the violent pounding in his temples was pumping out of him, with all the toil of Sisyphus, a mental slime of which his brain must rid itself, even if the pumping rubbed and scrubbed it raw.

This much he knew: Bompard now had him in the palm of her hand. One of her friends had witnessed the state in which he left her room—he was irredeemably compromised; she need only open her mouth and speak the truth to ruin him socially, as he was already ruined morally. Was he already ruined morally? Something like a lust for horror and self-pollution overcame him. Suppose this act had certain natural consequences? he thought. Suppose I have made her pregnant—*I made pregnant the murderess of Gouffé, whom I set out to avenge?*

This was such an atrocious idea that he was forced to sit up; resting on his elbows, he sat staring at the tips of his boots. And to his inner eye there appeared with absolute clarity the little revolver as he saw it in the gloom of the room, a dangerous, handy little weapon, a compact object of nickel and mother-of-pearl, with its accurately tooled, pretty round cartridge chamber between barrel and handle. The picture was so fascinating that he could not take his eyes off it, and it was as though he had to bring himself back from far away before he finally became aware that someone had already knocked on his door several times.

"Who is it?" he called out, turning his eyes toward the door. It opened and there stood a great hulking shape. The visitor stepped to one side and closed the door behind him. "Gaunt," he said briefly. Jaquemar did not answer. The young American struck a match on his trousers and lit up the room; in the flickering of the flame, his beautifully ugly face with the deep furrows was at once paler and more mobile than usual, and the melancholy eyes had an insistent life.

"I have a message for you," he said, looking at the half-upright Jaquemar with a deep but uninterpretable gravity. He waved out the match and came closer in the darkness. "Madame Carapin asked me to tell you that you should not stay here. You're to leave tomorrow morning on the ten o'clock train. Your ticket has been left with the doorman."

"Leave?" burst out Jaquemar. "Where for?"

"New York." The visitor parted the short tails of his coat and dropped onto the foot end of the bed.

"I—leave?" Jaquemar burst out again. He was trying to think it out and shook his head.

Gaunt turned his face away; he kept his powerful chin in the soft white shirt collar lowered, stared down at the floor, and said, speaking straight in front of him: "I am no one's judge, I can't even pass a verdict on myself . . . but you want to abduct her, that much is clear."

Jaquemar burst out laughing. "I abduct her! God bless your simple heart."

"What a night," said the young man, ignoring Jaquemar's remark. "First we took Tulipan to the hospital; he was taken ill during the farewell dinner; Madame ('Ma'am') was furious. 'Why does he drink one brandy after another, when he's already half gone?' she said. But it was serious. A heart attack. The doctor holds little hope. And now *this!*" He turned his face toward Jaquemar; his lips looked torn and bitter, and he remarked in a tone of somber finality: "I love her, and you are taking her away."

"If it were like that . . ." rejoined Jaquemar equally somberly. "You don't know what you are being spared!"

"Well," said Gaunt, standing up with a clatter, "that was my message." He walked to the door and had already taken hold of the handle when he turned around again. "I don't want to lie to you," he said dryly, "not even to you. I was there all the time. I was in the bathroom, Madame ordered me in there; I was to come out if she called for help, but only then. 'What you hear,' she said, 'will do you good.' No doubt she wanted to cure me." He gave a very faint laugh and said: "Heaven knows, you are discretion personified. And I poured out my heart to you! I'm ashamed of myself."

"You don't know anything about it," exclaimed Jaquemar. "If you had an inkling what infamy and unutterable baseness, what suffering and misery and despair lie behind it! Don't you see that the whole thing was prearranged? That you were ordered to witness my degradation out of craftiness and malice and for purposes of blackmail? I abduct her! I abduct that beast. . . ."

"So you're leaving," stated Gaunt in a calm voice. Jaquemar stared into space; once again he saw the little revolver before his inner eye. "So you're leaving?" reiterated Gaunt.

"I shouldn't dream of it!" roared Jaquemar. "This is my chance—even if I myself go to perdition through it! Say to the filthy trollop: 'Jaquemar travels when it suits Jaquemar!' And let her beware!"

He fell silent as abruptly as he had begun to shout, and for a few minutes there was nothing in the room but silence and the immense insect concert that swallowed and outlasted all other sounds with its rhythm, repeated with all the patience of eternity, the croaking, drumming, chirring, trilling, and warbling, the jubilation of the world of night and love outside that ceaselessly enjoyed itself, uncaring for any human suffering and anguish.

"Good night, sir," said the young American in a curiously hollow voice; the door shut behind him and Jaquemar, who did not follow him with his eyes, was alone once more with the vast, merciless drumming of nature.

3

AMERICA. SECOND STOP: THE FOREST

Jaquemar stayed, Bompard left—that was what happened. Apart from a certain feeling of emptiness that kept him wandering restlessly to and fro throughout the whole of the following morning, this fact remained concealed from Jaquemar, until a presentiment of it came to him in the afternoon. Struck by the lightning of half realization, he came to a sudden stop on his way across the hall, just in front of the Negro boy who had recently had his ears boxed by Bompard on his account. He looked at the thick-lipped, smiling face with recognition and burst out: "Where is she? Madame Carapin?"

"Left at daybreak, yessir," with her big trunk on the back of the light carriage that had come from "somewhere else." Where was she going? The boy didn't know. Jaquemar turned and walked with his new officer's gait to the reception desk.

"Where has Madame Carapin gone? Where did the carriage come from?" The man sitting behind the desk shook his big liverish face blankly and raised his heavy, drooping lids to reveal melancholy eyes. But when he saw Jaquemar's thumb and forefinger slowly and seductively drawing a bank note out of his waistcoat pocket, his lips moved as though in slothful but awakening cupidity and he answered gloomily, his eyes on the note in Jaquemar's hand: "Four Corners in

the Vermont forest is a place often recommended to our clients for
their convalescence. It's three times three hours' journey from Saratoga,
with good horses."

Early the following morning, Jaquemar was once more on the road,
with good horses. Sitting on the rear seat of the trap, he gave one last
look behind him and saw the Grand Union gradually move away and
disappear, shimmering festively in the opal light of dawn, a grotesque
Versailles of shame decorated with a multicolored flag, which, however, curled slack and joyless around the short, sturdy mast on the roof
of the central section.

The coachman on the front seat was an unfriendly, gaunt man with
a bulbous nose in his gray, emaciated face; he had one walleye, and
curiously enough this intensified the impression of lechery for some
reason evoked by his unappetizing thinness, as though the eye had
been damaged in some indecorous erotic combat. He had not replied
to Jaquemar's greeting, and later, too, he spoke not a word, except that
every now and then he pointed with his whip, broke into a completely
uncalled-for laugh, and uttered the name of a village or some other
topographical detail. But this happened for the first time after they
had been traveling for three hours toward a mountain range that cut
across the horizon like a gigantic wall or the towering shoreline of an
inland sea.

Now they were at its foot. The powerful horses were going at walking pace; the soft white sand of the track trickled out of the wheels
as they wound their way up through the dense forest of deciduous
trees and conifers to right and left. The aromatic scent of resin in the
sun gradually freshened into little wavering breezes; the coachman
laughed in his moronic way, raised his whip to point at the track, and
said: "Old Mohawk Trail."

Finally the trees thinned out, they were at the top, the track
plunged on into the open, affording a magnificent view of the land
across which they had driven and a hitherto unnoticed little town
nestling close by in a hollow of the hillside, its glazed roofs glittering
and trails of pale pink and ochre smoke hanging above it. The sky,
undisturbed by the cry of any bird, stretched out endlessly overhead,
golden-blue and dotted with motionless balls of cloud; the silence was
almost eerie. But in front of them the white sandy track ran on in
long-drawn spirals down to the valley, and there below the land ex-

tended in all directions, broken up into fields and forests and cut across by a flashing stream, until it ended in a hazy blue ridge of wooded hills; it was quite a different landscape from the one at their backs, more dreamy and unawakened, inviting in its unspeakably peaceful muteness, so that the coachman's cackling laugh sounded if possible even more foolish than before, as he pointed straight ahead and down at an angle toward the hazy blue forest in the distance and said: "Big Forest of Vermont."

At many points in its rising and falling course the track narrowed, rounded a steep wooded slope, and opened out beyond to afford magnificent views. Then thickly wooded hills and mountains could be seen far and wide beside or behind one another beneath the motionless clouds of the summer sky, their richly varied shades of green shot through by birch trunks like white dashes; at several points the bluish smoke of campfires curled up from among the trees, scenting the rich, hot air with their pleasant, pungent odor.

Finally, the trail became a forest path that led down into the depths of the dense timber, bordered on either side by bellying, humming bushes. At first everything was still fallow, then patches of gleaming brightness appeared among the shadowy brown, now on the right, now on the left, and flowering meadows stretched out on both sides, above whose grass green and buttercup yellow the vertical sunlight boiled into a froth and shimmered in the shape of a smoldering haze. As Jaquemar gazed out, dazzled from the moving carriage, he suddenly became aware that his face was glowing as though with fever and that his body was wet with sticky, hot sweat. Something like apprehension or terror came over him and he asked almost in a shout: "Have we reached our destination?"

The driver laughed his stupid laugh and pointed to one side with his whip. There, crooked and only half visible, a moldering wooden notice leaning among the bushes announced: "ENTERING FOUR CORNERS / Founded 1739." Yes, he had reached his destination. In front of him the road plunged into a covered bridge of a kind no doubt necessitated hereabouts by the heavy winter snowfall, and looking like a barn, the missing ends of which constituted the entrance and exit. The carriage drove through with a thunderous clatter, and in the darkness Jaquemar saw rows of long tins set along the inner walls with names painted on them in black, and red metal tablets, some of which stuck up in the

air to attract attention—letter boxes, which bore witness to the fact
that this village deep in the heart of the great forest of Vermont was
not entirely forgotten or destitute of links with the world and life
outside.

All the same, it lay deep in the heart of the forest, amidst inviolable
peace. Jaquemar could see it; there could not be much more to it than
the single dead-straight street before his eyes. Through the rich green
of many gardens, old-fashioned houses of white wood peeped, and
the bright pastel colors of flowers shimmered in the heat haze.

Jaquemar's carriage bore left to a gently curving lawned hillock
comprising a cemetery, on the topmost terrace of which a little white
wooden church with a low, square tower was perched contentedly like
a broody hen. But even this, the highest point of the village, still
nestled in the protection of the giant trees that stood in utter stillness
with their enormous, wrinkled trunks and winglike tufts of foliage.
Everything remained concealed beneath their impenetrable cathedral
roof and steeped in enchanted twilight, in which every color and
every object became a boon to the eye and life itself a gentle dream,
a friendly specter, insignificant yet entrancing—for instance, the old
man who was just making his way between the graves on the cemetery
hill with a cow on a halter and who vanished into the greenish glimmer
beyond, as though the luxuriant and familiar growth had swallowed
them both up without sound or suffering.

Jaquemar had little time to surrender himself to this enchantment.
No sooner had it swung left than his carriage came to a stop outside
a multistoried building, and the coachman turned his emaciated face
as though inquiringly toward his passenger, who did not notice. He
was looking at the building. It was encircled by a wooden veranda
raised two steps off the ground and full of empty rocking chairs; the
windows of the upper stories were filled with reflections of the surrounding greenery and flanked by red shutters at present thrown back;
the whole was topped by a rickety tiled roof from whose thick, cubical
chimneys bluish-white oven smoke was billowing, and this mute sign
of activity gave the prosperous and well-kept building something of
the atmosphere of a German fairy tale, as though it meant: "Welcome, unexpected visitor, we are already cooking a meal for you!"

Jaquemar clambered out of the carriage and made for the building,
until the lecherous driver whistled shrilly with two fingers in his

mouth to call him back. The man growled and shook his forefinger threateningly, made the gesture of paying money, and watched craftily with his walleye as Jaquemar handed over the fare. He did not thank him, but merely said "Luggage!" jerking his head back toward Jaquemar's bag. "Wait here," Jaquemar replied curtly and walked away.

He mounted the two steps to the veranda. The double-leafed sliding door in front of him was already moving apart to both sides; a gray-haired but youthful-looking and very slender lady hastened toward him, all welcoming smiles, stumbled, wrung her hands with delight and embarrassment, and brought out bit by bit, in a voice interspersed with tiny laughs, the forms of greeting usual in this country. "A wonderful day, sir, warm and sunny, like a gift from the Almighty, sir, just right for a trip . . ."

"My name is Jaquemar," he interrupted.

"Oh, yes, yes, of course," she warbled, intensifying her almost whimpering little laughs, brought her hand up to her cheek, turned around from the waist and cried to Jaquemar: "If you don't mind, sir, please, perhaps I may . . . Will you follow me, sir?"

She took him up to the second floor and into a room the walls and doors of which were lined with antique tapestry worked in large-scale pictures, filled with furniture of highly polished birch or lemonwood, and all in all delightful, except that it contained an extremely wretched iron bedstead or camp bed with chipped black paint and a feather mattress already pressed down in the middle, an eyesore in the otherwise fastidious, though curiously chaste, style of the rest of the room.

"I thought, sir," stammered the lady, giggling painfully as she followed Jaquemar's gaze, "I took the liberty, but of course, sir . . ."

"I want a decent bed," growled Jaquemar.

"At your service, sir!" cried the laughing voice of Gabrielle Bompard.

She was standing in the doorway leading into the next room, looking up at Jaquemar and tidying her blue-black curly hair, with the strong light in the room glowing healthily on her delicate cheeks and the damp red of her lips and the sparkling black of her eyes. Heaven knows she had no need of fine clothes! She was dressed in a bright-colored checked shirt and workman's trousers of smooth blue cloth with a dull sheen, while on her feet were buckskin moccasins.

Her sudden appearance so startled Jaquemar that he did not notice that at this moment his traveling bag was brought in by the man in the hunter's cap and dungarees, who was greeted with incredulous disapproval by the lady. "Well, now, really . . . Cooley Lane!" The man took off his cap, looked shamefacedly at his feet, and murmured, but actually without servility: "I beg your pardon, Miss Dimple. Balthasar was going to throw the bag into the road. He wouldn't wait."

"The rascal wants to fall off the box and break his neck, does he?" cried Bompard merrily, adding curtly: "Leave us alone."

As the door closed behind the two of them, Jaquemar walked slowly and threateningly up to Bompard and said: "So this is where you got to. I suppose you thought nobody could find you here!"

"It's nice and snug here," she answered, as though agreeing with him, shrugging one shoulder. "We're on our own, you've got your way."

"Not yet!"

"Everything in good time," she said beaming, and suddenly broke out laughing. "What must the dreary old goat have thought? A bed? What do you want a bed for? Really, your whims are just too crazy. A bed! Isn't one enough? Or how did you imagine things? Did you expect to come marching up like troops going on maneuvers every time we felt like getting to work? In-out, out-in? In the morning, for example, just when it's nicest, when you've slept yourself into a heat?"

"Your filthy talk doesn't deflect me from my purpose," he said calmly, but with grinding teeth amidst her laughter. "Cowardly beast! You wanted to dodge me again, as you did when you left France, I suppose?"

"Because I preferred my American friends' yacht to the Orphée?" she inquired with interest, beaming down at the floor. "But you were welcome to come with us. I waited for you in the hall of the Hôtel Corbeau, you only had to ask me. I was sitting there."

"You hoped to slip away under cover of darkness, eh? It won't do you any good, don't delude yourself!"

"What do you mean?" she asked in the same childishly attentive tone. "You came after me, didn't you?"

"I certainly did!" he cried with a laugh. "You won't escape me, hide where you will!"

"Hide? Well, yes, one of us had to start. The forest is deep, and that's where Bruin the bear has his den. Everything is the way you wanted it—as if I didn't know you! You must admit that it's absolutely ideal for two people who want to be alone."

He seized her arm and whispered with fierce joy: "Quite right! For two people who want to be alone. . . ."

"What!" she cried, as though only now beginning to understand. "You really believed . . . ? Of course, it's perfectly true that Chester was worried about me; he would have liked to know that I was somewhere out of reach of your lasciviousness. But I ask you: where is there such a place? Besides, love too has its rights, and those who say 'Let him who has the itch scratch himself' don't know what they're talking about. So as a sign of my willingness, I left my address with the porter and told Balthasar, who is an old business contact of mine, to explain the route to you as he brought you here, so that you could find your way back again, if you felt like it, after you had had your fun."

"Didn't you first order the poor lad to be a witness of my degradation," yelled Jaquemar, shaking her by the arm, "and then send him to me to tell me I should—leave?"

"But you did leave! And what do you mean 'degradation'? You had a wonderful time. And I slipped Chester, who had come to help me pack, into the bathroom for protection when you forced your way in to rape me. One has to take certain precautions. I did it out of good nature. Lust sometimes sends young tomcats jumping off the roof, you know."

"What a poisonous toad!" Jaquemar burst out disgustedly. "One ought almost to feel grateful to her for trying to slip away into the darkness!"

"No!" she cried indignantly. "Is he starting that old rubbish all over again! Slip away into the darkness? Hide? Don't be ridiculous! Just look in the next room! Why do you think I ordered Dimple to bring the beautiful big double bed in—for a joke? And why do you think I booked in under *this* name?"

"*This* name?" he stammered. "What do you mean?"

"I'm sorry," she said reasonably, "but it was unavoidable, since I made my bed yours."

"Under which name? Answer me!"

"Your face is all patchy again," she remarked in a matter-of-fact voice, looking at him closely.

"You didn't dare to call yourself by my name . . . not Madame Jaquemar?"

"You've no idea how prudish they are in this country. In order to couple, people slip under one name together as elsewhere they slip under a blanket. One must howl with the wolves and do as Rome does, unpleasant incidents only spoil one's fun. But about those patches on your face, you should quickly bathe it in the Androscoggin, Eau de Cologne is no good in this case."

"Madame Jaquemar!" he whispered with hard, pale lips, shut his eyes, opened them again, and gulped: "Good, that's good. Even if I wanted to, there is no turning back now! Madame Jaquemar! I swear I shall not take one step back! I fear, Madame, that you will not bear that name for long."

"We shan't get any gray hairs about that. The main thing is that you are here at last!" she cried merrily and burst out laughing again. "Don't forget the Androscoggin! One might think your hot desires were breaking out on your face in the form of chicken pox. You ought to be ashamed of yourself. . . . But who am I to poke fun at you! I too can hardly hold myself in. Just feel my dear heart, it's racing. Feel it!"

With a deft movement she grasped his hand in hers and thrust it into her blouse, in which the firm breast with the nipple like a nut was naked, naked, soft, and sweet, so that in spite of his overwhelming feeling of horror, a thrill of carnal delight ran down the young man's spine.

"Don't tickle me," said Gabrielle Bompard, breathing through her little tiger's nose and pressing his hand around her breast. "You are anxious. In broad daylight!"

She pressed herself against him as though entering into him, her octopus arms held him in their firm embrace, and the slippery wetness of her merciless snail's mouth drew in his lips in short, vigorous sucks. Once more he opened his eyes; her lids were chastely lowered, and she was groaning as though racked with pain. They staggered back and in the next room knocked against something hard and ribbed. Gouffé's trunk! shot through Jaquemar's brain. In this trunk is the revolver, be of good cheer, Gouffé, however I may lose myself!

"What's the matter?" she groaned from underneath him. "Curse these trousers! Come, sweetest! How I have waited for you! How I love you! Love me, Jaquemar! My darling little goat! Oh, Jaquemar, Jaquemar. . . ."

When finally he sought to free himself from her, she continued to hold him fast in the iron grip of her arms, belly, and legs; in the corner of each eye, on either side of her nose, there was a tiny, brownish blood vessel; under her eyes lay an enchantingly delicate violet crescent; and the closed lids with their long, slightly curved lashes cast a fine, deathlike shadow on the cool, sated face.

"No, stay," she murmured lazily. "We aren't flies. You're not heavy. How I yearned for you—oh, long night! My wonderful one. It was a good thing Balthasar—"

She broke off thoughtfully and laughed softly to herself, before continuing in a dreamy voice and without opening her eyes: "We'll push him off the box, he must be punished, he was disrespectful to you. Besides, with his horrible eye he arouses unhappy memories in me. Don't struggle, Jaquemar, stop that, it disturbs me. He reminds me of Catherine, the poor dear, who was with me in the convent during the glorious days of my youth. Because of the queer shape of her head, we used to call her 'the Half Moon,' until out of kindness I gave her a new name. Later she took the veil, because she couldn't get on in the world outside either; you see, apart from the odd shape of her skull, she was disfigured. Two friends were swinging her by her hands and feet and, overestimating their frail strength, they accidentally dropped her into a thorn bush, which tore one of her eyes. We meant no harm, we were only playing with her, but as long as I remained with the good sisters I was reminded of the little accident; the torn eye looked like the eyes of the boiled haddock we had to force down our throats every Friday on account of the fast, notwithstanding the high boarding fee, and for this reason—out of the kindness of my heart and to set her free from her contemptuous nickname—I called her Catherine Friday."

"For God's sake," groaned Jaquemar, "let me go."

"Is it already dinnertime?" she asked with a yawn. "All right, darling, straighten yourself out, tidy yourself up, so that you can look a proper gentleman when you take me to dinner."

Jaquemar sat gloomily at the gay meal; for gay it was, or should have been. The menu was exquisite, tasty hors d'oeuvres, carp from the Androscoggin, Virginia ham roasted with mustard and brown sugar with slices of pineapple; the well-cared-for, cosy room, with its brightly painted timber walls and the shelves running around them bearing a multitude of antique bowls and vases, ships in bottles, gilded china dogs, and Dutch tiles, was aglow; there was an enchanting fragrance compounded of the sweet scent of flowers, the cool smell of floor polish, and the melting wax of the candles on the table that flashed in Bompard's merry eyes. She was in the best of spirits and kept encouraging Jaquemar.

"Fortify yourself, Monsieur!" she cried. "Refinement alone won't keep you going; the prudent man builds up his strength."

As she spoke, she was already looking with anticipation at the next dish, which a very lanky young girl with a good-natured but curiously chalky mask of a face was carrying in with the zealous speed of a coach and pair through the pantry door that fanned this way and that as she passed, after which she brought it gliding down onto the table with a fine sweep of her arm. At one point Miss Dimple herself put in an appearance; a certain severity lurked in the flashing glance of her black eyes as she peered over the table, to the accompaniment of embarrassed murmurs, nods, and hand-rubbing. She wished them a good appetite and withdrew with a multitude of tiny bows and still more embarrassed murmurs, after asking whether there were any further orders and being curtly dismissed by Bompard with the words: "We'll tell you if we want anything."

But to Jaquemar she was amiability and encouragement personified, humorously understanding and misunderstanding the taciturnity of her ill-tempered table companion.

"Don't worry, chéri," she said, looking with shining eyes at the bowl of dessert that had just come to rest in front of her. "Don't worry, you won't have the blues for long! The little bit of messing around you had on the trunk was just an introduction! But once you take a real look at me afterward and I get my nails into you again, sap will shoot into the sagging stalk, I can tell you, and our love will blossom as never before. Just rely on me."

In the room with the bluish figured wallpaper (the wallpaper in the next room displayed the same pattern in red—a cock, an anchor, a ship, and a house encircled by a garland of flowers repeated over and over again) Jaquemar undressed, pulled a long linen dressing gown on over his nightshirt, and listened to Gabrielle Bompard rummaging, rattling, and shuffling about on the other side of the wall. Will she forget to shut the trunk? he wondered and felt his breathing quicken. He stared into space. Next to the ugly camp bed stood a pillar table with four claw feet of metal; on the circular table top, beside the lighted candle, lay a thick little book with silver clasps which—he was quite sure—had not been there before. He picked it up, opened the clasps, and turned the pages. It was a manual of devotion containing Sunday sermons, edifying thoughts, and extremely naive woodcuts; in particular, there was one showing Jonah sitting with crossed legs in the belly of the whale, and Jaquemar was struck by the pious passenger's appearance of comfort.

"Do you know," asked Bompard, who had stepped unobserved into the doorway and was plucking with lowered eyes at her batiste cami-knickers, "that they call these things 'modesty garments'?"

As Jaquemar did not answer, although he looked up so that the candlelight was reflected in his squinting eyes, she too raised her eyes, saw the little book in his hand, and could not help laughing.

"Do you say your prayers every night, Jaquemar?"

"You're right," he replied, shutting the book, "it's blasphemy."

Or isn't it? he wondered, and became lost in thought. Bompard was rummaging about in the next room again; she was whistling and humming softly to herself and wandering gaily to and fro; finally there was a sigh and a contented purr, evidently indicating that she was snuggling down in her bed. This was followed by complete silence that lasted a long time, both in her room and in his.

"How much longer is it going to be?" cried her voice. "What are we waiting for?"

Jaquemar walked quickly into the next room, carrying the little book, saw that the trunk was shut, and hesitantly approached her bed.

She was holding the thin blanket pulled up to her throat, her fists on the inside. Her eyes were modestly closed and her white face lay slightly askew on the pillow wearing an unutterably sweet and contented smile. As on the very first day, the beauty of this face struck the young man with oblivion, terror, and delight. The loveliness of the cheeks and the expression of unsatiated thirst in the curve of the full lips that were only just touching one another, the petal-like shimmer of the eyelids, the charming, slightly disreputable discoloration of the skin by the bridge of the nose, where the sinuous veins were clearly visible, the bold, shell-like shape of the nostrils, the shiny, pale-pink wall dividing them, and the gentle groove running down to the little heart-shaped protuberance in the center of the upper lip— all this lay there in total purity and indestructible innocence, embedded and framed in those flamelike locks in whose bluish-black the reflection of the candlelight danced and flickered. Intoxicated by a lust that was no longer of the body, he sat down on the edge of the bed. She stretched her bare right arm out from under the bedclothes, took hold of the book he was holding, without opening her eyes, and flung it across the room. She grasped the back of his neck and pulled him down toward her, whispering with her lips on his: "Darling, are you going to come to me properly this time, all night through, really properly, no more of that silly kid's stuff, a quick do and off again? Oh, how I have been craving for you, how I love you!"

She tugged at his dressing gown and tore his shirt open, she snuffled at his chest, her head quivering like a dog's as it searches for a scent and lamented: "No, really, all these prudish complications still! Am I to smell starch instead of a man? Man is naked, and he must be loved naked! Everything serious is naked! Down with all that rubbish!"

The shirt ripped; Jaquemar staggered to his feet in order to throw off his dressing gown; she pulled the thin blanket to one side with a gesture of invitation and motioned him to her with her outstretched right arm. He hesitated; for she was intoxicating to look at in her nakedness and bewilderingly different from what he had expected to see: she was at once softer and harder than in her clothes. There was something boyishly solid, something archaic, about her curiously straight, low-arched feet and rounded calves, and yet they did not appear too powerful, because they passed in perfect proportions through small kneecaps into the twin goblets of her voluptuously extended thighs. Her thighs were full of controlled strength and enchantingly lovely where they converged at the hill of Venus, conjuring a soft, alluring patch of shadow into the spotless mirror of her body; they seemed to reflect in broader form the delightful constriction where the outer curve of the hips narrowed in toward the navel, an extraordinarily expressive valley that forced the observer to recognize the suppleness and fertility of this young female body. The same shape was repeated for the third time in the triangular shadow of the collarbone below the rounded, warm-looking shoulders, where it emphasized the fruitfulness of the breasts, whose buds, now at rest, had settled down almost into slits but were encircled by granulous moons, like pistils in the interior of a flower.

In contrast to the white face, however, the whole glorious body was as dark as Isis, as though burned by the Ethiopian sun, and it looked so firm and succulent that it gave the young man the feeling of being confronted by a fundamental and final manifestation of life, an extreme expression of the phenomenon life, a uniquely inspired creation that would oppose to its own destruction an immensely robust power and fury of resistance; and this existential fanaticism slumbering in the flesh was perhaps the most captivating thing about a body that must ultimately, like all bodies, be destined for death—or of what other substance could it have been made?

Jaquemar felt her body with his hands. She was completely and utterly different from what he had expected. Judging by her behavior all the time up to the present and her extreme outspokenness, Jaquemar, who detested exuberant women, had naturally anticipated unrestrained ardor—yet now he found a chaste young woman, though one who was in love and therefore awaited smiling and with yielding acceptance the gratification which the loved one would perform on her.

She pulled the blanket up over herself and him, and with a thrill of delight that ran through all his nerves Jaquemar noticed that although a clammy heat prevailed in the room—for nightfall had raised rather than lowered the temperature—she was in the literal sense of the word cold, ice-cold in fact, and not only in her cautiously inquisitive, hard, thin fingers and the smooth flatness of her stomach, but also where her flesh swelled and blossomed, on the twin goblets of her thighs and on her breasts, whose nipples, now that the male body she desired was close, had burst forth like firm little nuts. Nothing more stimulating than this coldness can be imagined. It streamed into the young man's blood; he immediately found himself in a firm and hard, almost savage embrace; a tiny cry of delight, a bird cry, slipped out between her lips, and although her eyes were still chastely closed, her mouth, unable any longer to master its thirst, was half open and quivering in anticipation and the desire to feel and make itself useful.

Jaquemar slid his arm between her thighs and up over the small of her back toward her shoulder blades; the wiry hair on his chest scrubbed against the elastic, budlike fullness of her cool breasts, and the mouth and breath of the lovers sank and burrowed one into the other. But when Jaquemar finally possessed her, the heat of the tight belly burned him, her eyes opened, she was squinting slightly in the turmoil of lust, and if he had been fully conscious he would have been terrified and horror-stricken by the soulless gleam in the eyes that stared at him out of the white face with the little tiger's nose through which the breath came in a hiss—but when in the act of generation (if we were only aware of it) does soullessness not stare us in the eyes, as in the villeinage of pleasure and pain that binds us to an unplumbably greater soul we sow and reap and are reaped, without kindness or mercy?

He was protected from the recognition of these unfathomable depths (as we all are) by the intoxication of enjoyment, and it was a long-lasting enjoyment that heaped up stroke by stroke an ever blinder and wilder urge to self-liberation in his cells and finally poured itself out in such ecstatic convulsions that he simply fell asleep on the bed of the beloved body. But this man, usually so cantankerous, who had now made of himself, as she wished, a joyful sacrifice to her, was no burden, and a smile of innocently happy gratification and peace played about her lips. Yes, innocence was in her, only innocence sleeps such a diaphanously light sleep after lust as she slept by his side when he later lay beside her, looked at her, and without any feeling, without any thought for what had gone before, merely said to himself in the crystal-clear vision of total freedom from desire: "An innocent young woman, satisfied in the depths of her womanliness to have been loved by her lover."

How young was she? According to the calendar, twenty; but that was not what he wanted to know. The eyebrows that rose in the middle with the pained expression of a clown, generally as smooth as though painted on, were a trifle ruffled; the shadows of her lashes created the appearance of fatigue on her pale face, and the violet rings under her eyes were marked by slightly greasy little folds suggesting dissipation. The furrows running down from the nostrils to the corners of the mouth, which normally looked simply like a smile, although they were fine, were very deep as if cut with a sharp little knife; a cloud like the gravity of ancient experience seemed to lie even over the peaceful serenity of her smile, a hint of something that must have been far earlier in origin than the very oldest man; and her body revealed an erotic maturity not found in young girls. How young, how old was she? Like life, like death—and like mankind's great poems—she had in this respect no attribute; she was present. And she was also present in a more banal sense, although she did not open her eyes under his gaze, but murmured sleepily in a velvety yet scratchy, deep voice: "We could have saved ourselves a lot of unpleasantness, darling. Why didn't you come to me instead of the man of Millery? Why didn't you hand that colorless goose, Chottin, over to him?"

At this, the old hatred blazed up with unprecedented intensity in Jaquemar's heart, and so great was the shock that his paralyzed lips could give no utterance to it, but said in reply to her question: "Suppose I loved her?"

Still with her deeply satisfied smile, she replied in a low and languid voice: "How could you have loved her, dearest, when you were waiting for me?"

Impelled by his rage, he rose on both elbows and let his eyes run down her body. They came to a stop at the pit of her abdomen, and he discovered a splendid motive for his hatred: How he hated her hands! Both were now lying chastely over her belly; on a different partner these hands would have amused him, for there was something distinctly comical about their shriveled, knock-kneed shape; but on her they had an inhuman look. In their yellow crookedness they suggested bird's claws; they were claws, jagged gripping implements, and although they could inflict pleasure and pain, that was not what they were made for; they were made to grasp and cling to the prey, they were the claws of a bird of prey, and the fact that at the moment they were lying quiet made their fitness for their cruel purpose almost more threatening—their indifference sprang from a horrible assurance!

"Anyhow, darling," murmured Bompard drowsily, "all these speculations are nothing but smoke and straw in your heart and mine; forget them! You were waiting for me, I was waiting for you . . . I'm patient by nature."

She raised both hands and gathered in his head, hooking one little finger in Jaquemar's ear, and laid the resisting man to rest on her bosom. She ran the nails of her left hand over his body like a comb, a sly smile now suffused her features as the quivering Jaquemar gazed at her, and she whispered: "I'm a virtuous woman, God knows, but of all my virtues I prize my patience highest. You see, it always pays."

She looked down at him animatedly, gulped, and whispered, breathing heavily but quietly: "My dearest love, I am craving for you, and you, who are not lazy in spite of your sluggish blood, are craving for me."

Yes, he was craving for her! He was nothing but desire and exuberance, obscene, it appeared to him so long as he was able to grasp a thought from amidst his terrible desire, his fury, and his turmoil. He took hold of her; a fresh love struggle began, even wilder than the first; he loved her with the violence of fierce hate, an almost unbearable rapture of hate; for lust and hate were one in this love; the rattle in their throats anticipated the death rattle of final destruction; he was filled with a savage urge to murder, to desecrate. But she, the partner and victim of this ghastly act, felt none of this; for any orgasm suited her, and she cared little what fired the man of her choice so long as he was fiery; it was strength she lusted for, since her whole being was in the flesh; with her unerring instinct she had scented strength in Jaquemar, and for his unawakened strength she had chosen this quiet and retiring man.

Dawn was breaking. Bompard had fallen asleep from one moment to the next. Her smiling face, the image of immaculate virginity, lay at an angle on the white pillow amidst the cloud of her curly locks. What malevolent spirit created you, venomous, innocent-looking beauty? thought Jaquemar. His gaze roamed to the window; within the greenly shimmering arch of a treetop reaching almost into the room, birds like flashes of blue lightning were darting hither and thither, magically beautiful creatures to look at, but giving vent to the harshest and most quarrelsome screeches that were an offense to the ear and aroused some vague memory in Jaquemar. He laughed evilly and said, as though in self-mockery: "Bompard's birds!"

With a gloomy face, he rose from the bed, picked up his torn night-shirt and his dressing gown from the floor, started to walk away, and stubbed his right big toe on the lumpy little book with the silver clasps. The knock hurt him out of all proportion; he kicked the book angrily aside, bent down with a groan, and clasped his injured foot.

"Where are you going?" came the almost inaudible question from the bed, like a lament whispered by the morning wind.

But he went on, his body hot and sweaty in a way that disgusted him, his heart pounding, because the uncooled, thick, humid air was almost unbreathable. He sat down on his camp bed and felt a thought sweep unexpectedly across his brain: Where have I landed myself? What kind of a country is this, where you need gills instead of lungs in order to live?

But what he actually said was this: "I know her power. I know my hate. I know the unfathomable depth of them both. Don't be misled, Gouffé, by what seems to you my weakness, I have drunk with her from the bitter, murky, Stygian waters of pleasure. It was a magic draught. It has made me as hard as steel; and if she thinks she has weakened me, I need not even smile. Let her illusions cast their web around her, the denser the better! I shall be on the alert until my hour strikes and is fulfilled: *she must be done away with!*"

The following morning—and every morning after that—Bompard was gone, off and away "hours ago" as Jaquemar was assured by the little waitress, looking delightfully fresh in a cotton frock and a starched white apron. She brought him an excessively copious break-fast, trundling in through the swing door with arms waving: iced fruit juice, fragrant coffee with cream, toast, butter, and strawberry and raspberry jam full of fruit, preceded by an imposing bowl of scrambled eggs or mountains of golden-brown pancakes covered with slices of bacon or maple syrup—all of this, according to the waitress's cold response to Jaquemar's protest, "specially ordered by *Madame*." If he then stepped out of the flower-filled fragrance and coolness of polished floors indoors onto the veranda, the summer heat struck him, and the air was so laden with moisture that he felt himself suffocating, like a drowning man. Striding on over the cork floor, he saw Cooley Lane, the warty man in the stiff dungarees, behind a barred window or standing in the doorway. Lane would raise the hand in greeting, but never spoke, though he would occasionally send a jet of tobacco juice spurting out of his mouth in an arc as the stranger descended the steps.

Feeling benumbed, as he had felt as soon as he got up, Jaquemar strolled around in the village. There was no point in walking beyond the constricting clasp of the brick and wooden houses, except that the stroller liked to see the way in which the street narrowed down in the distance to a bridge, rose in a hump over the soundless swirling of the Androscoggin and disappeared into the trees. But here in the center of the village stood the general store, in front of it a railing consisting of a single beam for tying up horses, and inside an all-pervading smell of soap, in spite of the fact that it also contained a multitude of goods of all sorts, dangling, piled up, and stowed away in drawers, as well as the local post office behind a high counter and a little frosted-glass window.

Sauntering on toward the little church that looked like a broody hen, Jaquemar caught glimpses of flowers shining like lamps and the damp, dark green of close-cropped grass, coruscating lawn sprinklers, the glitter of blue glass balls reflecting the clouds, and sections of white-painted wooden houses gleaming through the foliage. He climbed the cemetery hill, fascinated by the curious winged solar or angelic faces on tilting stones, granite tombstones in the shape of tables on four short legs and fluttering red and blue American flags stuck here and there into the soil of the graves, as though the honor of having belonged to this nation was a pass to the next world. But incomparably more beautiful than what man had built and cultivated was the green twilight of the huge and venerable trees, all of them together a cathedral of nature arching its gold-flecked roof shelteringly over the lost and forgotten little settlement.

The young man rarely caught sight of Bompard before midday. Then she would come marching gaily along, swinging a bunch of little keys which she generally kept dangling between her breasts or in her trouser pocket on a piece of coarse string. She took no trouble over her dress, and wore the same things almost every day: a checked blouse and rolled-up jeans of dully-shining blue cotton that had worn gray in patches on the seat—which on the untrammeled young woman, and over the taut curves of her figure, looked rather vulgar and highly exciting, so that Cooley Lane, as he gazed at the fly-screen door through which she had disappeared, spat out an arching jet of thick tobacco juice. Where did she come from, from what place, from what pleasures? Jaquemar did not know.

Of course, he was anything but happy. The pounding of his heart, his gasping for breath, the dulling of his brain, and the stumbling flaccidity of his limbs, and what was left of his energy all gave the lie to any feeling of happiness. But enjoyment—that was unfortunately true: he enjoyed all too thoroughly! And that was the primeval pull which continually sapped his will, so that night after night he poured himself out, under the black star of lovemaking with Bompard, weaker every time and every time lusting more intensely for the pleasure that convulsed him with an ever fiercer orgasm. She no longer had to invite him, he came of his own accord. She lay there naked, archaic, a young wrestler with round calves and low-arched feet, her skin an Ethiopian brown, smiling, and with lowered eyelids that shimmered silkily like the petals of blue tulips—thus she waited demurely till Jaquemar came to her and she drew his strength into her, she greeted his penetration with bird's cries, and spurred his ardor with dreamily confused exclamations: "Oh, my little stallion! How well I feel you, how strong you are! But keep it up. Give it to me good and hard! Look here, I'm a woman of flesh and blood, I need more, more, more. . . ."

All the time her skin felt icy cold like a fish, the only cold thing in the heat, and yet she was the flame that set it all alight, her womb the primal source of all other incandescence, and this duality was an even more unprecedented stimulus than what she did to him with her sharp bird's claws, the rocking fullness and unfathomable magic of her body. No, Jaquemar could not contain himself; bitterly as he hated her, his hate only served to whip up his lust and magnify his insatiability, whose phallic tumescence delighted as much as it disgusted him.

Dazzled by desire, debilitated by the unusual heat, poisoned by the idyllic green glimmer of the ghost village, sleep of a frightfully all-pervading and manifold kind took possession of him and bemused his mind; now, as so often before, he might have recalled Gilgamesh of Uruk, of whose weakness on his journey to the demons the old song sings, "Like a snowstorm sleep rushed in upon him." But Gilgamesh rose again after this test that he failed, otherwise his song would have come to an end at this point; and at this point Jaquemar's song, too, would have come to an end if he had been a Carapin or any other of the crowd of suitors.

But he was Jaquemar, and Jaquemar could not be completely lost; for the significant man is not distinguished from the insignificant man by the fact that he cannot succumb to temptation, but by the fact that there is a small core of diamond in him that no defeat, no pleasure, and no suffering can shatter; he is brother to eternity, with a fragment of indestructibility in his being which this ephemeral life cannot harm and which death alone can take back into the everlasting store. Jaquemar's being was constricted; but one thing remained firm in him, though very inconspicuous: the thought of the little nickel and mother-of-pearl revolver in Bompard's trunk, which glowed unceasingly in his gloomy breast; it was the last remnant of self-awareness in Jaquemar's mind not reduced to dust, the signpost before his inner eye on what seemed a trackless journey through the mist. He was always thinking of it, on every path he followed; when he listened to Bompard's gay conversation at the table; when he entered her room and looked first at the trunk that stood shut; and even when he slipped into the embrace of her thighs and surrendered himself, surrendered himself utterly, with the sole exception of this conscious thought: be my bed and my oblivion—yet you remain my purpose and will be my triumph, to the honor of Gouffé!

Meanwhile, preparations for the annual festival were being made. Once a year the young people gathered from far and wide and, mingled with the old, indulged in all sorts of innocent merrymaking in the square. Now, from morning to night, hammering and laughter, planing, the sound of splitting wood and friendly argument reached the hotel, the side and prison door of which stood open, since Cooley Lane, his hunter's cap with its blue feathers pushed back on his sweating neck, had no time for idle incarceration, but was working along with everybody else, the keenest of all.

In the square, watched over by the matronly little church, circular and elongated stalls of wooden trestles carefully planed and nailed together were going up, along with a shooting gallery and a dais of planks for the musicians; between the gnarled branches and mighty trunks of the venerable trees a wire net had been stretched, on which hung brightly-colored paper lanterns, red and yellow tubes, and crinkly globes bearing naive faces of suns and angels, indistinguishably similar to those on the tombstones in the cemetery, winged like the latter and only occasionally painted with a mouth turned dejectedly down at the corners. Old women, who generally shunned the light of day and kept timidly to themselves, could be seen sitting under the striped or red sunshades in the hot gardens with their embroidery or knitting; the sound of eggs being whipped, coal shoveled, and roasts pushed into ovens could be heard from kitchens, and buttery vapors smoldered appetizingly in the incense smoke of the wood fires.

Yes, yes, thought Jaquemar, sauntering around, blessed be joy among men, what could be more needful! For the constructive activity all over the village was joyful, joyful in a pleasant way that was full of well-mannered expectancy; and most joyful of all was something that suddenly riveted the idle stroller to the spot: carefree laughter and thigh-slapping that could come from no one but Bompard, interspersed with jolly squeals and the cheerful laughter of peaceful men's voices.

The sounds came from a property that lay snuggled away in the woods, so that only the white-painted corner of the house was visible. Jaquemar forced his way through the underbrush, in the middle of which stood the house, rather dilapidated and entwined with wild vine, an L-shaped old Vermont farmhouse, the long wing of which formed the front.

Jaquemar pushed his way to the end of this main wing, stopped, and peered around the corner. Facing him, at right angles to the main wing and rather lower than the latter, stretched a shorter wing, containing tool sheds, an open coach house filled with piles of oak and beech logs, and various stables. But in the yard, a bucolic picture met the eye: laughing men were standing in a wide circle; half a pace in front of them stood Gabrielle Bompard, who was twisting about with enjoyment and slapping her blue-jean-clad thighs, while inside the circle a boy about twelve years old was chasing a pig that grunted and squealed in the excitement of the game, until with a bound the boy seized it by the curly tail and was dragged through the dust with feet acting as brakes. At this the expression on the bristly animal's face changed and its grunting assumed an indignant, groaning note. But this availed him nothing; four or five men immediately surrounded him, grabbed him by the ears, throat, and feet despite his furious struggles, and dragged him over to a low table unmistakably reminis-

cent of the table-tombstones in the terrace cemetery, except that it was
not made of stone but of soft, roughened wood.

Bompard stepped eagerly toward them. All of a sudden she was
holding a knife with a long, pointed blade, which she handed to the
boy, crying: 'À la bonheur! You caught him, Matthew, my little
fellow; in reward you may do him in!'

The men had laid the pig down on the low wooden table and were
holding it in place by its legs and tail; it lay twisted half sideways,
while Bompard, offering the knife with her left hand, busily wetted
her right forefinger, dabbed a point on the animal's throat with it,
and cried: "No hemming and hawing! To work! Take the knife and
stab away! And when it has sunk in up to the handle, twist it to the
right and twist it to the left so that it crunches! For whatever we do,
we must do thoroughly, and we ought not to prolong the death agony
unduly."

But the boy took the knife unwillingly; with his long, close-cropped
skull and charming peachy-skinned face lowered, he looked first at the
knife, then at the pig, which lay quiet, and shook his head with an
embarrassed smile.

Thereupon, Bompard hit him hard across the nose with her bony
fingers.

"Cheer up!" she cried, and blazed out at him: "You heard what
Madame said! Stab away, was my order. Stab away, it isn't even
squealing yet, the beast is dreaming! Will you do as you're told?
Quick, get on with it!"

The boy looked at the point on the pig's throat over the windpipe,
on which Bompard's finger was pressing and boring to indicate where
he should strike; with his mouth suddenly contorted he overcame his
reluctance and drove the knife home to the hilt. The animal remained
mute, however, with its head to one side.

"He's a good lad, he'll do all right in life," cried Bompard gleefully.
"Now twist until there's a crunching sound! Bring the bowls, good
people! Don't let the delicious black juice spurt away unused!"

Buckets and bowls were pushed up close to the table; groaning, the
boy twisted the knife so that it crunched through flesh and bone;
the pig remained mute. But when, at a sign from the mistress butcher,
the knife was pulled out and the first geyser of blood spurted out of the
wound and poured foaming into the vessels, it began to scream. Yes,

it did not squeal, it screamed; the terrible scream of the death agony, like a human cry, rang out shrilly through the air. Overwhelmed by the knowledge that its life was at stake, the stabbed beast suddenly opened its eyes wide and let out an unparalleled wail of terror. It twisted and kicked in the iron bonds of the men's fists with the tremendous fury of the will to live; it struggled wildly on its back— and for a moment it broke free; it threw and rolled itself halfway around, and the jets of blood, which welled up and died down rhythmically in time to its pulse, sprayed out through the hot air and splashed with a hissing sound in the middle of Bompard's laughing face.

She turned around, exactly in Jaquemar's line of vision, spat, and wiped the thick, dark blood out of her eyes and from her white face and laughing mouth with both hands. Jaquemar staggered back; for the besmirched young woman was horrible to look at with her laughter, her spitting, her eyelids, which she opened wide and squeezed together, and the glitter and radiance that flashed out from the blood-stained mask. "Pooh!" she cried, shaking herself, but in such undiminished merriment that horror overtook Jaquemar and he leaned against the wall and shut his eyes.

For a while the young man perceived nothing but his own feeling, a feeling of abysmal malaise and powerlessness; then he became aware once more of the indescribable screams with which the animal on the slaughter block was gasping out its life in fear and anguish; for they were growing fainter, and the flow of blood was splashing softly into the frothing vessels in time to the hoarse, choking death rattle. Finally silence ensued; there was no sound but the scuffing of the buckets and tubs and footsteps on the gravel, when suddenly—and Jaquemar could not believe his ears—Bompard's voice rang out in a way he had never heard before, in a desolate, loud lament; it was as if the primal mother of mankind were bewailing the first death of a child, tearless with horror and pain.

"Woe, woe!" she wailed. "My saucy, pink little animal, you were so fat and sturdy and tubby and had sparkling blue eyes! You grunted in all innocence and did no harm to anyone! Now, sad to say, they have polished you off, your little eye is dull and all four legs stretched out. See, like a woman in childbirth I cry after your stolen life! And if I were to flog or otherwise punish the bloodthirsty Tom Thumb who raised his hand to you, so that he would never forget it, it would do you no good, you have breathed your last and everything is over for you! Oh, shameful misdeed, ah, horrible end!"

While she was thus crying, Jaquemar could not resist peering around the corner again. She was standing with her back to him, tearing her hair, throwing her hands above her head in furious conjuration, and twisting her body from the hips. She looked powerful as she stood there with her legs apart! The men were standing around the victim with bent heads, hats and caps in hand, and only the boy with the bloody butcher's knife in his right hand was gazing at the lamenter with an ecstatic ardor from which Jaquemar turned away with a groan.

"Above all," he heard Bompard continue her lament, "above all that grub and snuffle in the dust with their snouts for the purpose of building up good bacon, I shall always miss you, and my heart bleeds for you, as your throat bled for them!"

She ceased her wailing as suddenly as she had begun, for a minute silence reigned, then she said: "Now, let's slit his belly open."

She clapped her hands vivaciously and cried: "Roll up your sleeves, folks, and get to work! Take care that you don't spoil his nice leather with your knives, and slice him up with a will so that when the hour strikes we can regale ourselves on his sacrifice!"

Jaquemar left. Hate, fanned to a fresh blaze, was burning in his breast; but the horror that had overcome him would not go either, and he felt the urge to give vent to his feelings. He went up to his room. Home, he thought vaguely, I'll write home about it.

He entered his room, took out pen and paper and ink, and sat down at the one-legged table. But the paper was too porous; the faulty pen dug into it, and the ink ran out in splodges. Jaquemar threw the pen furiously across the room, drew a deep breath, and stared in front of him.

After a time that might have been short or long, someone could be heard coming up the steps to the accompaniment of a whistled dance tune. Jaquemar turned his head and peered through the half-open communicating door into the next room: Bompard walked in. Her face was washed, fresh and beautiful; but her blouse and her blue jeans were spattered with great stiff patches of black blood; and, pushing the door carelessly shut behind her, and still whistling, she undid the filthy blouse, pulled it off, and stood there with naked breasts.

She noticed Jaquemar watching her, and she grasped the underside of her left breast with her left hand and raised it slightly to display it. She came toward him with demurely lowered eyelids and murmured: "It isn't right when the dear sun is still laughing above."

"Isn't there any blood on it?" Jaquemar asked through the door. "Or have you washed that off already, too?"

"Don't be so superior," she commented.

"Ugh!" he interjected. "Wallows in blood and pain and stirs up blood lust even in children!"

"Matthew?" she interrupted politely. "He'll be punished for it. Just have patience."

"It's you I'm talking about! Have you no other way of spending your time except in butchery?"

With downcast eyes she was now plucking with the fingers of her right hand at the nipple of the naked breast in her left.

"That's country life," she said, shrugging her shoulders; she suddenly reached for the latch of the communicating door and shut it behind her.

"Are you the village butcher?" Jaquemar shouted after her.

The door promptly opened again, her face appeared in the crack, and shaking her head she exclaimed: "It was because of the feast. Do you inquire about the butcher when you stuff yourself with ham and sausages? Then Monsieur doesn't give a straw for his hairsplitting, he shuts his eyes to everything! Always refined at other people's expense, always a moral parasite, and I, poor woman, have to pay. . . . Hah!"

She pulled the door shut, then opened it a little and cried: "Is everything to live forever like the gods? Don't let me hear that old twaddle any more! I won't have it."

"And she's allowed to live!" Jaquemar whispered to himself as the door finally shut. "Wherever she goes, there is the stench of blood, the screams of the dying rise to deaf heaven! Will her downfall never come?"

But Jaquemar's rage was soon fused with joy. For the night of the festival and of joy had arrived. Heaven came to its aid; a soft warm wind had risen that whirled lazily and damply about in the treetops. Its rustling entered through Jaquemar's open window, together with the music of fiddles and the whispering and friendly laughter of the young people who had come pouring in from the farms, hamlets, and homesteads far and near and were now giving themselves over to dancing in the light of the lanterns outside, to the singsong commands of the rustic master of ceremonies.

Bompard had long since disappeared. In obedience to an impulse which he did not stop to analyze, Jaquemar wandered over from his room into hers and stopped in the doorway, drawing a deep breath. The big patent trunk stood wide open; cami-knickers, dresses, stockings, scarves, and also glass beads gleaming in the candlelight, and even chains of precious stones overflowing and dangling over the sides of the trunk—the lovely odds and ends of a beautiful woman who had had no time to tidy up in her eagerness to get to the festival— protruded and spilled over as though from another Pandora's box. The young man hurried to the trunk, thrust his hand in among the entrancing jumble of diaphanous and silky fabrics, and did not have to fish about for more than a moment; at once he felt in his hand the hard little shape he had so often dreamed of and now drew out.

He weighed the tiny revolver in his right hand and saw the nickel and mother-of-pearl glitter and gleam; the strong and evil joy that he had almost forgotten since Saratoga flared up in him again. Delicate death in my hand! he thought. Why do you wink so impatiently? I shall not fail you! He slipped the weapon into his trouser pocket and went out.

He stayed for a while on the veranda below, watching the festivities in the square, struck by their beauty—for beauty, like goodness and truth, is a mystic phenomenon, an act of primal truce, and only the dull-witted man remains totally unaware of the rancor breathing quietly within it. The feast lay in the greeny black velvet of the summer's night like a magic jewel gently glittering with iridescent colors. The central core was formed by couples whirling in the dance; around them wandered those comfortably resting from dancing; at the foot of the terraced cemetery the musicians were sitting on a plank dais, each firmly planted on his chair and yet in his own manner winged, with fiddle bow flung up, accordion pushed in and pulled out with a sinuous milking movement, and the plucking of mandolins, while the caller stood in front of them in white shirt sleeves directing the dancers in a rhythmic chant. "Take her by the right hand, now swing her on, / but hold her hand tightly, or she'll be gone!"

From time to time the music stopped; then the sighing of the wind became audible and other sounds beside: bangs, tinkles, croaks, scraping, and cries of invitation and encouragement from under the puckered roof of the tombola tent. For today everyone had to try his luck and skill, aiming a gun, bombarding old crockery with hard balls, and thrusting his hand into glass lottery bowls, in the hope of winning this, that, or the other—children's rattles, cardboard trumpets, all kinds of trashy ornaments, and especially ribbons for pinning on the clothes embroidered with saucy phrases. In other stalls fried sausages were sizzling on the grills, and milk and lemonade foaming in mugs. So much pleasure and so much youth! But in conformity with the restrained customs of this country, everything took place without haste or hubbub, in a kind of ghostly hush in which the warm night wind immediately absorbed any noise that was too loud and shrill.

Jaquemar was now sauntering about among the crowd. On the left, a dense circle of shirt-sleeved men had formed on the churchyard terrace to the right, and Jaquemar observed the lanky little waitress from Miss Dimple's hotel pulling and shaking first shyly, then angrily, at a lad's sleeve; then she began to snivel and, putting both hands over her pretty little masklike face, ran into the kindly rustle of the virgin greenery. Someone must have noticed this and shifted out of the circle, so that for an instant Jaquemar caught sight of Bompard in the center of the gathering. She was sitting full of animation on one of the low table-tombstones, a glass of milk in her left hand, a milky moustache around her laughing mouth, and her upswept curls entwined with ribbons from the tombola. With the index finger of her right hand she was pointing at Matthew her little butcher boy, who was standing in front of her; she slapped her knee and threw back her head. She was not looking at him, however, but at the lad facing her, the same at whose sleeve the waitress had tugged in vain; he bore a fraternal resemblance to the other boy, having a long skull and a face whose skin was still as downy as a peach. He shook his head bashfully and lowered it, then the circle closed again and Jaquemar saw no more.

But when the break was over and the music struck up again, he saw her dancing. Around the square sat old men and women; children crawled about between their legs; and the old people watched the turbulent activities of the merrymakers good-naturedly, their hands on their knees or folded in their laps. Jaquemar had taken up a position behind the spectators, unobserved by anyone, and was peering hawk-eyed into the well-controlled jollification. She popped up now here, now there, among ungainly but courtly bows, rhythmic hand clapping, serpentine winding lines, and yodeling whirlpools of dancers; above her head her curly hair rose like tongues of flame as she threw herself wholeheartedly into the revelry, the picture of rapturous youth, de-lighted with every partner; for every partner suited her—little Matthew, fat-bellied farmers, and Bearstruck Cooley, the victim of popular meanness, whose blue cap-feathers bobbed and swayed through the air; but the one who was most often near her, perhaps by chance, was the young man who looked like a boy.

No, no, it was not by chance! They had fallen for one another; every time he spun her around in a pirouette she gave herself with rap-turously closed eyes into his arms, while he gazed down with an anxiety compounded of bewilderment and happiness at this beautiful, aban-doned face. *This* sight, Jaquemar hated! It was only granted him for a moment and quickly withdrawn again; other couples hid these two, and they were swallowed up by the crowd; all he could see of her was an occasional glimpse in the distance amidst the turmoil, her hair, the tip of her nose, her upthrown hand.

What are age, maturity, status, and wealth! thought Jaquemar. The bitch is a democrat! So long as she can do harm. . . . Just get in front of my gun!

There was no weakness in the care he took, gnashing his teeth; he was an unskilled shot; if necessary he would have given his own life to bring down this game, but he did not wish to endanger that of a stranger. It drew a smile from his gravity when the master of cere-monies began reciting rather than singing something that sounded like a hunting song:

> Chase the rabbit, chase the squirrel,
> Chase that pretty girl round the world!
> Load your gun and aim it right.
> Hurry up, boys, don't wait all night!

Was it the pull of his anticipation, the youngster's guidance, chance? She was now dancing on the outside edge, barely four paces away from her hunter. His squinting eyes fixed firmly on his prey, Jaquemar cocked the little revolver in his pocket.

She was bedizened with tombola ribbons, on her taut bodice, her puff sleeves, her skirt, and in her flamelike hair; but since the ribbons were fluttering like banners, Jaquemar could distinguish the words on only two of them: "Hello, stranger, try and get me!" and the other mutilated, "I'm . . . angel," because the middle was tied around a lock of hair, so that it might have read "I'm an angel" or "I'm no angel" according to the decipherer's preference. For the rest, although she was wearing a valuable gold and beryl clasp between her breasts, she was dressed with rustic simplicity in a dirndl costume with white stockings and heavy, buckled shoes, hardly more gorgeous than all the other girls, but of course so incomparably more beautiful than they in her high spirits that it made Jaquemar tremble.

At this moment she came spinning, entranced, toward Jaquemar, her wide white skirts flying out as she was seized around the waist and then set rotating by her youthful partner in a kind of frenzied country waltz. Suddenly brought to a halt by her partner's grip, she stopped dead for a fraction of a second one pace from Jaquemar as though in a state of paralysis, a paralysis that seemed contagious and was almost more charged with energy than the force and agility with which she immediately afterward plunged into the general rhythm. With precision, her head with its little tiger's nose gracefully tilted, raising one leg so that knee and calf formed a right angle, she stamped and strutted in the orgiastic fury of physical enjoyment; she spun back toward her partner as he drew her to him, her laughing face thrown up, her eyes beneath her anguished brows open and giving out a cold and sparkling radiance in which glittered and shimmered the multi-colored light of the paper lanterns that were trembling and swaying in the summer wind.

The instant of Jaquemar's paralysis and impotence was already past; but how long (if such time is measurable), how long was it that her eyes met his? They were like a blow on Jaquemar's brow and chest. The fire of life spurted from her eyes into his, out of primordial depths of animality or divinity, an indeterminate, multiple radiation, fire or frost, something, at all events, on which one burned as on flames or ice, so that his cornea threatened to stick fast and tear, pleasure and terror, procreative lust, and the craving to destroy, all in one, but devoid of any feeling or any frailty.

Nevertheless, Jaquemar lifted the weapon in his pocket, and once again his will was disturbed, because the lowing of cattle rang out through this night of dancing. Bompard had long since whirled back into the general turmoil with her lad, a laugh on her lips; and as though only now noticing how he had been dazzled by the mute blaze of her look, he put the back of his left hand over his eyes and sank into the morasslike depths of a profoundly shattered ego. A horrifying and despairing revelation shot through his whole being and he whispered between stiff lips: "God, have mercy on me! I love! If it were with the flesh that can be burned, torn in pieces, and thrust with screams of agony into the next world or into the earth, to serve as a fertilizer for new flesh, what would it matter? But it is with the spirit, with the heart, with the eternal for which there is no name! Who can resist that? It is many thousands of times stronger than I, you see, and will survive me by aeons. I love. . . . "

Jaquemar withdrew. With lowered head, but walking erect, he hurried back to Miss Dimple's hotel; all his strength had gone, and just as he knew that he was in love and desperate, so he also knew he could sink no lower. The shame that no one else knew was unspeakably worse than the shame of Saratoga Springs; he was alone with it; nobody's scorn, contempt, or sentence could purge or punish it; there was no court to try it, only himself. And he—what sort of judge was he, since he could clearly feel that he must love this shame too, because it was part of his love, because it offered him *pleasure* like a narcotic?

He entered his room, undressed, wrapped his naked body in the long linen nightshirt, and went across into Bompard's room. Carelessly, with no desire to hide from her what he had tried to do, he threw the revolver on top of the lingerie in her trunk, walked over to the bed in which he had so often possessed her, and lay down on it. He waited; he heard that the wind outside had fallen silent, the heavy, humid heat was already gathering unfanned in the room. I am waiting, thought Jaquemar. How differently I am waiting than I was waiting an hour ago! I am horrified by myself because I cannot help loving this terrible woman. But the country music down below on the village green, fiddling, droning, tinkling, echoed on undiminished; the talk and the laughter of the festive throng was like a soft bed for their joy and his distress; and over his own horror he fell asleep.

He was so shamefully lost. But he could not become completely lost; the small core of diamond in his being could not be pulverized or destroyed; its hardness scraped and cut and agonized his weakness; in his sleep it sat in judgment.

Bompard did not come home until morning; Jaquemar watched from the window. Since the warm wind had given up trying to put the rainclouds to flight, they had settled over the forest, the wet heat had turned into hot wetness and was drizzling down with a rustling sound among the leaves; the drizzle was softening the paper lanterns in the netting above the abandoned square, hanging in the form of heavy moisture in the puckered roofs of the stalls and turning the soil into a quagmire, along with the dirty, trodden pieces of colored paper with which it was littered. Only chickens, cackling and scratching and pecking in the mud and the refuse from the feast, were there in force, and parted with outraged squawks before the splashing footsteps of Gabrielle Bompard, a bow wave of animal fear flowing off to left and right.

Bompard did not notice them as she beamed gaily ahead of her. She was wearing over her dirndl costume a raincoat that was far too large for her, with a long, pointed hood that stuck up behind her at an angle, and she let the rain run merrily over her cheeks and little tiger's nose in round drops—she was the very picture of good humor. She disappeared into the house below, and the thought crossed Jaquemar's mind that the night that had just gone by was the first for weeks that he had spent without her—just as though she attached no further importance to it, he thought absentmindedly.

Jaquemar waited in vain; she did not come upstairs, so he went down to her. She was sitting at their regular table in the corner, sipping with sucking lips at an iced fruit juice, and she looked at him gaily over the edge of the glass.

"Where have you been?" asked Jaquemar, standing at the table in front of her.

Her face assumed a vexed expression, she put the glass down on the table, and muttered sulkily: "Held up. . . . Someone was hurt."

"What do you mean 'held up'?"

"Have I passed into your ownership, just because you put horns on Carapin?" she retorted angrily. "Don't start acting the husband."

"You're so sure of me. . . . " he commented, sitting down thoughtfully.

She ignored this remark; her sunny mood had returned and, beaming down at the table, she watched the little waitress sullenly pushing things to and fro on it with jerky movements.

"It was Malcolm with the horses," she said, failing to notice that the waitress rushed out sniveling, and explaining confidentially into Jaquemar's disapproving face: "Malcolm, the brother of Matthew, the little fellow you were angry with because he butchered a pig. Do you remember? . . . Where the devil is my ham and scrambled egg? My tummy's rumbling. Hey there! Service!"

The pantry door was kicked furiously from inside, so that one leaf flew open and banged quivering against the wall, and the little waitress appeared, her lower lip protruding in her pale, convulsed mask of a face. In her right hand she held a bowl filled to the brim with the desired scrambled eggs; she approached the table sobbing, caught sight of the raincoat on the peg, and went rigid.

"Anyhow, this fellow whose name was Malcolm, as I told you," Bompard went on with shining eyes, "was completely taken up with his horses until I reminded him of his duty as a cavalier and, to correct his ideas, told him: 'Where I come from, young men are interested in horses whose eyes they can look into while they ride them!' The bad boy took this the wrong way, made all sorts of advances to me, and offered to take me for a ride in his buggy, which of course I refused, so late at night; but afterward he proved to be quite a lot of fun, to the best of his short-lived ability."

The little waitress suddenly let out a cry; the scrambled eggs slipped off the plate and straight into Bompard's lap.

"Loathsome toad!" screeched Bompard, nevertheless laughing quite gaily. "She wants me to give her a good hiding, I suppose? Get going, jump to it, hot water and a cloth, and be quick about it!"

She beamed at her dirtied clothes and waited till the girl came with the water and dabbed at them unwillingly.

"Do it properly!" she cried. "Down on your knees, and heaven help you if it leaves a ring!"

The girl dropped sulkily to both knees beside her; blubbering and sniveling, she rubbed and scrubbed at the clothing and winced as Bompard gaily continued her tirade: "It's all very well blubbering now! After it's happened, always after it's happened! No wonder her boy jilts her! She hasn't the slightest inkling of how badly she treated the poor fellow! Wicked, stubborn creature! Be off with you! Get out of my sight! And bring me some more scrambled eggs, and in double-quick time, or it will be the worse for you!"

Jaquemar had gazed steadily at the gaily scolding Bompard, throughout this scene, with an indeterminate, distrustful expression; now he stood up and left the room without a word, though she, settling herself confidently in her chair, took not the slightest notice of the fact. In the hall he met Miss Dimple, who greeted him with a profusion of whispered laughter, hand rubbing, and bows, and lisped something about the "nice warm morning"; but her, too, Jaquemar passed without a word. He stepped onto the veranda. Cooley Lane in his stiff dungarees was leaning in the open doorway of the prison; he raised the hand holding his pipe in greeting, pushed his hunter's cap onto the back of his neck, and scratched his head as he stared after Jaquemar. Outside, the boy Matthew was hanging shyly about and disappeared around the corner of the building as soon as he caught sight of Jaquemar.

It had stopped drizzling, but the wet still hung like a veil in the tops and foliage of the trees. The village lay as though abandoned, and not another soul greeted Jaquemar on his way past the post office and toward the Androscoggin bridge.

A breath of coolness drifted up from the black river; the young man squatted down, made a scoop of his two hands, and washed and bathed his face in the cold black water. Craving to refresh himself further, Jaquemar took off his shoes and socks and dipped his bare feet in the stream, in an unexpectedly strong current that seemed to be trying to push him angrily aside, yet could not refuse the longed-for benefaction—indeed, his feet were almost painful, as if freezing; then a dense swarm of tiny fish, vague shadows rather than visible objects, swam up and tested his toes and soles with little kissing mouths in the hope of food, causing such a prickly, tickling sensation of the skin that Jaquemar lifted his feet onto the bank with a laugh.

At lunchtime Jaquemar returned to the hotel. Bompard was not in her room; but the communicating door was open, and as he entered it drew his gaze, or rather it was Bompard's trunk that drew him. The hated piece of luggage stood wide open as it had that morning, and the revolver lay untouched on top of silk and batiste, just where he had thrown it the night before. The sight gave him a pang, he felt insulted and mocked, he hurried through the room and out onto the landing. The little waitress came running up the stairs from below, caught sight of him, and cried: "Lunch!" "Where is Madame?" Jaquemar inquired. "Downstairs, with a visitor," she replied curtly. "What kind of visitor?" Jaquemar asked sharply. "Another man, of course," she retorted pertly, but the next moment started sniveling again and ran downstairs to the sound of suppressed sobs.

The visitor was none other than Chester Gaunt, the young American from Saratoga Springs. Bompard was sitting beside him, sipping, as that morning, at an iced drink, a blood-red one this time, tomato juice; she peered at Jaquemar over the top of the glass, put it down, and cried with an impatient shake of the head: "There you are at last!"

Gaunt rose with a clatter and gave the ghost of a smile, but Jaquemar merely nodded in greeting with a set face and sat down. The young men did not exchange a word, only Bompard chattered with undimmed gaiety, telling the story of the village dance and of "Malcolm with the horses," plucking at Gaunt's sleeve with her yellow, shriveled fingers to compel his attention; she drove the sulky and frightened waitress to serve them quicker, fidgeted about in her chair, and looked with radiant appetite at every new dish.

"Tuck in, Jaquemar darling!" she cried. "That's the way to make our oats blossom!"

Jaquemar made no reply to this either; but she did not notice, being too busy heaping her own plate. Every now and then Chester Gaunt cast a quick glance at Jaquemar's face, which expressed nothing—no anger, no hostility, only reserve and loneliness. Then Jaquemar rose, without waiting for the end of the meal; looking over Bompard's head, he bowed briefly to Gaunt and left without apology.

"That's the way he is," he heard Bompard say, between chewing and laughing, "always tired, because he can never observe moderation. Well, that's what men are like, and Frenchmen are the worst of the lot."

Her words died away in his ears; he was already mounting the stairs, and as he entered his room his eyes were caught by an object he had not noticed before: a fat envelope plastered all over with stamps and postmarks that was lying on the pillow of his camp bed. He could not remember ever having seen the soullessly precise copperplate handwriting of the address: "Monsieur Edmond Jaquemar, c/o Grand

Union Hotel, Saratoga Springs, New York, U.S.A." He tore the envelope open and a smile crept over his grave, composed face, for he now saw that the letter was from his friend Germaine Chottin in Paris. From the land of the living, he thought animatedly. He looked up thoughtfully, put the letter in his pocket, and left the room and the hotel.

Jaquemar strode through the leathery grass and crooked trunks of the apple orchard, which in its neglected state still hinted at form and utility, and sat down on a tree stump, close to the high wall of foliage; and the seat, because the rotten wood gave as he sat on it, was as comfortable as an armchair. He took out the letter and, as he read it, forgot his surroundings; he plunged back into a time that was no longer within reach and not yet without significance; for Germaine Chottin's letter was a greeting and a call from his old life and home. It read:

> 5 Rue de l'Arbalète
> Paris 5ᵉ
> 23 June 1890

EDMOND, MY DEAR FRIEND!

How often, since you left us, have I asked myself whether perhaps you had no intention of writing to us, and since I am now writing to you I really ought to ask myself whether you will not look upon this letter, if it reaches you, as an importunity. But God alone knows whether it will reach you! I cannot tell by what route it will travel to you in your unknown hideout. I pressed Lebigot to try and think where you might be. He looked at me with his sour face and answered: "It pleases you to jest." Then he mumbled on and said that perhaps he could arrange for my "cry of longing" (for that no doubt was what it was) to be forwarded by Monsieur Dopffer or Maître Rebattu to your address, or rather that of the "swamp siren, Bompard." He must be forgiven for his venom, and you too must forgive him; he is ruder than ever, but he is in terrible straits. That is another reason why I feel I must overcome my modesty: I must tell you how things are and if possible ask for your advice. And I'm right aren't I, you keep silent, but your silence doesn't mean that you no longer think about your old friends, does it? It's just that you are a long way away.

What first gave me the idea that there must be more behind Lebigot's gloomy and savage mood than his usual ill-humor was actually a remark of Monsieur Goron's. Lebigot is now treating him, he looks in on him almost every day and he gave me to understand that in this case there could really be no question of "treatment," only his overconscientiousness made him keep up the visits, "so that the death certificate should be ready in good time." I fear there is no reason to doubt Lebigot's pessimistic prognosis: Monsieur Goron is marked by death. I visited him and brought him flowers, about which he was as pleased as a child. Heavens above, how the poor man has changed! I don't mean so much because he looks so dreadful and because his neck has grown so thin that it looks like the skinny neck of a plucked fowl in his turn-down collar that is far too wide, I mean especially his nature. He has become so different, so utterly different, he even speaks differently, softly, thoughtfully, almost dreamily, and his eyes, which used to be rather piercing, now avoid looking at you, and when they do turn toward you, they look as cloudy as puddles. But the most striking thing of all is his walk; it's hard to describe it, there is something waddling about his walk, it looks almost comical. It gives you the touching feeling that he has infinite time—he who never had time, and just now, when he really has so little time! He also giggles every now and then in a very queer, roguish way. He did so on the occasion I want to tell you about.

He was lighting one of his black cigars. "You will permit me, I hope, dear lady," he said, and added with his giggle: "Even Jaquemar's Dr. Lebigot permits it. He says, 'In your state it really makes no difference.' 'Now just a minute,' I said (for I couldn't help feeling a bit indignant), 'suppose I die?' 'Then we'll bury you,' he replied, and all of a sudden grew angry. 'What more do you want? You're a famous man! You'll probably get a state funeral, they'll carry decorations on black velvet behind the coffin and rest your head on a white silk pillow with showy tassels.' Heehee. A plain-spoken man, that Lebigot, he goes straight to the point and doesn't wrap it up."

But then Monsieur Goron glanced at me with his cloudy eyes and looked at the cigar in his hand. "No," he said thoughtfully, "not altogether plain-spoken, only plain-spoken in relation to other people. Unless I'm very much mistaken, he needs a doctor more than I do. You know how it is with me . . . but he is a young, useful man." Of course I pressed him to say more, but he dodged my questions and finally remarked, shaking his head and shrugging his shoulders: "I don't know. But there's something the matter with Lebigot. He's in danger, he's gone off the rails somehow, I don't know what it is."

This hint would not have perturbed me all that much, if I had not already begun to worry secretly about Lebigot on my own account. I was visiting him pretty regularly, because he was one of the few things you had left behind here, and I couldn't help noticing that every time I saw him he became more unbearable, more disagreeable. I have certainly never seen a more ill-humored man in all my life. Moreover, in spite of the warm summer weather, he always had a cold; he sniffed and snuffled and wiped the tears away from under his glasses with a filthy handkerchief. He also spent days on end lying unshaven in bed, and it became evident to me that even when he was up he did no work or anything else.

One day I could restrain myself no longer. I asked him straight out whether this kind of life did not lead him into difficulties, and when he laconically answered that it did, I asked him whether perhaps I might help him. "Certainly," he replied unabashed and took my check in his great hand without attempting to thank me.

The queerest thing, however, was that one day when he was in bed and I went to fetch his handkerchief from his jacket, I found his jacket pocket filled with black earth. "But Lebigot," I said, "what's this?" "Haven't you got eyes in your head?" he retorted. "What could it be? It's earth, good black earth." He refused to explain further. Wasn't that extremely odd?

After Monsieur Goron's remark, I thought very carefully about how I ought to behave toward Lebigot, and an instinct told me that I must take a rather firm line with him. At my next visit, he was, if possible, more spiteful and malicious than ever, so I suddenly got up and said: "I see that my visits are a nuisance to you, my dear Monsieur Lebigot. I am sure you will only welcome it if I draw the obvious conclusion. Good-by to you." But he reacted far more violently to this than I had expected. He seized my hand. "No!" he cried or positively yelled. "No! Not you too, for God's sake!" He clumsily stroked my hand with his red fingers (which, by the way, have curiously long and ugly nails), raised it to his crabbed mouth and kissed it, and said quietly: "Come, be a good child. I'm a horrible fellow, I know. Who will forgive me for it, if not you?"

All this took place in your room, room 12A, which Monsieur Chambron is keeping reserved for you. Lebigot had been sitting in your wing chair by the window and had not stood up; he made me sit down again on the stool in front of it, sniffed and blew his nose, and began to talk. "Deep thought, deep thought is my whole trouble! It was the same with Jaquemar's Gilgamesh; when his bosom pal Enkidu kicked the bucket, he wanted at all costs to know what lay behind it, and deep thought dragged him from one unpleasantness to another! Yes, that's what deep thought does for you! Mine has sent me slithering down into the snake pit of despair, into a permanent state of cerebral anxiety, from which intoxication alone provides an escape."

He stopped speaking, looked at me distrustfully, and said: "That's enough of that! Forget about deep thought and anxiety. Madame is far too appetizing, she's no Seneca. Let's stick to facts. I have also thought—and who hasn't thought the same thing before me?—that this life is an instant of twilight between two everlasting nights. What is left to us but intoxication? Come to my heart, intoxication, whatever be your name! Honored lady, you will understand that this is a matter involving a woman. I am horribly in love. There is much that is quaint about the little bitch, she has eyes as mild as oil and honey, and silky little hands with velvet knots under the tips of her fingers—not even the most naturalistically inclined would think of claws in connection with them! But in spite of it all, she creeps and crawls and tickles in my blood like a whole tribe of bugs, pregnancy urticaria is nothing by comparison. You understand what I mean, don't you?" "Lebigot," I replied, "I'm sure that everything you have said is absolutely true. But is it the whole truth?"

"Aha!" he exclaimed, taken aback. "There we have it! Once you start making a confession! The whole truth? Well, no, that it isn't, not by a long shot. We have taken the liberty of withholding a few details out of consideration for our listener, and what we have made public was, so to speak, utter nonsense. The whole truth? As you like. Let us begin with the deep thought. If our highly esteemed Dr. Lebigot is right in thinking that this life is nothing but a frightened instant of twilight between two everlasting, impenetrable black nights (and he is right about that, whatever you may say), well, my love, why shouldn't one at least make this hateful interruption of peaceful nothingness as pleasant as possible and, instead of lying on a fakir's bed of nails, wallow in puddles of laziness and debauchery? Why not soothing turmoil for the shuddering victim, even if it is bought with a draught from Granny Satan's cookshop?"

I think the poor fellow was in anguish as he delivered this speech. "What do you mean?" I asked. "Please, Lebigot, what do you mean?"

"Well," he said, stretching and dismissing my question with a wave of his big red hand, "if our much-traveled friend and mentor Jaquemar were here, instead of gadding about the world, he would undoubtedly treat us to a moving sermon on the sin against hope, for which, as we know, there is no forgiveness. He would administer a soul laxative of true Jaquemarian stamp and lay down the law something like this: 'Despair, scorn, and blasphemy before the awe-inspiring impenetrability of the world-spirit are no better than obscenity before the spirit of love.' That is how he would speak if, as I said, he were here. But the filthy and disgusting fact is that he is not here! Monsieur Jaquemar has gone away and is lost to us. Old Nick has slipped quietly and with folded hands into his place. And so we continue to sip at the sweet Lethe of the hours, good luck to us and let us do so once again! With your permission, Madame, poor widow that I am, with your permission I shall master our grief."

He jumped up, hurried over to the little hanging cupboard in the bed recess, and opened it with trembling hands. The shelf was full of bottles bearing red and black skull-and-crossbones on their labels. He took one out, spread out his left hand, and shook a heap of glittering crystals into the hollow between the thumb and index finger. He held one nostril closed and sniffed up the glittering dust with the other, blinked his eyelids, and gave vent to a long-drawn sigh of enjoyment.

Then I suddenly realized the terrible truth: Lebigot had become a drug addict! He frankly admitted it when I asked him. With his narcotics the Evil One had enslaved him, he reveled in the most glorious states of drowsiness and phantasmagoria, and paid afterward with terribly long, gray hours of destructiveness in which, as he put it himself, "nothing but the ghostly wind of despair blows across the brackish water." Opium, morphia, heroin, and cocaine, mescaline, peyotl, and hashish—Oh, I don't want to name all the loathsome substances by their accursed names, but he enumerated them all to me, smiling with closed eyes, entranced, like a man thinking of the unutterable charms of his beloved. That was why the pores of his nose had become as large as those of a drunkard, that was why his eyes were so hazy, marshy, or fixed and his behavior so intolerable! He was going rapidly downhill, the abyss was already yawning in front of him, for every child knows that this fearful vice leads inevitably to ruin, to demoralization, and finally even to suicide. That was also what Monsieur Goron said, when I told him the whole story, feeling that I owed him the truth. "Only a miracle can save him!" he said.

Since then something has happened that looks almost like a miracle. One night soon after my visit to the Hôtel des Mines, Monsieur Goron had a particularly severe attack; Lebigot stayed with him faithfully the whole night, and when the worst was over Monsieur Goron looked up from his pillow and saw Lebigot striding to and fro in the grip of some sort of inner conflict. He suddenly came to a stop by the bed and asked: "You know all about it, don't you? About me, I mean?" "I was once in charge of the narcotics branch in the Cité," answered Monsieur Goron. "Well," asked Lebigot, "what is your experience? Can a person get over it? Does that ever happen?" "Yes," said Monsieur Goron, "if you have will power. If you believe in something. But first comes the resolve. First you must renounce, then you become free."

Lebigot stared at him, fascinated; he sat down on the edge of the bed and said, without turning his eyes away from Goron: "I will take no more of the stuff. I swear that by my life." Monsieur Goron was very exhausted; he shut his eyes and said in a low voice: "You have sworn it by the bedside of a man delivered up to death, do not forget that." "I swear by my life," reiterated Lebigot. "By your life?" replied Monsieur Goron with a smile. "No! You might come to regard your life as of no account." "By Jaquemar's life then," interrupted Lebigot impatiently. "Do you believe me?" "I believe you," said Monsieur Goron.

Monsieur Goron told me all this himself, and you can understand, can't you, that from that hour forward Lebigot's oath has never ceased to trouble me! If only he had sworn by something else than your life! "Do you really believe him?" I asked Monsieur Goron fearfully. He swayed his head to and fro and at last he said: "We must believe him." That's as good as saying he *doesn't* believe him, isn't it? But I really have to believe him. And above all, I must ask your advice. If he goes back on his word, what shall I do? Please, please advise me! Forgive me for troubling you; but to whom could I turn if not to you? I have no one. Oh, how sad everything has become since you left us. Nevertheless, I do not believe Monsieur Goron who, when I lamented my fears to him, uttered this terrible sentence: "Madame, our soul is nothing but fear and sorrow." Is it not, above all, love?

Oh, I am rambling on; that was not my intention. About myself I will not and cannot tell you much. You already know all that there is to know about me. I am still the eternal wallflower and shall probably remain so.

And now, Edmond, my dear friend, good-by. I wonder who is now sewing on your buttons, making your Turkish coffee, and reading the Song of Gilgamesh to you? Or have I no longer the right to think of such things? In any case, allow me, Monsieur, as we once used to do, to give you a hearty kiss and a friendly embrace. You know that I am the same and shall remain the same, I am always

Your

GERMAINE CH.

Something hard to comprehend remained suspended in Jaquemar's brain and being after the reading of this letter, something somber and menacing that went beyond concern over Lebigot's peril. He took no notice of where he was going. He rustled through the leathery grass of the apple orchard and walked, lost in thought, wherever his steps led him into the overgrown gardens and backyards of what had once been homesteads.

In front of him lay another half-grown clearing containing a crookedly subsided dwelling. The veranda, widened to provide room for sitting, tilted down into the grass; birds were singing and warbling, awakened by the approach of evening, butterflies were fluttering and insects buzzing and whirring in the still air. But on the veranda was something peculiar—a young man absolutely motionless in the position of one about to turn a somersault. He had fallen to his knees, his head was twisted in an unnatural way under his chest, and he was supporting himself on his two outspread hands, while the foot and calf of one leg had disappeared into the rotten wood.

Jaquemar recognized him at first glance: it was Bompard's favorite from the evening of the dance, Malcolm, little Matthew's brother. His one open eye glinted glassily in his head beneath his chest and did not twitch when an occasional fly alighted on it; his mouth was firmly closed as a result of its compressed position; and this, together with the glitter of the eye, intensified to an uncanny degree the impression of stillness that radiated from the acrobatically bent figure.

Jaquemar hurried as fast as he could to his lodgings. The fear that had come over him earlier had completely left him, or had dissolved and become unrecognizable in his excitement, his indignation, and the hatred which, fired by the shock of what he had seen, was seething in his breast and brain.

Thoughts rose to his mind like bubbles, burst, and were dissipated. Why was any liaison with her followed by such terrible vengeance, which fell on all who enjoyed her, whether in the marriage of a year or of an hour? Did she belong to the world of no forgiveness, to Satan's anticreation, was she sin, ageless as sin and seductive and beautiful solely in order to destroy? But she was also innocence! Therein lay her magic power; without innocence she would not have been irresistible.

He walked in through the hotel door and, in his overstrung state, scarcely noticed little Matthew slipping past into the open; he saw that the candles were already burning in the dining room, their dull flicker penetrated the early evening dusk in the hall and he crossed it quickly. Bompard was already sitting at the table with Chester Gaunt, the young American, who half rose with a clatter to greet Jaquemar; but this, too, he only noticed fleetingly; he pulled out a chair and sat down, with his body at an angle to the table, on which he rested his right elbow; his right knee projected into the room, and he kept his eyes glued to the gay eyes of Bompard. But his voice sounded quite calm.

"I beg your pardon," he said, and continued rather more quickly, as she waved his apology aside good-humoredly: "I have a piece of news for you. In an abandoned house, on the rear veranda—"

"I thought so!" cried Bompard.

"Yes, yes, it was your conquest from the festival. The young man has fallen through the timber; he must be hurt."

"I told you somebody had been injured," remarked Bompard, suddenly sulky. "I heard a cry, the cry was short. . . ."

"The man is pretty seriously injured, you know."

"It's a pity," she said politely. "But it's always like that. Anyone who has once loved me and wants to leave me can't do so; it's generally not worth trying, he suffers injuries to body and soul."

" 'Can't do so?' " asked Jaquemar with a smile. "Does he break his neck?"

She, too, looked at him with a smile, a strange, ambiguous smile, and answered gently: "It's not always as bad as that; he may also bleed to death internally."

"The man is dead," remarked Jaquemar briefly.

"You don't say!" cried Bompard, clicking her tongue and shrugging her shoulders. Then she grumbled: "He wanted to cuckold you."

"The man is dead!" Jaquemar repeated loudly.

"I heard you," she replied huffily, and called out: "Hey, girl! Run at once to Frankie, the old man, and tell him to go with Bearstruck Cooley and a stretcher to the abandoned village, the first house on the left. There's someone stuck in the rotten timber."

"You seem to know all about it," said Jaquemar meaningly.

"He's the coroner, isn't he?" she retorted, misunderstanding his remark and showing off her superior knowledge. "He's the coroner and the sheriff; there might have been a crime."

"Yes," persisted Jaquemar, not taking his eyes off her, "there might have been a crime."

"That's what I said," she confirmed. "Law and order must be preserved. Somebody must recently have been tramping around on the veranda and made a hole in the timber with his foot, he's the guilty one."

Jaquemar's face turned pale, but he tried to laugh. "That's a pretty farfetched theory! But can you explain your part in the matter?"

"Where do I come into it?" she asked in surprise. "I heard a cry and that was that. Was I to run back? It might have been a trick to entice me in, after the blackguard had first tried to jilt me in favor of his peasant wench, the waitress here. I had taken his coat, for what further use would it have been to him, and had already left by the front door, when he cried out. But you can see—"

"Yes, the coat!" interrupted Jaquemar. "How could you tell when you took it that it would be of no further use to him?"

"Are you from the police?" she retorted, with an amused laugh.

"It had served for amatory purposes, it was too late for any more of that, the night was over."

"And what will your protégé Matthew say?"

"That's the limit!" she cried in sudden anger. "You wanted him to be punished! And now I'm to— Do you think I'm the whipping boy for your Pharisaical moral sophistries? You've got what you wanted, and that's that!"

Jaquemar looked across at Chester Gaunt, who was listening attentively, with bent head and protruding lower lip, both hands under the table. Something like a smile passed across Jaquemar's pale features, but he said nothing. He stood up and left the room without apology or farewell.

"You mustn't take offense at Jaquemar's bad manners," he heard Bompard saying reasonably. "He doesn't have an easy time with himself."

In the hall—he had already put his foot on the lowest stair— Jaquemar stopped, and through the screen door watched a little procession making its way along the village street. In front walked Frank Day, the aged cowherd, who had replaced his usual prunella cap with an old military cap, from beneath which the curls at the back of his neck peeped roguishly; then came a swaying brushwood stretcher; while the rear bearer was Cooley Lane in stiff dungarees, the blue feathers in his cap glowing, nodding, and shimmering intensely in the twilight.

Jaquemar mounted the steps. He entered his room, taking Germaine Chottin's letter out of his jacket pocket as he went, and came to a halt in the middle of the room. After a while he raised his head; he looked through the open communicating door into Bompard's room and saw the trunk with its lid still thrown back; he could even see the little nickel and mother-of-pearl revolver among the diaphanous lingerie. He quivered with anger, slammed the door shut, threw the letter down on the pillow of his camp bed, and went quickly over to the other wall of his room, where a slender-legged and fragile chair stood. He sat down on this chair and remained sitting, staring into space amidst the slowly falling darkness, his hands resting on his knees. One of those glowworms, which were so much rarer here than in Saratoga Springs, had strayed into the room and was testing the ceiling and the corners of the walls with a palely glimmering light, and this alternately brightening and dimming gleam became more and more golden and starlike the deeper grew the night.

Perhaps an hour had passed, perhaps two; Jaquemar had heard no sound in the next room; then there was a knock at the communicating door. He did not answer. Nevertheless the door opened. In the streaming flicker of the candlelight stood a great lumbering shadow, and for some reason this sight gave Jaquemar an irresistible desire to laugh; he laughed, while the shadow in the doorway stood perfectly still.

"What's so funny?" asked Chester Gaunt's voice.

"I'm sorry," replied Jaquemar, "but in the doorway you look like a horse in a living room."

"Do I?" said the other. "I have to ride away. Will you come with me to the post office?"

Jaquemar immediately stood up and left the room and the hotel with the young American. The young man was wearing his short tail coat, and in his hand he held an old-fashioned kind of top hat; he looked at it thoughtfully with his emaciated, furrowed face as he stalked along beside Jaquemar down the village street.

"Thanks for the letter," said Jaquemar.

"Don't mention it," said Gaunt. He looked gloomily at his companion and asked out of the blue: "Are you happy?"

"Have you no eyes in your head?" retorted Jaquemar with a laugh.

"I see," said Gaunt quietly, and added reflectively: "But you love her."

"The curse," remarked Jaquemar staring straight in front of him, "the curse is that I still haven't finished the business."

They now walked along side by side without speaking. The night was starless, and a lazy wind was rummaging among the trees, which rustled and fell silent, sighing like powerless beings concerned for their lives.

"I believe," Chester Gaunt eventually began again, "that I now understand things rather better. I'm sorry I was unjust to you that evening in your room at the Grand Union. Thank you for not having held it against me."

"It's not worth talking about," answered Jaquemar somberly.

"You see, I love her too," the young man declared in his honest, straightforward manner. "And when I can look at her it is like a hemorrhage of the soul. It makes one empty, one bleeds to death internally, she said so herself and it's true."

They had reached the post office and came to a halt. A fine brown horse was tethered to the rail in front of the low red house and looked around at the two of them. Finally the young American put on his old-fashioned top hat, untied the horse, and said, tilting his head slightly to one side: "I fear I cannot be of any use to you. Otherwise I would give you my address. What for? You will go your way. I shall never forget you."

He stretched his great powerful hand toward Jaquemar: "Good-by. I believe we should have become good friends."

"Adieu," answered Jaquemar, shaking his hand. "All the best."

He turned and strode back toward the hotel. After a minute Chester Gaunt trotted past, high up on his horse, and wearing his curious top-hat; he waved the outstretched index finger of his right hand, with a quivering gesture that looked like an admonition, and vanished into the darkness. The clatter of his horse's hooves, as he rode across the covered bridge, rang dully in Jaquemar's ears.

Jaquemar went to enter his room and stopped dead on the threshold. On the table by the camp bed, the candle, which he had not lit, was burning, and it had been moved close up to the bed. Germaine Chottin's letter lay on the pillow torn into a thousand pieces, heaped up into a little pointed mountain, and the pile of jagged scraps of white paper covered with black writing seemed to be in trickling movement on account of the flickering candlelight, as though it were melting away. The sight caused him a brief, stabbing sensation that was not really either surprise or pain or anger; he looked up, saw that the communicating door was not shut, and went into Bompard's room.

She was lying in bed and kept her face demonstratively averted and the thin blanket drawn up under her chin with both hands inside, so that only the thick mop of curls, gleaming blue-black in the candlelight, was visible on the white pillow.

"A vain act of jealousy, Madame," said Jaquemar venomously. "When I have read a letter through twice I know it by heart."

She jerked quickly into a sitting position under the blanket, which fell away, uncovering her beautiful torso with the rounded shoulders and succulent breasts that tension caused to stand out like two great lemons.

Her eyes under the anguished brows were darting fire as she cried: "Do you want to behave like your Gouffé, whose memory should serve as an example? To lie with me and dream of that sentimental goose? That would have been the last straw! For your sake, just so that you shouldn't be disturbed, I let myself be talked into going to this God-forsaken little place—and that's your thanks? Do you think I didn't realize long ago what was behind your apathy and edginess?

"That would just suit you," railed Bompard. "To let that dreary goose, that scrofulous offal, pay court to you, and use me as a concubine! What are you thinking of? Nobody can rape a woman like me for nothing!"

"Quite so, quite so," said Jaquemar without irony, and his eyes were now resting on her breasts. "I know that. On the contrary, it costs more than anyone possesses."

But she did not continue her argument. She said nothing, suddenly lifted her left breast a little and said in a low voice: "Come to bed, Jaquemar."

"After . . . what happened in the ghost village?" he whispered, shaking his head. "No, not today!"

"When?" she exclaimed indignantly. "On your fiftieth birthday?"

"You're in a hurry."

"Certainly," she replied ill-humoredly. "Firstly out of love and secondly because one shouldn't waste one's time. The little time we still have left here."

"The little time?"

"We're leaving," she said briefly.

"Leaving? Why? Where are we going?"

She shrugged her shoulders and mumbled, making a vague shaking and rocking gesture with her outspread, skinny right hand: "Some-where else."

"Why did Gaunt come?" he asked. "Where has he ridden off to, now, in the middle of the night?"

"Not to Saratoga," she replied evasively. "Not back. That was impossible. On your account."

"No," said Jaquemar obstinately. "I'm not leaving. This was the last stop."

"I'm no gypsy. We can't stay. On your account."

"What do you mean, on my account?" he asked suspiciously, trying to look into her eyes, which he was unable to do, because she had lowered her lashes.

"Carapin is in Saratoga, darling, back from Buffalo," she reported, with a sigh through her nostrils, and afterward set about unbuttoning Jaquemar's shirt and undoing his braces. "If you knew Buffalo you would readily understand that meanwhile he has had second thoughts and become aware to the core of his being of what he has lost in me. And he's as vain as a peacock. If he ever finds out what passion has made you do with me! He only needs to meet Chester or Balthasar the coachman (though as a matter of fact he can't meet him any more), but people in the Grand Union know too. It would be awkward if he surprised us here, the man would make such a scene that the church bell would fall out of the belfry, and he might shoot you in a duel. Who knows?"

While she spoke she disordered all his clothes, pulling up his shirt and unbuttoning it; and he was so dazed by the news that he allowed himself to sink down on the bed beside her. With a few dexterous movements she stripped him naked, threw the bundle of clothes on the floor, snuffled about over his body, and kissed his chest.

But he squinted up at the ceiling and muttered as though in meditation: "Yes, it would be awkward. But to run away? From Carapin? Who is Carapin that I should run away from him?"

"We must move on, there can be no doubt about that," she stated, shrugging her shoulders.

"Move on, move on!" he cried. "From whom are we running away? We are free people."

"I am free," grumbled Bompard on his chest.

"Oh, you are? But I'm not? Is that what you mean?"

"You're too sensitive, my heart," she remarked, and watched herself with interest as she ran her clawlike fingers over his body, so that the thrill gave him gooseflesh and his excitement swelled up, in contradiction of his whole state of mind. "Your sensibility makes you unfree."

All of a sudden she was sitting on top of him; she uttered a loud groan, supported herself with both hands on his shoulders, and the lids were closed over her eyes. But this act of taking possession did not interrupt her speech. She sat on him calmly and entranced, gripping him with her powerful thighs, an enchanting smile playing around her mouth and tiger's nostrils, and went on coaxingly: "No man is more perfidious, chéri, than he whose vanity has been wounded. If Carapin discovers us here and you drive him out of the temple, he will vent his rage and grief in some other way! I know him better than you do! The newspapers here and in Paris will be full of the story that Monsieur Edmond Jaquemar, brother-in-law and sole heir of the murdered Alphonse Gouffé, has fled into the woods with the same person who was half accused of being an accessory in the murder—utter rubbish as it was, pitifully stupid and an outrage against justice—and that they are billing and cooing there like turtle doves. Then people will remember the persistent rumor that we were always hand in glove; and if Carapin can now swear by God, because he has now seen it with his own eyes, that this was true, wouldn't it rob you of your sleep and all pleasure in life? Would you ever be able to go back home again? Yes, wouldn't the scum of police laugh up their sleeves and immediately block and annul your inheritance, so that we should go hungry until you had answered for your conduct? But how can you answer for your conduct, when you really have become involved with me, incessantly, and are still doing so now?"

In this way, with common sense, wheedling, and lust, Bompard persuaded and convinced Jaquemar that their sojourn in Four Corners must come to a rapid end and that they must set out on a hejira into the unknown. He no longer contradicted. Like an Amazon, beside herself with joy, Bompard rode him skilfully, lingeringly, and then wildly into a heating of the blood and an orgasm of self-surrender such as he had never experienced before (the deeper the shame, the greater the ecstasy), thrilling and shattering to the point of pain, a firework of nerves and senses in which the last fragment of consciousness and strength was shot away. The picture of her naked, her panting breath through her bold nostrils, and the blue-black hair that seemed to be streaming out behind her like tongues of flame, was the last image his eye, like that of a man sinking into a quagmire, was able to take in before gratified pleasure thrust him entirely without transition into a sleep which, if it had a place anywhere, must have lain fathoms deep under the earth and as if cushioned on black pillows; he lay inanimate in this sleep, close and soft, and greeted by not a single ray or drop of light.

Once only, when dawn was breaking did he wake. He heard the screeching of birds, and closed his eyes, nauseated, and with an icy shiver between his shoulder blades.

They left that morning. Bompard's trunk was strapped to the back of the coach. Miss Dimple rubbed her hands, bowing continually and lisping incomprehensibly between a whisper and a laugh; Cooley Lane watched the farewell through his barred window. Bompard climbed into the coach, followed by Jaquemar. On the box stood, not sat, Matthew, the little lad; whooping and yelling, he spurred the horses to a gallop and frenziedly lashed them with the whip. Hooves thundering, they plunged into the shadow of the covered bridge and Jaquemar, benumbed by the din, thought: *With view halloo and cracking whip we're on your way, Gouffé!*

4

AMERICA. THIRD STOP: MOONSTONE VALLEY

They had set out on a long journey. To the accompaniment of whoops and whipcracks, the boy Matthew's carriage brought them, after many hours' travel through pretty wooded mountains with granite crags and waterfalls and through a hilly region that became gradually bleaker, to Albany, in New York State; after this, a day and night express that snorted and uttered long-drawn cries for help took them to Chicago, in Illinois, and here they boarded the great overland express.

This was a luxury train of the first order. The long straw-yellow carriages were decorated, in the ostentatious taste of the time and the country, with paintings of Indians' heads wearing feather headdresses, wigwams, and the like, the dining car with twisted golden conch shells out of which beribboned and brightly colored fruits and flowers were overflowing into baskets on a blue lacquer background. The traveling restaurant was called *The Palace of the Golden West*, according to an inscription richly ornamented with flourishes; and only the locomotive, a squat monster of black iron with a bumper grid at its feet, had no other ornament than its power, such a grim and menacing power that the name *The Great Challenger* announced by a brass plate beneath the single chest-wide Cyclopean headlamp eye seemed highly appropriate to this colossus of weight and energy.

For it must indeed have been a great challenger that carried the travelers in comfort through the measureless corn fields and prairies of Illinois, Missouri, Kansas, Colorado, New Mexico, and Arizona, and on toward the West. Jaquemar realized the distance they were covering not so much by what he saw, as by the time that rose and fell around him as they raced tirelessly onward: it was a cumulative experience derived not from signposts, but entirely from the duration of the journey, just as a true knowledge of life ripens within us less as the result of particular events than of the experience of growing old.

No wonder he was gradually possessed by the feeling that movement through these geographical spheres must be correlated with a different clock from that which applied elsewhere. At sixty miles an hour they seemed to be traveling very hesitantly through the vast emptiness, because although a trail of black smoke occasionally flitted past the windowpanes there was hardly ever a tree or a house—they raced forward, yet never moved from the spot. The growling calls emitted every now and then by *The Great Challenger* died mournfully away; they sounded like a steamship's siren—heaven knows what purpose they served in that wilderness; perhaps they were meant to bring consoling memories of the sea; only the sea moves and has spray, fishes, and dolphins; here they were in a timeless no-man's-land, to whose empty vastness the young traveler's rate of perception was not adjusted. Was he being carried by ghost horses? The rotation of the wheels bore a strange resemblance to the clatter of horses' hooves and gave a completely fantastic character to the aimless journey through plains of rye and wheat and sandy prairies. Along with the concept of time, those of place and destination were annulled and invalidated.

Seven days and seven nights in nothingness—ought not Jaquemar to have felt bored? He was anything but bored! He looked out, he saw, felt, and knew that the vast expanse outside extending right into the sky before his eyes was inconceivable to the human mind; yet there it was! It was inconceivable, it was undeniable; its existence set up an insoluble conflict in Jaquemar's breast, and the sight of its measureless void exercised an unequaled fascination, in which even the image of Bompard paled and vanished. She sat facing him, confidently rummaging through her things and laying down the law in her amusingly brazen way, as much at home here as everywhere else; and for hours Jaquemar did not see her, as though she were sitting in line with his blind spot. When he did see her, however, it seemed to him that she had imperceptibly changed, as though an aging process had begun to take place in the very heart of her agelessness—probably an optical illusion brought about by the merciless light of the plains, which gave a sharper, harsher outline to her lovely features as though etching them with a finely pointed graver.

Meanwhile it was not as if the journey through the vast waste of this landscape was mere empty monotony. There were diversions. Once the plain outside crumbled, sank into a wide depression, and became a forest of stumps, stunted trees, and gray gypsum; no bird nested and no green leaf grew among the petrified boughs or on the gnarled trunks; it was a forest of dried clay and death. The train sped across a bridge with iron arches and the travelers caught a glimpse of the calmly flowing Mississippi, which at some time or other had over-flowed its banks and suffocated the forests in its valley with its mud. Another time the train stopped; beside the track stood a corrugated-iron shed and next to it a structure built of strong metal scaffolding supporting a large black tub, from whose snakelike outflow pipe glitter-ing water was still spurting and dripping as *The Great Challenger* started up again and quickly gathered speed.

The meals served by Negro attendants in the dining car were also diversions; and so, in a sense, were the nights. On returning from supper the travelers found the train transformed: the open space in the center of the compartment had vanished, leaving only a narrow gang-way curtained on both sides by walls of felt that swayed gently in the semidarkness under the dimmed ceiling lights and brushed against the shoulders and cheeks of those passing between them. Behind these were concealed two bunks one above the other, set up between every set of two facing seats and extending along the whole length of the compartment; a small retractable ladder led to the upper bunk, and both were covered with piles of soft white pillows on which it was indescribably comfortable to lie.

After Jaquemar had undressed in a kneeling position between the mattress and the bunk overhead, he let the roller blind over the win-dow run up and, lying flat, gazed out. The countryside lay like a thin black plate in the vastness of the night, and all around myriad lights and patches of fire glittered and flashed in the blue-black ether, in clusters and precise geometrical figures, radiant single stars and shimmering nebulae. Borne by the faithful clatter of the ghost horses, he was in the middle of the universe and—tiny ego that he was—he had a share in eternity; for his existence consisted solely in the fact that he was breathing, and this alone distinguished him from the everlastingness, the loveless, motherly everlastingness, which the born brain cannot conceive or the circling hand of any clock measure.

There were also diversions afforded by the disappointment of expectations. According to the sketch maps in the timetable, rivers with melodious Indian names—the Havasu, Chemehuevi, and Mohave—should have been flowing through the area they were now traversing, but they were no more than wide pebbly channels without a drop of water that wound their way through the reddish-yellow sand, full of whitish flints and rubble; unfulfilled promises such as the Petrified Forest had been the day before yesterday, a feature the map described as covering mile upon mile, but which appeared to the eye as nothing but a totally empty stony desert. But there was one diversion that got on Jaquemar's nerves. Bompard was now frequently missing, not only to the young man's blind gaze, but because she was drinking, gambling, or gossiping in the dining or observation car with other travelers.

Returning to the compartment one morning, after having washed and shaved, Jaquemar found the two bunks gone, along with Bompard. The two upholstered seats facing each other, rearranged for daytime use, formed a niche in the green felt corridor. No sooner had he sat down than the mist outside began to clear. It was exciting to watch how it cleared: with a boiling, clouding, swirling movement like the shaking of a gauze curtain, a trickling and flickering, in which the heavy, dull gray willingly disintegrated and began to glow with a charmed and charming radiance as of blossoms. This was the purple morning light of California, the most virginal and soulful light Jaquemar had seen in America, clinging, cool, and chaste.

The landscape they traveled through in this purple light was exceedingly lovely. It was dotted far and wide with southern-looking, flat-roofed stone buildings and thin-walled timber shacks, and also planted with gardens, groves, and flowerbeds. But what rendered it beautiful above all was the multitude, softness, and purity of the colors, the sharp-cut character of every line, the lively gentleness of breeze and growth. The great faces of the sunflowers glowed innocently; the fan palms waved their rounded frond-arms to and fro in a dreamy gesture, and the crests of the sixty to a hundred feet tall date palms were combed by the morning breeze and gleamed and glittered with an entrancing rustle. There were also deciduous trees of every kind and species, ancient-looking, ash-gray northern pines and tropical trees whose foliage was interspersed with the blossoms of fleshy creepers. Birds took off and darted like jets of paint through the purple peace, as though in a park in some Eastern fairy tale.

Jaquemar barely noticed that Bompard was back and, as so often, busy with packing, that the Negro porter in the short white jacket and black trousers carried out their luggage, that the railway carriage, reconverted into a daytime lodging, once more had seats, windows, and occupants. He looked out and took with him as the last acquisition from this long journey a picture of amiable insanity: in the wide open window of a timber shack wreathed in flowers stood an old man in a nightshirt; silvery hair fell in curls over his ears and a silver beard covered his half-naked chest; he was looking out with a furrowed, weather-reddened face and tear-dimmed eyes and brandishing a toy American flag in his right hand; he waved it in greeting to the train and glided slowly past.

Then Bompard turned to her companion. He looked at her calmly. With a beaming face she made a polite, boyish little bow and said: "Would you mind? We're just arriving."

"I must admit," commented Jaquemar thoughtfully, "that I am consumed with curiosity as to where you are dragging me off to."

"Have patience, my heart!" she cried, boldly grasping his hand with her clawlike fingers. "You won't be disappointed, you're in for a big surprise."

The station, which stood well back behind a flat expanse of gravel, was built of porous tufa and painted peach-pink; it glowed warmly in the early light and palm trees were rustling beside it. "San Geronimo Junction," Jaquemar read over the round-arched entrance gate as they walked toward it; and *The Great Challenger* started up again behind them with a loud, powerful puffing followed at once by the low but rapidly accelerated sound of the rotating carriage wheels.

Meanwhile, Bompard strode out cheerfully and was as beautiful and lovely as the morning. Her costume of blue horsehair fabric had a comical hint of the convent or the Salvation Army about it, arising from the farthingale that was almost as wide as a crinoline and the little tight-waisted jacket with the modest shoulder frills, but especially from the poke bonnet which cast a sweet shadow on her face and from beneath the front edge of which the wayward curls protruded like a diadem.

In front of the station, a high-wheeled open carriage was waiting, with two seats surmounted by a striped rainproof canopy decorated all around with a short frill. Bompard's large trunk had already been strapped on at the back; in front, a sorry-looking hack stood in the harness and someone was busy stowing away the hand luggage between the seats up above.

The smacking of the coachman's tongue rang out like a wet kiss in the air, the whip cracked slackly, and the unexpectedly lumbering vehicle moved off with a creaking and grinding noise.

San Geronimo Junction—less a town than a garden settlement, with one street and side turnings that petered out into sand and vegetation by the second or third property—San Geronimo Junction was soon behind them, and now they were traveling, bumpily to be sure, but at a gentle trot in the play of light and shade of a tree-lined highway. The light grew clearer and clearer, gradually changing from purple to pink and finally to gold. But the air, although it became warmer, remained fresh and sparkling, with an aromatic, sweet smell of honey, resin, and flowers, and fanned the travelers' faces with gentle breezes: it was mountain air.

They were on a plateau. Through the swaying branches of the trees lining the roadside they caught sight, first on the left and then ever more frequently on the right, of wooded mountaintops, mere images in the margin that passed slowly by as they advanced along the highway. It stretched out ahead of them into the distance, like a tunnel, but free from any monotony; for unlike the beautiful avenues of poplars in Jaquemar's homeland, this was bordered by trees of the most varied species. They bewitched Jaquemar's senses, only his delight was perforated and split in pieces; for the coach was thumping and bumping ever more unbearably in stony ruts; Jaquemar had to keep his jaws clenched to prevent his teeth being knocked together, he was shaken this way and that on the seat, and yet they were not going fast enough for Bompard.

She jabbed the hunched-up man on the box with the tip of her parasol and railed: "Get a move on! Give your scurvy beast a taste of the whip, and God help you if I'm not at Joshua by dusk!"

She looked at Jaquemar (the reflection of the blue jacaranda blossoms in her radiant eyes was indescribable) and remarked with her sphinxlike smile, shaking her head and raising her eyebrows: "They simply don't know how to behave, these scum, you mustn't hold it against me, chéri, I'm doing my best."

Jaquemar stared meditatively at the wretched figure in front of him on the box. His shirt was torn into long strips, the crooked line of the spine showed through and so did the shadows of the ribs under the shimmer of the material; the pointed straw hat added a fantastic touch to the miserable apparition, and as the result of either fear or effort, sweat was pouring in precise, heavy drops out of his armpits onto his ribs.

"Can't she see," said Jaquemar thinking half aloud, "that he can hardly hold himself upright? He's dissolving."

"Hey, you!" cried Bompard, jabbing the man even more savagely in the ribs than before. "Stop sweating! The stench is annoying the señor!"

Satisfied with her work, she settled herself back on her padded seat, plucking at her skirt; Jaquemar clenched his fists and said nothing. The Mexican imperceptibly turned his head and it seemed to Jaquemar as though a long, sad look came to him.

The road must have led straight into the mountains, and had lost itself in the grass. They were driving along a forest ride a mile across, thinly planted with trees, and saw to left and right mountains shaped like crests, heads, and sugarloaves, which, to judge by the pure ether blue surrounding them, must have been of towering height, although they could only sense rather than see the gorges and ravines between them; the grassy surface of the ride cut horizontally across these wooded summits, which very slowly shifted position in relation to one another, covered each other, and reappeared. The coach bowled along gently as if on soft, springy turf; but this seemed to strain the horse more than the rough ground they had traversed previously; its trot turned into a walk, and the shadows of the bones under its sweating skin bent and stretched laboriously, as though it were carrying a burden of ever-increasing weight.

Fortunately, it was already midday. They came, unexpectedly in this desolation, upon a tiny homestead: a small house out of whose steep roof the beams protruded; in the yard a few lath sheds and a tree stump that served as a chopping block, with an ax sticking into it. Although the place proclaimed itself, in painted letters that had run, an inn, the room inside was no more than a mud hut; there were not even any panes in the windows; and the ragged innkeeper, cringing before the energetic Bompard, displayed big white teeth in a crafty rogue's grin as he declared, hand on heart, that he had absolutely no food available.

Exhausted and in an agony of thirst, Jaquemar sat down at the one crooked table, had an earthenware jug of black local wine set in front of him, and drank from it greedily. The inky beverage on an empty stomach made him fuddled, so that he took little note of what was going on. He heard Bompard's hardhearted orders, the lamenting and beseeching of the innkeeper, then the mortal squawks, almost like screams, of a hen, which pretty soon afterward appeared on the table, roasted and enveloped as though in a cloak in a slice of bacon. The roasting must have been done in the same room; the cave was filled with acrid smoke, through which the innkeeper made his way outside, looking like a specter. He was bull-necked, with great round shoulders, and in his hand he carried a tin plate on which Jaquemar could just make out the chicken's severed neck and head with the comb on it and two yellow legs—lunch for the driver Alphonso, as Bompard explained, shaking her head at the foolishness of his question.

Starting awake out of a doze, Jaquemar found himself being once more thumped and bumped in the carriage next to Bompard. In the feverish instability of thought that often follows the enjoyment of strong alcohol, it suddenly struck Jaquemar that the innkeeper in the pothouse had reminded him of someone and that Alphonso the coachman also reminded him of somebody, the latter in a melancholy, the former in a repulsive manner. He soon forgot about it again, and now looked out at the region through which they were bowling along at a moderate trot.

It bore no resemblance to the countryside they had previously passed through. The road, which had reappeared, wound along white and treeless through bare hummocks of gray and dull-green sand; here and there stood some thorny bush, a small tree, or a stunted fir, and there were a few patches of scrubby undergrowth; for the most part, however, there were stones, smooth, flat, or loaf-shaped flints, which in places were heaped up into positive bastions and flanked the road on both sides like fallen gateways; the sun was high in the sky and blazed down unhindered on the bumpy plateau.

The extremely colorless expanse of multitudinous but insignificant hillocks, like the surface of a relief map, was not calculated to hold his attention. The only fascinating thing about it was its apparent endlessness; they had been bumping along among the mounds and hillocks for several hours, making detours around circular eminences and finding themselves on the other side once more confronted by long stretches of winding road, and the only observable change was in the scanty vegetation. The low trees and stunted firs disappeared and made way for other species, occasional solitary cactuses, agaves, and ocotillos, the latter the most extreme example of hardened and woody plants Jaquemar had ever seen; for they did not bear a single leaf or fibre of green, but stuck up out of the yellowish sandy soil like bundles of bare black rods.

"Will this never come to an end!" cried Jaquemar, staring malevolently into the distance.

"You'll be surprised," commented Bompard.

And Jaquemar was surprised—if surprised is the right word to describe the state of mind and emotion of a man whose breath is taken away by the picture he sees before him. He lacked the power to take in the immense stillness and heart-crushing grandeur of this picture— and, in God's name, who are we, mere chroniclers, reiterators of a truth within anyone's comprehension, to presume to describe what was beyond Gilgamesh-Jaquemar's comprehension? Since, however, we must make an attempt to do so, let us enumerate the facts with all the sober accuracy we can muster.

Our travelers' carriage drove along the edge of the plateau, which lay a few feet to their right and dropped, without any gradual declivity, so steeply that it looked as if it had been cut off with a spade. The drop was so great that a look over the edge evoked no sense of measurable depth, but merely one of immensity. The immensity of the drop amidst the utter silence produced in the spectator a feeling of being pulled down into the depths, a feeling that he must jump over the edge.

In this frightful, lifeless scrap heap of earth and rock there was nothing to which any feeling could attach itself; it did not even repel, it was not even indifferent. By comparison, the prairies through which Jaquemar had traveled on the train had been deserted gardens. The human mind is unable to tolerate the existence of anything that cannot serve as an echo of any human thought, of any human feeling; such a thing it calls "nothing," and nothing must be invisible. But the huge primeval mountain across the valley was visible in its ghastly softness; it *was*. It was only weight, yet light as air, nonform, yet the coagulation of heaven knows what fluid, in which every attribute was canceled out by its opposite: it was as heavy as it was light, as old as it was young, and, in the absence of any standard of comparison, as high as it was low (the observer could, no, *had* to picture the giant spirit, his sudden shadow as his foot came to rest in passing on the little heap of primordial grit that made up this mound and trampled it to dust, a grinding sound and it was gone); the primeval mountain was and was beyond all comparison.

The sight took Jaquemar's breath away. He shook his head, as though to rid his brain of irritating mosquito swarms of unthought; he opened, closed, and reopened his eyes and wanted only to see— yes, only to see, and with what eye, if not the eye of life? Can life feel itself, except in relationships and comparisons? Poor Jaquemar, poor life; so much ambition within such narrow limits! What had man's shame and man's nobility been since the beginning, if not passion for the eternally denied, gnawing love of the impossible, the thirst for truth?

Jaquemar was very thirsty; his throat was parched from the black wine he had drunk and was growing more and more leathery from the waves of dry heat that were billowing up from the corner of the desert in the depths below; for they were already on the way down. Winding thousands of feet downward, the multiple-spiral ribbon of the road glowed white like white-hot hoop-iron on the almost vertical slope. Jaquemar squeezed his eyelids together again, a grotesque little image in his eyelid. Bompard angrily hooked the crook of her parasol around the coachman's neck, dragged him back, and snarled cheerfully: "Put the brakes on, carrion, the señor is chalky white with dizziness!"

Jaquemar looked across again at the ridge, which in his own mind he called the Moon Mountain, but he could give no name at all to the un- and super-reality of the scene that was being enacted over there. The sun above the plateau was departing, the lifeless mountain opposite was its mirror, the shadows lay purple on the protuberances and clefts, and down below the pearl-gray slope covered in slag and debris was suffused with a shell-pink glow. It blushed as though in sweet innocence, and it was impossible to imagine any event of greater charm than this virginal blushing on the part of the sinister mountain —Jaquemar felt almost ashamed to be spying on this poignant im- maculacy. Yet what was happening there was far too spotless and supernatural for two eyes that watched it to have any effect on its otherworldly detachment: in its unparalleled loveliness it thrust the young man savagely back into himself, for it meant nothing.

Impeded by the brake block on the rear wheel, the carriage jiggled down the white roadway with the canopy frill swinging. It was going along very easily and steadily, but for some reason not to the satis- faction of Bompard, who was still staring malevolently at the neck of the miserable fellow on the box and shaking her head with an em- bittered expression. Far away from them, where the vertical wall of the plateau broke up into loftier wooded mountains, the peaks and slopes showed inky-blue, and among them motionless trails of mist hung and blossomed olive-green and ochre-yellow in a cold, gaseous glow. The narrow corner of the desert lay extinct far down below in the abyss, gray and humble, grained with a somewhat darker pattern, while the giant crest of the Moon Mountain opposite took on an ever more fiery and magnificent orange-yellow and blood-red incandescence, like fanned cinders.

"Can we stop?" asked Jaquemar softly. With his left hand he took hold of the parasol which Bompard had already poised to jab and heard her voice call out: "Stop, you horrible menial."

"It isn't usual, sweet mistress," muttered the Mexican dejectedly, casting a reproachful glance back at Jaquemar from the hat-shadowed putrefaction of his face.

"Shush!" went Bompard, threatening him with her eyes; and the coach came to a halt.

The silence, now that the grinding and regular bumping of the vehicle had ceased, was incredible, and suddenly had the effect of an unending thunderclap. A total, thick, dense silence that assailed acoustic duct and eardrum in an indefinably horrible way, like cottonwool, winding itself around heart and temples and drawing itself tight like a rapidly twisted garrotte. Yet it was really nothing but silence, only it was perfect and therefore beyond all human measurement.

"Courage, beautiful!" cried Bompard boldly. In an instant she was in the roadway on Jaquemar's side of the carriage, took his hand, and helped him to alight. "Don't be a coward, Jaquemar, what can happen to you?"

And so mighty was the silence that her cry hung in it, thin and echoless like something solid. Jaquemar freed himself from her assistance; but after he had taken a step nearer the edge of the abyss, the sight of such depth brought back the old vertigo; he staggered, reached out behind him, and took Bompard's hand again. In his grasp it felt cold, horny, and sharp like a bird's claw; he was glad of its support, and for the space of an instant was somehow moved by it.

The primeval landscape, in which the young man stood like a dwarf, seemed only a further solidification of the hot, unprecedented silence, to which he had to listen not only with his ears but with his whole being, and he felt himself turn pale. This process of turning pale was a kind of stupefaction such as he had never experienced before; his thoughts and sensations grew pale and faint, and the sharp pain he felt in his left ankle, although it now rose into his calf like a cramp, was numb.

"What is this?" he whispered, with hardened lips and trying to be ironic. "Are we entering the kingdom of the bloodless, of the damned?"

"Come, come," she exclaimed, in a subdued voice and with the hint of a sulky laugh, slapped him on the forearm with her hand, and added didactically and full of self-confidence: "This is Moonstone Valley."

Then he forgot her. He surrendered himself to the inconceivable muteness; and everything that is expectation in us, except for the physical, which kept him breathing, sank to rest in him, but without solemnity or peace. He had no sense of how long he stood there; his pause was neither sleep nor waking; perhaps he was in that silence in which the souls of the unborn timelessly exist.

All of a sudden something gentle touched his heart. Out of the unfathomable silence there rose a single high, clear, trilling birdsong;

the notes darted like a hair-thin flash into the cottonwool emptiness and density of the atmosphere, which split in pieces under the impact, and as it mutely disintegrated became light and airy, and above the primeval stillness of the scree the creature's sweet, unintimidated song blossomed and rejoiced.

The song had the same shattering effect on Jaquemar's gravity as it had on the great silence. A sob wrested itself from him, and at the same moment he had to laugh at Bompard, who worked herself up into a state of misdirected concern and cried indignantly: "Does the miserable bird have to make that ghastly din? Nasty bunch of feathers! It can't keep its beak shut, it whistles, trills, twitters, and has no consideration for your nerves, my poor dear! May Satan pound it to a jelly!"

"Forgive my squeamishness," he muttered malevolently. "I'm really overwrought. This heat . . ."

"Definitely, my beloved," she interrupted, "this lovely, dry warmth will do you good, it's a real panacea. Whatever ails people, whether it's gangrene, rheumatism, impotence, anthrax, or cancer of the kidneys—everything gets better here."

"Everything gets better here," repeated Jaquemar meditatively, and felt the heat of the desert scorching his face and searing his entrails, so that he could hardly swallow.

"What are you babbling about?" he growled peevishly, glancing at Bompard suspiciously. "I'm not ill."

"Just nerves," she replied, as though to herself, with modestly lowered lashes and turning bashfully away.

He fixed her with his suspicious gaze. She laughed, made her polite little bow, slipped her arm under his, and drew him away from the abyss.

"Are you limping?" she inquired in astonishment.

"I took a false step," he answered briefly.

She supported his elbow as he mounted, climbed in after and past him, and settled herself in the seat beside him, plucking at her skirt. With a smacking kiss into the void and a shake of the reins, Alphonso put his tired horse into a trot, and the cumbersome vehicle trundled on down toward the desert with a grinding clatter.

The mountain of slag and debris on their right was completely extinct, a huge ridge of black cinders. Behind it the early night sky glowed a deep, pure apple-green, lit by the radiance of a single fat star. The glowing veils of mist on the slopes of the wooded mountains at the travelers' side were also extinguished; but on the peaks, as though hooked to them, sat round balls of cloud glowing and blossoming with a golden hue—the day's last greeting, filled with a melancholy rapture. And with a feeling of having missed something that could never be made good, Jaquemar answered the farewell of animate nature and watched the light overhead turn gray, while the balls of mist squatted like blind wads of cottonwool in the hairy blackness of the peaks.

The carriage clattered on down into the darkness with its brakes on. In the narrow ravine between the two enormous arms of the mountain they bowled along in the shadow of the mute evening; as they descended, muteness and heat seemed to grow denser, to become a different element of firmer consistency, into which they plunged as into the sediment of silence; and Jaquemar felt the blood pounding in his temples, unwillingly and threateningly as though flowing through calcified veins and on the point of coagulating.

"In God's name," he cried with a short laugh, "everything gets better here!"

"I'm glad you're seeing sense at last, darling," replied Bompard promptly, in the tone of a governess. "Just remember how much trouble I've put myself to on your account, although I was always very much in demand elsewhere; then you will certainly do your duty and satisfy my needs."

She looked away and muttered to herself: "It's high time."

The road finally ran down into the desert valley and flattened out. Here, where they now drove faster, without brakes, shaking to and fro at a regular trot, it was lightless—not pitch-black, however, but smoky with gloomy heat, so that, in spite of the absolute dryness, the vegetation Jaquemar saw at the foot of the slopes as they drove past looked as though it were under water: creosote bushes like thick-stemmed algae; smoke trees with delicate, trembling leaves that seem to be made of smoke or merely the reflection of smoke; and joshua trees, half palm, half cactus, the last survivors of a sea-bed forest, that advanced with their powerful trunks and bunches of dagger-shaped leaves right up to the roadside, while a few isolated specimens stood farther out in the emptiness of the desert, blown aslant—by what storm, by what ground swell?—in this deathly sandy gorge where not a breath of air stirred.

The huge black arms of the mountain, to right and left, were already moving slightly farther apart; with sand trickling from its wheels, the carriage was bowling along in the middle; and although he had difficulty in breathing, Jaquemar felt strangely entertained by the journey. Saguaros stood near and far in sparse forests, cactuses, taller than a man, of venerable age and grotesque shapes; their multiple fat torsos, like bottles or cucumbers, were streaked from head to foot with triangular thorn furrows and sprouted sideways in similar thick extremities, which they extended outward or upward in a paralyzed gesture like shapeless baby's arms.

"You must know, Jaquemar, my sweet," Bompard informed him, as though she had been eavesdropping on his fantasies, "if their arms are hacked off, they don't dry up, they rot, they feed on so much water, where everything goes thirsty. In your goodness of heart, you have no idea at all of the vulgar obstinacy with which life asserts itself. There are beasts here, tiny, but armed with scales and horns, and others that blow themselves up out of pure boastfulness and to strike terror, and this brood refuses to make water, but retains its urine out of malicious meanness until it finally comes out dry like dung. All so as to avoid paying its tribute to the beautiful silence!"

This chatter, with its arid, false sophistry, appeared to our young traveler half insane; he glanced sidelong at his companion, who made a gesture of conclusion with her outspread yellow fingers and settled herself back in her seat, as though after finishing an argument.

Suddenly the thought crossed his mind: Why am I here—with her? He looked around and felt the burning heat in the black air enter into him with an unspeakably horrible effect: his heart contracted painfully and the hard, hot pounding in his temples became for a moment as furious as a raging attack of migraine.

The wider the corner of the desert opened up before them, the sparser became the vegetation. The saguaros ceased; the last of them held both arms outstretched toward heaven, a figure of petrified horror at some unidentifiable cruelty of destiny—that it was not screaming seemed perverse. Now there were only a few deerhorn cactuses here and there, a tangle and jumble of hard twigs and branches shaped like stag's antlers, and the whitish colors of lamb's

wool; every now and then isolated prickly chollas squatted malevolently in the gloom, looking like wildcats crouched to spring with their
hair bristling; and the bleak bundles of rods of the ocotillos stuck
naked out of the sand and gave no hint that even they, when their
time had come, would burst into a little flower at every tip, fiery like
the glow of a cigar.

The carriage rumbled along faster. The Mexican with the fantastic
pointed hat turned his face almost imperceptibly back to Jaquemar
and muttered some sort of warning out of the corner of his mouth, of
which the young man caught only a single meaningless word: "Otto-
queechee," or something of the sort. The same moment, the tip of
Bompard's umbrella struck the wretch in the side with such force that
he almost fell off the box. Jaquemar clung to the rail of his upholstered
seat in sympathy. Shaking and clattering, they crossed the flat bed of
a dried-up river, such as he had seen many times during his journey.

Then they were really in the desert. It was completely flat, nothing
but grayish-yellow, colorless sandy soil, through which little islands of
matted vegetation erupted in places like scabs on skin. Thus it
stretched endlessly, and would have given the eye nothing to which
to attach itself if a long, bushy block of shadow had not emerged one,
or perhaps two or three miles ahead of the travelers. Within this block
of shadow a dim, reddish flame was flickering, while above the center
of the black shape a simple cross, also black, stood out very clearly
against the gray and gloomy brightness between desert sand and starless sky, inanimate darkness, inanimate light—the primordial twilight
of the time beyond time, when day and night were not yet separated.

The oasis of shadow grew very slowly before Jaquemar's eyes. Yes,
it was something like an oasis, with an extensive but only single-
storied four-winged building as its core, from the center and around
the circumference of which rose isolated palms and even a few willow-
like trees with pathetically dangling foliage. The house itself, in Spanish
style, whitewashed, with a dark roof of undulating tiles and bordered
by garden beds in which grew decorative cactuses and carefully
trimmed box trees, opened out in front into an arcade of short, sturdy
columns and round arches, within whose shadow black bars of old-
fashioned ironwork could be distinguished above window sills at little
more than hip level. A cast-iron oil lamp hung above the central arch,
a dim star, and above this again, on the tiled roof, stood the cross of

the only saving faith, plain and smaller than might have been thought on seeing it from a distance.

But before Jaquemar had time to familiarize himself with these details as they drew nearer, a gate opened with a creaking sound in the shadows of the arcade, an indefinite reddish beam poured out, and with a suppressed whine of jubilation two large dogs bounded forth and almost the same instant, with one wild spring, were in the carriage. The animals, a male with a bushy tail and long red locks, and a female with cropped hair, threw themselves on Bompard, completely covering her; and the ecstatic snarling, panting, and pressing and writhing looked almost like a perverse act of love, in which— sounding most strange—were mingled tiny cries of delight uttered by the raped woman.

A memory flitted through his brain. He had once encountered a dog like this red-haired one in a nightmare, in a stony underground passage; he had seized the beast by the hind legs, with an unspeakable feeling of horror, and smashed its head against the pillar of a round arch, beneath which a stairway led upward. He had no time to reflect on the enigmatic semi-identity between the dream of yesterday and the experience of today, because he was fighting as though for his life. It was a good thing they had reached their destination!

In their excessive enthusiasm, the dogs jumped down and raced this way and that between the arcade and their carriage, barking and howling. Beside one of the short, thick pillars of the arcade stood an old man, with silver hair and beard, wearing a dark cowl; he nodded with a smile on his kindly face and said over and over again: "Welcome, Mademoiselle Gabrielle. Welcome, my daughter."

Bompard, laughing, her cheeks and little tiger's nose white with the dogs' saliva, stepped rather ceremoniously out of the carriage; she looked around and breathed the burning air of the desert night with enjoyment. The fact that she uttered no word of reply to the old man's greeting was a foretaste of the comical lack of respect with which she behaved everywhere here. She waited for Jaquemar to clamber down from the seat, told the limping man to support himself on her arm, and led him to the reverend gentleman in the cowl.

"I hope, good father," she remarked in her didactic way, before she had quite reached him, "that everything has been done to accommodate us as desired. Monsieur Jaquemar here, my protégé, craves thorough rest and enjoyment. Through the fault of Alphonso, who should be soundly thrashed, he has sprained his ankle. The warm humidity of the Green Mountains was not to his liking, and he loves truth."

The old man, whom she did not consider it necessary to introduce (his name was Father Junipero), continued to nod in his friendly way, and now looked at Jaquemar, who for his part, prevented by his breathlessness from joining in, gazed past him into the darkness of the arcaded walk. There stood a completely motionless figure, a man with stony slit eyes in a Mongolian face; his forearms were crossed over his body and his hands concealed in the sleeves of his gown; from one of these hidden hands a thick, serpentine whip dangled, which gave the unmoving apparition a menacing and dangerous air. With his monk's garb he wore a brightly colored kerchief wound around his head and running out into a point at the back, and this incongruous combination left the observer doubtful as to whether he was looking at a man of God or a Red Indian chief. Bompard, however, suddenly let go of Jaquemar's arm and advanced with her venturesome stride toward the silent figure.

"Old Gabriel!" she cried, and kissed him on both his rounded cheekbones. "If we get too much overheated you may fan us!"

Alphonso staggered past the group carrying the travelers' luggage, groaning, and sniffed at distrustfully by the dogs.

The nodding old man said to Jaquemar in his mild, sonorous voice: "Welcome to you too, my son, heartily welcome, and may you be enlightened that there is only one path to truth."

Jaquemar replied, with a blasphemous laugh: "Faith!"

"Love," the silver-haired old man corrected him, continuing to nod good-naturedly.

"Enough of ceremony!" cried Bompard gaily. "Enough! Forward march, darling, and don't plead tiredness; let us get to work! For this is our wedding night; let him pray for its success!"

With this she made one of her nice little bows to Father Junipero, who even after such a brazen remark did not cease smiling and nodding. She took Jaquemar's arm and drew him inside the house, into a spacious hall, where a fragrant smell of incense and stone impregnated the black heat without cooling it. The dogs romped about around the two of them; their unrestrained jumping, mute with the profundity of their delight, appeared to Jaquemar's mind like the darting of supple fishes' bodies, and intensified the curious feeling of being under the sea, as he strode through the gloomy hall on his companion's arm.

It was very dark; the presence of wall niches and round arches could just be guessed at; only a single oil flame, halfway up the wall facing the entrance, flickered in a bowl the color of mother-of-pearl and just sufficed at one moment to illumine the painting over it, while at the next the picture disappeared again, in a quivering alternation of light and shadow through which the immensely penetrating eyes of the face portrayed gazed down steadfastly at the floor below. Painted on a flat board, it was a black-bearded face that stared down with parted lips and an expression of utter hopelessness, muter than all the silence around and paralyzed by a question to which there would never be an answer.

Ghastly futility, thought Jaquemar. Even the Redeemer does not know to what purpose he should redeem us.

Meanwhile, Bompard swung gaily along on Jaquemar's arm, light-heartedly chattering. "Old Gabriel," she informed him in a loud voice, "is a child of sin, begotten by a highly placed cleric of a Quiguit-amcar Indian woman; while still a baby he was rescued by the friars for the salvation of his soul and baptized with holy water. He was formerly the lay doorkeeper and is now day and night porter at Joshua Springs. They say he is the oldest man in the world."

They passed under the first painting and came out into the un-roofed courtyard of the old monastery, the typical patio of an Hispano-Moresque house. It was square, bordered by the four wings of the building, with their undulating tiled roofs, and paved with large, smooth slabs of stone; in the center—the heart of this place of comfort in the desert—stood a pool of water encircled by a low wall, at the four corners of which stood four tall, thick-stemmed palms that spread out their fan-shaped arms umbrella-fashion, so that it was almost impossible to catch a glimpse of the sky, and no chink was left through which the sun could penetrate to this secluded corner during the day. Everything was clean and tidy and beautiful even in the darkness. All kinds of decorative plants, blossoming cactuses, and gnarled and stunted growths like Japanese dwarf trees could be distinguished, standing around the walls of the house in simple faïence vessels and earthenware tubs; not a leaf littered the stone slabs of the floor; and if it had not been for the swish of the bounding bodies of the dogs it would have been impossible to conceive a more tranquil peace.

But Jaquemar was in no mood for enjoyment. The odd sensation of moving under water like a diver, with insufficient lead in his soles, who cannot get his feet on the bottom and therefore moves through the element at an angle, half swimming, half treading, at once light and heavy—this abstruse transmutation of his specific gravity was still increasing and plagued him greatly, particularly as the more he breathed in the desert heat the more it seemed to contribute to this effect. Blown up by it as though by a noxious gas, he moved across this apparently bottomless patio as through an aquarium, choking and dizzy.

Now, of all times! he thought with a curse. When everything depends on it! Longingly he measured with his eye the distance to the door, which must be their goal, because it was the only one that stood open and discharged a gently flickering and flowing shimmer of light into the still darkness of the courtyard.

They did in fact make their way to this door and enter it. In passing, and without much surprise, Jaquemar first noticed the lay brother and doorkeeper, Old Gabriel, who, having mysteriously preceded them, was standing in one corner with crossed arms in the gown, and his head-cloth, motionless as an Indian. Two honey-yellow tallow candles, as thick as an arm and with zig-zag edges—altar lights, in fact—burning with tall, curly flames that sometimes smoldered black, stood to right and left at the head of a very wide, low couch and made it possible to distinguish a few little delicate rococo chairs and tables around the walls and a simple washstand with a zinc basin let into it; no other furniture was visible, and the corners of the room lay in almost complete darkness. A gray-black light, shot through with gold, filled the room and lent a mysterious life to the unexpectedly artistic mosaic floor. It was not absolutely flat, but slightly undulating, and composed of two pictures alternating at regular intervals: one set showed the intertwined bodies of dolphins, the other audacious *putti* riding with outflung hands on fish; and the ordered confusion of the two sets of images created the impression of a mute, blissful turmoil moving past by turns in the flickering dusk.

With comic pride, Bompard set her arms akimbo, so that the little parasol, like a feather duster, stood out at an angle from under the shoulder frills of her costume, and cried: "Now let anyone say I don't look after him! Well? What do you think of this place?"

She looked at him, her face beaming. He dropped onto a chair, which creaked fragilely under him, and groaned in disgust: "Have pity! If only one could breathe! This is hell!"

Bompard went rigid. The next moment she was seized by a rage such as the young man had never seen before. She stamped her foot, tears spurted from her eyes, and she screamed: "Well, I'll be damned! You can go to hell! I drag myself halfway around the world, forget all the harm he's done me, and devote myself to him as though he were the crown of creation! And that's the thanks I get!"

When Jaquemar looked up, at a loss to understand, he saw her far away from him, leaning on the half-caste's stony breast, weeping and whimpering.

Suddenly she began to scold between her sobs: "You never know where you are with them! It's better to have nothing to do with them! To hell with love and kindness! You get nothing but annoyance, chagrin, and disappointment. . . . You tell me, sweet Old Gabriel, what would a man like that deserve, if there were justice?"

The face with the slit eyes gave vent to a brief growl like that of a bad-tempered dog—and the dogs were, in fact, sitting with ears pricked in attentive peace at the head of the bed, each under a candle.

"The woman is as stupid as stone," said Jaquemar, to himself but aloud, and looking with hatred at Bompard. "She can't even grasp the fact that a man can't breathe in this infernal dry heat."

"The fellow doesn't know what he wants!" she cried, sobbing, in response, and stamped her foot at every word. "First it's too damp and then it's too dry! He doesn't know whether he loves or hates! Does he want to live or to die? And all of it just to spoil my fun!"

Jaquemar looked up and saw the old Indian standing in front of him, massive, almost square. The Indian withdrew his right hand from the sleeve of his gown, raised his index finger, and looked up at the ceiling with his slit eyes, as though listening for something. Sure enough, a jangling of bells started up somewhere outside, interspersed by slow single strokes.

The Indian lowered his eyes to Jaquemar again and growled through unmoving lips: "Midnight, my son. The twelfth hour."

"What does the fellow want with me?" asked Jaquemar uncomprehendingly.

Old Gabriel glanced over his shoulder at Bompard, who was standing in the background, and now shrugged her shoulders. He thrust his hand back into the sleeve of his gown and walked with measured tread to the door and out.

An atmosphere of ill-humor and hostility gathered in the hot room, its malevolent silence growing more stubborn with every instant. Jaquemar began to feel like a fly in amber; it already seemed to him that he could make no more movement than if he were enveloped in half-set plaster of Paris.

He made an impatient gesture and cried: "No scenes please! Not that as well!"

"There's an odd fellow for you," scolded Bompard, in a vague, grumbling kind of voice. "He won't resign himself to the inevitable. Carapin will never think of this place, it would never occur to anyone to go to Joshua Springs in summer. Is there any safer spot for a marriage and a honeymoon with a stolen loved one? But for him it's too hot, the heat is too dry, or some other nonsense. Devil take him; in future he can arrange his own furtive intrigues! Am I his maître de plaisir?"

"Plaisir!" he cried with a laugh. "I don't want to argue, but plaisir is a bit of an exaggeration! You forget that where the feminine virtue of insensibility is concerned, you represent an unsurpassable maximum. None of your lovers has so far been able to offer a similarly tough constitution. We mustn't lose sight of that fact."

"Is it my fault, if men overestimate their capacities?" she grumbled sulkily.

"Your favors have proved too dear for all of them up to now. The 'plaisir' brought them all to grief. Let me remind you. Who was the first one you belonged to? Wasn't it at Angoulême, in the convent?"

"Baptiste, you mean?" she inquired in a matter-of-fact voice. "But it was his cowardice that killed him. I didn't tell him to jump out the window."

"Then there was Gouffé," said Jaquemar gloomily.

"But that was Michi! Michi did him in, not I."

"Yes, your Michi! He had it coming to him."

"Of course," she confirmed, as though missing his meaning. "The penalty for murder is death, everyone knows that."

"Then there were your favorites at Saratoga Springs. Mr. Tulipan, for instance."

"Oh, that old dotard!"

"And Malcolm at Four Corners."

"Somebody put his foot through the timber, it was his fault."

"And Carapin, who as you say yourself—"

"But he's alive!" she cried impatiently. "That's why we're here!"

"And who's next?" asked Jaquemar relentlessly, staring with a composed expression into space.

"You bore me," she remarked, making a brief, dismissive gesture with her hand.

"So much the better."

"Why all this petty spite? Did we travel three thousand miles to amuse ourselves by quarreling?"

"You'll celebrate no wedding with me," said Jaquemar in a low voice. "I'm not going to be the next one."

"God above!" she cried in exasperation. "You and your everlasting crazy notions and tilting at windmills! Your speculations go in at one ear and out at the other, as far as I'm concerned. I'm a realistic person. Do you seriously mean to tell me you now want to drop the bone and snap at the reflection?"

"A nice expression," commented Jaquemar, taken aback. "But it's quite out of place here."

"Oh, it's out of place, is it? Why have you been pursuing and harassing me, at someone else's expense? Why did you rape me in the hotel room, which again somebody else paid for? Why did you grab the first excuse you could find to stick to my heels? Why the irksome journeys across the wide ocean and through the empty states after me, thinking of me, together with me? For the sake of the climate? That's not what I heard! I thought you were sick and tired of the whole dreary business, that you itched for . . . well, for reality! Are you seized, where I am, with longing for your demi-vierges, for the simpering geese of Paris? Go on, then! I don't care! I shan't shed any tears on your account! Turn back!"

She stopped, then repeated with a tiny, evil laugh: "Turn back, Jaquemar. No one is stopping you."

"Without you," replied Jaquemar hesitantly, "without you I couldn't find my way home. Is that what you mean?"

"Home!" she retorted sullenly. "Don't be ridiculous."

He glanced across at her. She was sitting on the edge of the low couch and looked lost as she gazed around her in the flickering semi-darkness, joyless, disappointed, and morose.

"You may be right," said Jaquemar gloomily. "Perhaps I have no 'home'—after all this. But that makes no difference. Do you hear? You won't celebrate any wedding with me. I shall not touch you."

Bompard rose, whistling to herself in a bored way. In a dark corner of the room, where Alphonso had piled it up, stood the luggage; she now began to busy herself with it; in a dejected, negligent manner, she swept the top pieces to one side and opened her large trunk, which had accompanied her faithfully on all her journeys, to the suppressed rage of Jaquemar, who now squinted across at it with an evil expression.

Jaquemar's will to survive grew all the more determined. He felt down to its very foundation the enigmatic nature of the depraved, soul-consuming love to which he was delivered up, in a worse and more hopeless state at every stage. For now he understood what he had so far suffered; at every step he had taken at Bompard's side he had left behind him more and more sources of protection, he had gone from the familiar into the excitingly insecure, from there into the injurious, then into the unviable, and finally into the utterly empty and deadly. Into the heart of *her* kingdom, he thought. And even if I can no longer return home, I can turn back or away, because I am still alive and need only say "*I will.*" And it struck him that Goron, the doomed, had said to Lebigot, perhaps as a kind of legacy, "First you must renounce, then you will become free"—yes, a legacy, which at first sounded trite, but which was nevertheless earnest and profound; for it meant "Let him who strives to achieve the difficult not ask after the reward or how to attain his goal; before every fulfilment is set the resolve, there are no gifts and no promises, only achievement, and that is entirely in your own hands."

At intervals he heard, as though momentarily coming to the surface from the dull buzzing in his ears, the ill-humored footsteps, the pleasureless rummaging, of his companion, little muffled bumps caused by her careless hand thrust into the trunk, the rustle of silken fabric and then the brief, hard clink of something that must have fallen on the mosaic floor, a compact, heavy little object, to judge by the sound, and then there was silence and even the buzzing in his ears died away.

Perhaps he slept; in any case, time, and with it anguish, desire, and conflict, went to sleep within him. Relaxed and still, he sat on his chair, and finally looked up slowly with a shudder, because he felt Bompard's cold hand on the back of his neck. She sat cautiously down on his lap, put her right arm lightly around his neck, and gazed about her with an expression of sulky sadness. She stood up and led him to the couch. But halfway to it he stumbled, began to stagger, and became aware that he had been tricked by a hallucination: he was alone, Bompard was lying on one half of the low bed, turned away from him and wrapped in a rug of thin, silky black wool from which not even her arms emerged, but only her flamelike locks and some of her white face with the chaste shadow of the lashes.

Jaquemar was too tired to be tempted by anything but this tiredness; he sat down and heard the firm bundle of wool and flesh on the other side of the bed, shaken by the mattress springs, give vent to an angry growl. And now they both lay still, Bompard on her side and Jaquemar stretched out on his back. From time to time the broad candle flames flickered mysteriously and crackled, then a fluttering, as of veils of dull gold being shaken, passed through the dull air, and a blossomlike, reddish glow suffused the ceiling above Jaquemar. This was a lovely sight, especially as the faintly visible ribbing in the porous stone converged like a star in the center, thereby giving the room a beautiful and somehow significant depth, as though it were something intimately enclosed and separate from the rest of the world, a crypt or the interior of a mystic rose.

A feeling of comfortable heaviness filled Jaquemar, his eyelids dropped, and he sank into sleep as into pleasant cool pillows. The sleep he enjoyed, a boon of peace, may have been long or brief; it was deep enough to revive, light enough not to submerge the sleeper's ego; it was a breathing, vital slumber.

When Jaquemar awoke the room was already filled with heat like an oven; but the early morning light was beautiful, and it played with bubbling rings and blobs of sunshine on the ribbed ceiling, gay and intimate, as though a golden glimmer was glowing and flashing through the petals of the mystic rose which this room resembled. From outside he could hear the boisterous frisking, whining, and leaping of dogs accompanied by the merry plashing of water.

Jaquemar was still too drowsy to identify the sounds; but in a trice Bompard was standing in the doorway. She was stark naked; wetness was glittering like a trickling serpentine shirt on her firm flesh; silver drops flashed and rolled down her body, sparkling; and with gaily fluttering eyelids she blew a silver spray from her lips and little tiger's nose. She stood there, a single shaft of radiance. She made a little bow to Jaquemar, bent down with legs together and reached out with her strong and shapely arm for a large white bath towel that lay ready on a small chair by the door.

Jaquemar raised himself on his elbows. He looked at her with a sad yet detached expression and said calmly: "It must be clear to you that we have already parted."

"You're loony!" she cried, and laughed and disappeared.

But she reappeared, even before Jaquemar had time to change his position. With a sulky expression, she wrapped herself in the bath towel, so that it enveloped her like the drapery of a statue, hanging from her shoulders to her feet in austere folds. She raised her shining eyes, in which there was now a dangerous glint, and said softly in the midst of her smile, which looked icy: "All right then, as you like. Don't imagine anyone is keeping you. Just try being happy in your own way. I'll have the carriage harnessed for Monterey."

She was gone. Jaquemar rose from the bed and rummaged in the little leather case containing his shaving kit. He could not find what he was looking for, but all of a sudden—for the first time in how many months!—his fingers grasped a delicate little object of smooth gold.

Yes, Gouffé, he thought in confusion, and looked at the gold heart on the long, thin chain. Sentimental talisman! How did you put it? With what words did you leave it to me? "To you, Edmond, friend and brother-in-law, for—when it is over." Is it—over? Oh, souvenir of an unknown soul! Does it mean the fruitless death in the world? It has the shape of a heart and is inscribed: "*Shaddai*, The Eternal." An amulet. It brought Gouffé no luck, and isn't likely to bring me any either. Have I deserved it of you, Eternal One (if you exist)?

In my own way I have striven, and yet have not learned, to love you.
Well, since it comes from Gouffé. . . .

He slipped the thin chain over his head and neck, raised the golden
heart with the ancient sign from his bare chest once more, looked at
it, and thought with a smile as he let it fall from his fingers: Remind
me then and make the miserable business entertaining for me.

In spirit we are standing on the plateau, at the same spot where
Gilgamesh-Jaquemar stood and allowed himself to be seized by the
pull of the depths and by giddiness at the sight of the too abrupt drop,
as he faced the grim, bleak heights of the primeval mountains. We
are looking down into the abyss, into the humble corner of barren
land far down below and farther on, to where the scorching heat of
the sun flickers over the open desert. We narrow our eyes: a black
dot is moving out into the vast expanse. We know that it is Jaquemar's
carriage, with a swaying frilled awning; Bompard in her poke bonnet
is sitting beside him, bored, occasionally jabbing the sharp point of
her feather-duster parasol into the back of Alphonso, the hunched-up
figure on the box. The shadows of the bones bend and straighten out
laboriously in the ragged, sweaty coat of the wretched horse, and the
sand trickles and dribbles out of the creaking wheels. We even know
that Jaquemar is furrowing his brow, because they are now passing
a rough wooden notice nailed to a post driven crooked into the soil.
Old Gabriel put it up, when he was still a boy and frequently scourged
by the Holy Friars for the sake of the faith, and daubed on it in smeary
letters: "Christ saves you." A curious promise and advertisement for
God in this uninhabited infernal heat.

We turn away; what else is there to see? The tiny vehicle down
there below, on the way to the last stop in the party's adventurous
journey, the insignificant black dot, has soon vanished; and silence,
blazing heat, and solitude lie abandoned as before and as if never
trodden by a human foot.

5

LAND'S END

Jaquemar, old soul, surely we can't separate just like that?"
said or asked Gabrielle Bompard—but neither *said* nor *asked* is the
right word, since she mumbled and grumbled in a way that rendered
her words almost unintelligible, very much as she had mumbled on
the occasion of her first visit to the Hôtel des Mines. "Jaquemar,"
she said dejectedly and sulkily, "is it really all to fizzle out in a dreary
ending like any insignificant love affair? As they say: 'Who will shed
tears when the time comes to part? / When one love is ended the next
love will start.' I just can't imagine it like that."

She spoke thus in the little Blue Whale Hotel at Monterey, leaning against the doorpost in the falling dusk and twisting her body this
way and that in anguish, as she addressed Jaquemar, who was lying
stretched out on his bed, his hands clasped behind his head, squinting
across at her out of the corner of his eye with a malevolent expression.

He answered dryly: "Since our account has been settled, I am in no
hurry, Madame. I am at your disposal."

She began to twist about more violently and mumbled: "If that's
the point we've come to, then I will tell you that apart from a request
for some cash—say fifty or seventy thousand, I leave it to your generosity—there is one small wish I have at heart."

She looked at him inquiringly with her shining eyes and went on as
though tempting him: "I know a place, only a few miles from San

Philippo by the Sea, where there is a queer rock formation, a deep funnel in the cliff which they call the Great Gorge. And apart from the screeching of a few birds and the swish of water, the most restorative stillness reigns there."

"What, another excursion?" replied Jaquemar with a distrustful laugh.

She shrugged one shoulder: "You simply can't go to Monterey and not see the Great Gorge. The funnel has an enormous attraction for people—hence it not infrequently happens that one looks down and sees below the bloody top of a head with flattened hair and seaweed, and underneath it the man it belongs to, in a striped bathing costume, standing erect and bobbing up and down as he is raised and dipped. A long bath. He swam out for fun, and the arm of the current grabbed him by the scruff of the neck, and it's no use the San Philippo coast-guards on their wooden towers waving red flags and shouting through megaphones: 'Hey, you out there, hello, come back!' The current pulls and swirls, so that he spins round and round like a top, and hurls the swimmer up against the Gorge, smashes his skull in on the lower edge, and stuffs him into the mouth of the funnel for safe-keeping. There you can see him raising and lowering his arms in the rise and fall of the swell, as though to say: 'Well, there's nothing I can do about it.' And if he is left there, he will keep much longer than an ordinary corpse, because the Pacific water is pure brine and pickles him."

"What a piquant local knowledge you possess," commented Jaquemar, without shifting his position. "Here as everywhere."

"One gets around," she answered vaguely, looking at him with eyes shining, and cried with a laugh: "But you don't have to look at it! Only it's such a lovely spot. Just one more tête-à-tête, Jaquemar. Yes, we will have a banquet, a love feast and funeral repast for something that was beautiful and will never return. We'll make the corks pop, and when we have eaten, drunk, and talked our fill we will smash our pointed goblets on the sharp-cornered rock, as a sign that we were fond of one another; for it is to an evening picnic with champagne and dessert that I herewith invite you, and when it is over we shall part as you desire."

She made her polite, boyish little bow, and Jaquemar said coolly and calmly as before: "I'm in no hurry, Madame, I am at your disposal."

Their conversation took place on the third day of their stay in Monterey, a town as Spanish as any in America can be, with pretty little white houses and red-tiled roofs, and winding streets bordered by gardens overflowing with brightly colored flowers and flowering shrubs. In the morning this was all steeped in the sweet lilac-blue of the Californian dawn; by midday the shadows cast by the houses and trees lay deep black and precisely outlined on the white sand of the streets; at dusk the spectator was drawn to look up at the giant date palms, whose only foliage, a spherical crest like the headdress of a Negro medicine man, at a dizzy height, moved soundlessly in the evening wind, a silhouette of blue-black, shiny and pliable strips of steel that glittered and flashed in the greenish light.

When Jaquemar declared that they must part, Bompard apparently couldn't be bothered to talk about it; and yet she responded both actively and with satisfaction. Having politely explained that Monterey was the most convenient connection for San Francisco, from which in time he could travel eastward, she had brought him here in her carriage. . . . and then had not left. She had been overcome with hesitancy; it was as though some web were being spun around her, making it increasingly difficult for her to walk. All the same, she did occasionally go for a stroll; she would be gone for a quarter of an hour—and then she was standing mumbling by the doorpost again. There was a theater here, she gave Jaquemar to understand, shrugging her shoulders offhandedly, as though this might explain her absences. She would stand there sulkily pouting her lips, and casting an occasional watchful glance at her ex-paramour. Jaquemar observed her sulky behavior in silence and with mixed feelings, and was glad that the whole affair was about to come to an end.

The following afternoon they carried out their plans, although the weather was not particularly fine—it was hot, with a glaring light and yet no sunshine. When Jaquemar came out onto the wooden veranda of the little hotel at the agreed time, the carriage was harnessed and Bompard already up on the seat, plucking at her skirt; Alphonso ran around the vehicle on padding feet in torn moccasins and helped Jaquemar to ascend. He behaved in a distant, servile manner and now actually addressed him as "Your Honor." Supporting his elbow, he whispered in a hoarse, piping undertone, as though talking to himself: "Let His Honor take care not to twist his ankle for good and all." After which he hurried away and clambered with an odd fuss up onto the box.

Thus they set out on their last adventure. Alphonso sat there with bent back, wearing a ragged shirt and pointed straw hat; he bestowed his damp kiss on the air and slackly cracked the reins, and the cumbersome vehicle lumbered off, grinding and bumping over the cobblestones of the narrow, winding street, between gardens that now blossomed joylessly, past small houses that snuggled timorously away into the greenery, across squares that lay deserted in the heat of the midday sun, overcast by a whitish haze, and out onto the highroad that led across country to San Philippo by the Sea.

Bompard remained as taciturn as Jaquemar. Gathered around her she had all sorts of boxes, vast receptacles, and even a zinc bucket from which the necks of champagne bottles protruded at an angle. On her lap she was carefully holding a small, beribboned basket, the padded interior of which was covered by a lid embroidered with flowers; and her feet, with their powerful ankles, were in high, white lace-boots that inspired wanderlust, like Hermes's shoes. But as on the road into the desert, she wore her nunlike garment with the shoulder frills and poke bonnet. The rare, stabbing spears of sunshine and patches of light that seeped down through the dense vault of foliage glided caressingly over the smiling, animal face, shimmering on the damp red of the lips and pink of the nostrils and sparkling in the shining eyes; and in the slight breeze created as they drove along the locks protruding from under the curved diadem of her bonnet fluttered in a half-constrained way, like Diana's curls. She was lovely to look at, as lovely as always; but what mood she was in and what was going on in her mind Jaquemar could not guess. God alone knew.

Meanwhile, the road ran out into the open, petered out among sand and weeds, and was at an end. The carriage stopped. They had reached their destination.

Now the open sea lay before Jaquemar's eyes, billowing like silk, a milky blue beneath a glaring gray sky that did not arch up from the distant horizon, as is usual over the sea, but hung close above it, like

a low-pitched roof, and a very long way away became one with the
water, merging without a dividing line into the waves, as light and
darkness merge in the corner of an attic. There was something harsh
about this sky, although it was neither a stormy sky nor a sky that
presaged a storm; but the light came down from its glaring gray only
in a diffuse and piercing form, giving the immense milky expanse
little more than a dismal gleam that brightened here and there into
a malicious-looking, pallid gold and silver glitter.

The surface of the ocean appeared all the more immense because,
from where Jaquemar was standing, no line of beach was visible. They
were on a plateau bordered by a steep cliff, an enormous block of rock
shaped like a balcony or terrace; and they felt this under the soles of
their feet, which, as they stepped on it, were received without
springiness, and firmly, and yet remained skeptical, as though treading
on unsafe ground. The fact that the faint, melancholy tolling of a bell
and even organ notes that sounded like sighs drifted across to them,
probably from nearby San Philippo by the Sea, helped to make the
billowing sluggishness of the ocean seem unreliable and the atmosphere of the whole place almost baleful and sinister.

Even Bompard must have felt this. For in the middle of piling and
suspending parcels and boxes on Alphonso, to the accompaniment of
punches and imprecations, she suddenly looked up, pushed the hair
back from her temples, and said: "Hey, Jaquemar! Don't let that
miserable clanging and droning dampen your spirits! The golden juice
will soon be prickling in our noses!"

The little troop advanced in single file toward the shore. In front
staggered Alphonso, panting, really no more than a shadow in the skin
of his burdens, swaying and sometimes stumbling with the pail
rattling; it looked as though a ghost were fleeing with a collection of
stolen goods toward the sea, the measureless sea, that hides and buries
everything in its gloomy silence. Behind him, at a quickly increasing
distance, followed Jaquemar, who from time to time listened to
Bompard's footsteps behind him; they tapped so cheerfully, positively
frolicsomely, and made a harsh rustling sound as she passed through
the leathery heather. The gaiety of her walk struck him as suspicious;
he did not know why, preferred not to notice it, and therefore stared
hard out to sea.

This was not quite so calm as it at first appeared. Far out, long, low

breakers ran together from various directions and poured foaming
into one another—and this, by its contrast with the great tranquillity
of the scene as a whole, created an effect of dangerous stealth, as
though hidden forces were about to break loose and as though some
amorphous demonic being were showing its teeth.

"Yes, it takes you by surprise," said Bompard behind him with a
laugh. "You must remember that here the seven currents converge.
Where else is there anything like it on the whole earth? What has
that basin in front of you not already swallowed in the way of boat
and man and mouse; and afterward it lolls around harmlessly, momentarily sated. Sated! I ask you! A man would have to be a fine simpleton
to trust that calm!"

"I thought the stillness was so 'restorative'?" retorted Jaquemar
irritably; he looked around and saw that she was holding the basket
slightly in front of her and very carefully, as though it contained eggs.

"Why not?" she replied in astonishment and shaking her head
didactically. "Everything is as it should be. *Honi soit qui mal y pense.*"

For a while they wandered on in silence. Jaquemar gazed out to
sea as before; on the shore a silhouette was moving, already quite
small—Alphonso against the gray glare of the sky.

"Darling," began Bompard in a conciliatory tone, as though after
an argument, "please don't take it amiss if I'm in a rather depressed
frame of mind. For the moment. My word of honor, I bear you no
malice."

"I'm touched," sneered Jaquemar.

"Michi meets his end today," she said briefly.

Jaquemar came to a stop. His fists clenched, his teeth grated, and
he cried in a sudden burst of malicious joy: "So they sped him on his
way after all! In the end he beat the good Goron in the race for death!"

"What are you talking about!" she retorted sullenly, stopping beside
him and looking around with a pout. "He bit the dust long ago.
When was it now? A fortnight or three weeks. I don't care a fig for
him, the fat boor. He was an utter fake, all his sturdiness nothing but
bad-tempered obesity. But Michi was a different kettle of fish, and
I forgive him the many acts of violence he perpetrated on me when
we were burning with love for one another, now that I picture them
pushing him out into the asphalt yard at La Roquette, in a greasy
frock coat, without a collar for practical reasons, his oily hair all

tousled and his carp's eyes full of unbelief. If I know him he is hurrying, stumbles with a curse on his long lips and toddles along shivering —then they grab hold of him and bend him down over the block, the knife comes swishing down, and hopla, the head jumps into the basket! The loss of blood in this form of death is quite unbelievable, it gushes out. Yes, yes, it's a pity. But why did he have to act so stupidly in the Villa des Fleurs? He got nothing out of it at all, only the trouble that followed his misdeed. Now he has got his reward; a whole year has passed since then."

She shrugged her shoulders and stared with shining eyes into the vegetation in front of her, unable to suppress the smile that lay as always around her lips and little tiger's nose.

"How do you know?" asked Jaquemar, eyeing her suspiciously.

"There was an old copy of the *Monitor* lying about in the lobby of the Blue Whale. The announcement of Goron's death, the rejection of Michi's appeal, and the date of his execution were all there, word for word; the execution was fixed for today, exactly one year after Michi's crime. Great God, time passes in a flash, and men's lives change with it."

"I'm glad they've cooked his goose!" burst out Jaquemar.

"Of course," she replied. "Naturally, justice must be done. After all, he beat me."

"Come on, talk!" yelled Jaquemar, suddenly losing control of himself, and seizing her wrist. "Bloodthirsty scum! Admit that you were in it!"

She gazed down with wrinkled brow at his hand on her wrist. He let go, and she said coldly: "I was there when it happened, that was my bad luck."

"You arranged it, you were in the secret!"

"I, poor worm!" she replied with a false laugh. "I knew as much as you. As much and as little as you. We are one."

Suddenly giddy, Jaquemar staggered back a pace.

"Careful, careful!" exclaimed Bompard. "Otherwise you'll come a cropper."

"I knew about it?" yelled Jaquemar, beside himself.

"As little as I!" she cried, still laughing. "And I, heaven knows, am a thoroughly good woman. I don't want to plant any moral crab lice in your hair. Only, just to get things straight, let me quickly remind you of the sum of money, an appropriate amount, which you were going to give me, please, before your departure, the sooner the better."

Jaquemar ignored this.

"I knew about it?" he burst out once more, breathlessly.

"God forbid," she said roguishly, digging him playfully in the ribs and winking. "How could you have known that when Gouffé took your advice and squinted around behind the scenes he would see me?"

"I didn't even know you!" he snarled through clenched teeth, stamping his foot.

"Of course not," she confirmed readily, slipping her arm under his, pulled the unwilling Jaquemar on, and continued as she strolled along: "That was just the trouble. One has to be ready for surprises. But why are we stirring up that old brew again? No man can be another's keeper. Now let's forget about it! It's all over and done with, and only this evening is still ours. Tomorrow, Jaquemar, you will never see me again. Oh, we poor women! There you walk with your discontented frown. You will never understand how it hurts us women when we have given ourselves to a man in love and then have to tear him out of our hearts. He is as good as dead, he no longer loves, and no lament will bring him back to you. For when you think: He lives, you also think: What other woman is he lying with now? And at once you wish that he were dead. Oh, what anguish! Each one of us has her cross to bear, and gasps because of it, and has to put on a cheerful face in spite of all her suffering. This is our last evening. And see, here we are, this is the spot!"

Half blinded by her babble, and his own brooding thoughts, Jaquemar looked up and out into the lonely expanse of sea and shore all around.

"What's that hullabaloo out there?" he asked irritably.

"Life, darling, innocent joy in existence!" cried Bompard with a cooing laugh. "It is seals, sea lions, and similar creatures, gamboling on the rocks behind the cliff and the Great Gorge and enjoying themselves. And so shall we, if it pleases Monsieur that we sit down to a meal?"

She made her polite little bow, holding the basket in her right hand and motioning with her left to the edge of the plateau, where Alphonso was standing obsequiously in his rags, peering, as though conscience-stricken, at the picnic table he had laid on the ground.

Bompard linked arms with Jaquemar; arm in arm they strolled across and sat down to eat at the freshly starched damask cloth on which stood all kinds of delicacies, served by the bag of bones in the pointed hat, who, vigorously spurred on by his mistress, handed plates, bowls, and silverware, oysters in their shells, little forks and tongs to crack the lobster's armor . . . until Bompard, angered by his padding walk, ordered him to go down on his knees, so that he now served the diners, uncorked bottles of *vin rosé*, filled glasses, and removed empty plates slithering to and fro and completely out of breath.

"Here, my good and beautiful one," cried Bompard in her gay fashion, "do reverence to the truffle-flavored goose liver from Strasbourg, because the animals that provided them, according to the ancient tradition, must have been made to hop about on red-hot oven tops so that their organs became soft and tasty for your enjoyment! Hey there, you—the señor's goblet is empty; stir yourself, you useless specter!"

Thus, then, they took their meal. The light wine, with a delicious slaty bouquet, refreshed Jaquemar but also numbed his senses, and with unconscious greed he inhaled the odors which, hardly noticed before, gently impregnated the potent salty and seaweedy breath of the sea. The vanilla sweetness of the heliotrope, the herbal pungency of the heather, peppermint coolness of eucalyptuses, pithy pine resins, perfumes of orange and jasmine, they all mingled in an exquisite natural incense and grew stronger and more emphatic as evening began to fall. For sunset was already beginning to shimmer and bleed through the cover of clouds, breaking out here and there through cracks in the low-pitched roof of the sky with a powerful golden glow, a sharp, dazzling glare and glimmer that was quite distinct from the remaining gray and red shafts that were thrust down into the sea at an angle like shiny, thin knives, and further out, where the water was frothing and foaming in small breakers, steeped the spray in a scintillating ruby-red glitter and gleam.

"So Goron too. . . ." said Jaquemar, nodding pensively. "And there was so much he wanted to do."

"And he had such bad manners," added Bompard tartly. "He didn't know how to behave toward a lady."

"Do you know," asked Jaquemar, looking at her, "that in his day 'to sit down to a meal' had a very special meaning in Paris?"

"We aren't in Paris," she replied.

"You said, 'Shall we sit down to a meal?' "

"I don't speak *argot*; I'm not interested in the policeman."

"In Goron's day," Jaquemar went on stubbornly, keeping his eyes fixed on her, " 'to sit down to a meal' meant 'to make a confession.' "

"No, in the name of three devils!" she cried indignantly. "Is he really starting that all over again? You have nothing to confess. He wanted to lie with me for pin money, your Gouffé, old wreck that he was, and dream of somebody else as he did so. Just imagine it! And if things hadn't been like that, so that my fond heart was sad, I might have kept my presence of mind and been able to protect him, when Michi came in and saw red, because he caught us at it. How could you have foreseen that? I tell you there is no sense or point in having qualms of conscience about it. You are no more guilty of this unfortunate affair than I am. Forget it, since it is past all changing now, forget it for good and all and don't spoil our last joy. Come, dear, take some of the Turkish violet preserve in this jar, it's the real thing, I got it specially for you, to round off our feast."

She pushed a tubby little jar toward him, and Jaquemar, who had looked at her angrily, now followed her movement with troubled eyes.

"Or," she added, "is it only on account of the unpleasant gossip? Because you and I . . . ?"

She had leaned right over to him, she tapped him with her crooked index finger, and whispered confidentially: "You rascal. I loved you! Under such circumstances no one can say 'no'! That would be absurd."

Jaquemar swallowed and made no reply.

"Thirst," cried Bompard furiously, lashing out with her clawlike hand and catching Alphonso a savage blow in the face. "Thirst, as any weakminded child can see, is tormenting the señor, so that the words dry up and his throat is as parched as old smoked meat, and you, ungrateful phantom, pour him no wine? Come here with the juice, slit open the peaches—and make off, that the sight of you may no longer disgust us! At nightfall, wait for me by the edge of the forest, and have the horse saddled and bridled for a long journey! For my widowhood, now that the man I loved is leaving me, drives me with its pain into the wide world, and no one knows where I shall rest or on what pillow I shall lay my head. Oh, what grief on your account,

Jaquemar! Have you thought of that? Come along, give us the bottles, and away with you, carrion! Be off, get moving, out of my sight!"

Shuffling along on his knees and panting with the effort, Alphonso did as he was bid, washed two large peaches in rose water and transfixed them with a silver fork, so that drops of juice issued from the glossy, colorful velvet skin and sparkled golden on it. He placed the luscious fruit in two capacious crystal goblets in front of Bompard, lugged along the bucket containing champagne bottles at chest height, so that the action of slithering along on his knees looked curiously ecstatic, put it, too, down before her and scuttled shy-eyed past them. He staggered to his feet and padded quickly and almost soundlessly away. As if at a loss to understand, Jaquemar looked up and followed him with his eyes. As he hastened away in his stooping posture, the fleeing man seemed to be wringing his folded hands in front of his chest; looking around, he raised them in a despairing and imploring gesture, but immediately drew his head in between his shoulders, as though cowering under a blow from a whip, and hurried on with face averted. He grew visibly smaller as he went.

Meanwhile Bompard was squatting on her knees, her heels under her thighs, fingering at the wire closure of one of the champagne bottles. She removed it, twisted and squeezed the cork with her hard little hand, and gazed after it laughing as it shot up into the air with a pop.

"Rude things," she grumbled gaily, swept the hair back from her temples, looked at the neck of the bottle, over the edge of which a little cloud of smoke was billowing, and sent the gurgling, hissing liquid spurting into the crystal goblets.

Jaquemar, too, was now kneeling. They were kneeling opposite one another, Bompard handed him one of the goblets and cried: "Jaquemar, you rolling stone, we are about to clink our glasses, and this, because you so desire, is the Last Supper of our love. What use to me are Jeremiads? It is true that I should like to scream, but I hold myself in check out of decorum and swallow my pain and the yearning that you are no longer willing to still; and now I drink to you entirely without guile, frivolity, or lamentation. Yes, bitter is the end—and lovely the loveliness we have had, and they are not spoiled by the bitterness. On the contrary, the bitterness is the price of the loveliness;

only by the price we have to pay for it can we measure the value of
the pleasure we are throwing away. O bitter woe! I cannot think of
you in any other woman's arms, so much do I love you. I love you
as on the first day! Woe is me, that you must go away! And yet because I love you I must wish you a pleasant journey. Good luck on
your travels, Jaquemar, my beloved, adieu and good night! Here I
raise my glass to you in farewell and cry: Your health!"

Jaquemar, squatting on his heels, brought his left hand to join his
right on the strong stem of the wine glass. He looked at it with a
malevolent, composed expression and said somberly: "You, whom I
have never named by name, you nameless one, thank you; you have
taught me much. I set out only for the sake of justice, and if it could
not be justice then it was to be truth. Justice, truth, judgment, and
confession, all that has been dashed in pieces on my weakness, on
your nothingness. You tugged me into your bed, you dragged me
through the empty land. Instead of the answer I so hotly desired,
I heard in my ears only the panting of your lust, the buzzing of
emptiness. Imperfect that we are, what is the thirst of our spirit to us?
In this thirst I ran across half the world after you, you who are nothing. Seduced, besmirched, and weakened in your arms, your belly, your
insatiable belly, I have ended up here—like a schoolboy playing truant.
This is land's end, the earth goes no further. I look out—what do I see
out there? Out there it is empty. Empty and malicious, just like you.
I no longer have any right to condemn you; in our love even that came
to nothing. How am I to live? There is nothing left of which I can
be proud. Nothing left at which to look, and nothing of which to
think. Therefore, because, heaven be praised, it is time to say good-
by, I think of the fruits that you gave me, the beautiful, bright-colored
fruits which, when I bit into them, were full of dust. I think of your
love that had everything, was everything, except love. I think of your
body, your eternally lustful body: where is the man who could resist
its beauty? Cruel beauty, as murderous as war! It remains, so that I can
appeal to it in my shame, and for that I give thanks. You are beautiful,
you who are nothing and nameless—oh, beautiful beyond measure!
Confronted by your beauty—dignity, spirit, and even the curse you
deserve are blown away in the light that is growing gray, because now
dusk is falling. You are so beautiful that my heart weeps over your

beauty. Then live, as far as I am concerned, live in joy—and when night falls, turn your back on me."

"Many thanks for the compliment!" cried Bompard.

And without looking at one another, they clinked glasses and listened until the thin tinkling died away before they drank.

The first glass was emptied at a draught and the second already filled. Bompard was lying stretched out charmingly in her long dress with the shoulder frills, the sea behind her. Resting on one elbow, she sniffed, smiling and with mobile nostrils, at the effervescence that formed a little cloud as of icy steam over the top of her glass; she sipped and chatted incessantly. Jaquemar sat facing her among the plants; he had both arms clasped around his knees; from time to time he lowered his head to the wine glass and took a sip from it, and gazed out to sea again as before. He looked very handsome, a man of the world and gravely mature; his hair, streaked with gold, created a curiously elegant impression in conjunction with his rugged forehead and lips that had now become firm, and even the squint in his eyes, which were only rarely opened wide, gave an added touch of intelligence to his face.

Perhaps he was listening with half an ear to what she was gabbling away about to the accompaniment of comical sighs: the hardship of a life of perpetual travel, "always on the run from desire," the "relatively poor remuneration for the art of loving" and a lot more extraordinary rubbish of the same sort. She watched herself as she raised her thumb and index finger bent into a circle to illustrate her words and said: "And if a woman has only a heart like this, black and wrinkled like a peppercorn, she will nevertheless lament the man who has made her warm. She will be overcome by anger and grief, and no one can blame her."

It was not worth hearing. Jaquemar watched the sun setting over the ocean. Huge blades of light were still pouring diagonally down out of the glowing fissures in the flat gray sky; but now they were white as though white-hot, and they flashed icily in the water, out of which something like frosty steam rose in a jagged cloud. Then shadows began to flutter among the shafts of light; they faded away; the water, shortly before still flecked with pools of blood, turned gray and the line of the horizon was now a distinct black streak under the oppressive cover of cloud. It was warm, but the falling dusk gave the lie to the fragrant warmth of the air; the very scents seemed to grow somehow older and coarser.

The damp breath of seaweed, mud, salt, and putrid fish smoldered amidst the perfume of flowers. The hoarse, deep-throated barking of the seals in the distance sounded closer and more labored, and sharper the thin hissing, snarling, and sucking of the sea on the beach and the soft slapping of the swell on the cliff face below them.

"The earth is no longer beautiful," said Jaquemar.

"You're right," answered Bompard. "And the day is ended."

She leaned over to one side and fished the second, almost empty bottle out of the pail and filled their two crystal goblets three-quarters full; she actually shook the bottle and slapped the bottom of it with the flat of her hand.

"That's the way it is," she commented, with a skeptical shrug of the shoulder. "Every pleasure comes to an end sooner or later. It can't be helped."

Carefully, with a glass in either hand, she rose at the same time as Jaquemar and passed one of them to him. They stood facing each other, Bompard with her everlasting smile, Jaquemar with a distrustful glance she did not notice. For the last time they clinked glasses.

"All for the best then, the way you want it, my angel," said Bompard, "and no hard feelings."

She emptied her glass at a draught and flung it, boyishly twisting the whole of the upper part of her body, at a not too-distant, moss-free boulder, on which it smashed with a crunching sound into countless tiny splinters; only the foot remained intact, flew up into the air spinning around and around, and fell with a little thud into the vegetation.

"Good night, Madame," said Jaquemar, as though to himself, and smashed his glass on the same stone.

They knelt down side by side on the damask cloth to pack the things. All at once Bompard clapped her hands together, put her left hand on her hips, and let her buttocks drop onto her heels as if felled by a blow.

"Well, I'll be damned," she exclaimed in amazement. "I drag around from dawn to dusk, I see to everything like a Yiddish momma, and now at the eleventh hour I have almost forgotten about the best surprise of all. Jaquemar, the dessert! The mere thought of it made the expense of the whole thing worthwhile! The dessert, my true love, was the first and the best thing I thought of. Well, it isn't too late, even now. Come on! But first I must blindfold you, according to the old custom, otherwise it wouldn't be a surprise, especially not for you, Jaquemar, you're such an inquisitive fellow."

Jaquemar, still on his knees, stopped gathering the things together. The melancholy emotion he had felt over the close of day had given place to a great indifference in his heart. Like her, he let his buttocks sink back on his heels, held his hands outspread on his thighs and murmured: "I'm waiting."

From somewhere or other she pulled out a very white table napkin, shook and flicked it out, and came shuffling over to Jaquemar.

"My God!" she said softly, with a false laugh. "He's kneeling as people kneel to be executed in China, poor thing! I'm not going to treat you to my dainties like that. Come here."

She jumped up and dragged him over to a stone that resembled a pouffe, because it was round and flat on top like a large pumpkin, and there Jaquemar now sat.

"You're not afraid of my cloth, are you?" she prattled foolishly, fingering and plucking with great care at his head. "The cloth suits you. Yes, just sniff. It has been lying all the time in my trunk with bags of lavender I picked myself. It smells wonderful. Cool, clean, and—as you can see for yourself—knotted by a tender hand. The back of your head, my friend, is stubborn, but that will avail it little—it will be over in an instant."

She kissed him on the ear and stepped back to admire her handiwork. As if looking for something, Jaquemar turned his face covered by the white cloth, which gave it a masklike appearance. He heard nothing. With a bound he was on his feet and tore off the napkin.

"No!" he shrieked. "I don't want any of your sweetmeats! Not blindfold!"

He saw the little revolver pointing toward him. He bent down, seized the stone he had been sitting on and raised it above his head to hurl at her. The shot made a popping, swishing, wet noise; he saw the little cloud at the end of the barrel; the stone fell to the ground behind his back with a thud; he himself fell to his knees and sank back. He lay with the back of his head and his shoulders on the stone.

He felt the warm blood dirtying him under his shirt, trickling and dribbling and flowing down to his hip, and he whispered with hard lips: "I knew it all the time."

Jaquemar's head lay at an angle; the world looked crooked from this position; he lowered his eyes and gazed into the swirling vapors of late evening. The figure of Bompard stood out very large in the midst of them. She flung the revolver away from her in an arc with her right hand and with her left the basket, tore the poke bonnet from her locks and made off. Because the trails of mist were creeping dense and languid over the ground, however, she seemed not to be running, but to be gliding through the dark air in her long dress, almost as though she had both feet raised above the earth at a slight angle, like the angels in old paintings. He even imagined that he could see the childish collar-cape that lay in multiple frills on her back and shoulders, making a gently fluttering and undulating movement, as she was carried off in this ghostly manner and disappeared far away among the black rock and seething mist of the cliff. Then there was nothing more to see; for Jaquemar it was night.

Hours later, he was awakened by the pain of a clumsy movement. It was still night, not yet black night like nights on land, but a lightless, glimmering sea night, in whose swirling mist colorless visions emerged and evaporated again, stones on the terrace floor, round and plump, and others of bizarre shapes, and far out on the reef the ghost tree, a cursing shadow giant that flung up its arms over the sea and was dissipated in billowing grayness. The vast expanse of water lay in dull, gloomy tranquillity; no breaking of waves was audible, and only the half-concealed coughing, baying, sneezing, and splashing of the invisible seals troubled the mist. Lazy waves of filthy vapor billowed from time to time through the windless air and brushed palpably against the face of the fallen man, creeping whiffs of oceanic ordure; they had an invigorating effect on him, as though in his distress and loneliness some lower form of life were visiting and snuffing at him.

He slipped his hand under his shirt, to feel his left side where the pain was burning him. His fingers came upon the little amulet, completely bent by the bullet that must have bounced off it; apart from this there was nothing but lacerated flesh and blood that was sticky like mud and began to trickle, fresh and warm, the moment he touched it. He withdrew his hand from his shirt, it dropped beside

him on the hard ground, and he sank back into a half-slumber, overcome by weakness.

But his features wore an alert, intelligent, and sober expression,
his thoughts were awake and talked with him in pictures. Very
clearly he saw his room in the Hôtel des Mines. It was afternoon, the
windows were open, and along with the hum, the sound of turning
wheels and ringing bells of the traffic in the Boulevard Arago, the
early summer wafted in smells of asphalt and syringa and playfully
fanned his cheeks and temples. He was sitting in an open, baggy
silk shirt in his wing chair, his legs wrapped in a light woolen rug,
his hands in his lap, looking at Germaine Chottin, who was sitting
in front of him on the *pouffe,* a tea apron over her dress, a large pair
of horn-rimmed spectacles on her nose. He fidgeted impatiently and
groaned: "It's no longer true."

But little Madame Chottin opened the book on her knees and
read: "Were I to tell thee the order of the earth that I saw, thou
wouldst sit thee down and weep."

Her words, uttered without dismay, rang out distinctly as though
spoken into Jaquemar's ear. He murmured, "That's true," and listened
more attentively.

As he listened, picture and sound faded away; he opened his eyes.
Dense mist was still swirling, although the first hint of lilac-blue now
glowed within it. With a groan, Jaquemar raised himself into a half-
sitting position on his elbows and listened. The seething mist stopped
up his ears; even the labored coughing of the seals now seemed to
come from far away—and from even farther the tolling of a bell, and
a sound like a sigh, perhaps the notes of an organ being played in
San Philippo by the Sea, or perhaps only a memory, for he had heard
it when he came here, before this night had fallen. But it remained.
He shut his eyes and pulled himself together. He tipped himself
over onto his knees, bit back the pain, and began to crawl toward the
sound.

In spirit we emerge from that forest in which the path peters out
among sand and weeds. But a dense mist is billowing over everything,
even over the terrace of rock. We peer into it, anxious to bear witness,
we shout through our cupped hands: "Hey, Jaquemar! Gilgamesh of
our day, where are you? Are you succeeding? Are you bleeding to

death? Are you still on your way?"

We wait. It seems gradually to grow a little lighter. Far beyond the sea, on the horizon, the sun must already be rising. A pallid glimmer filters into view through the dark clouds of chaos, and suddenly, in the uncertain play of the light, towering from our feet to high overhead, the huge shadow of a crawling man looms up in the surging gray mist. A gigantic insect. Now he raises one arm to the sky, perhaps to beckon—or because he is falling? We do not know, the vision vanishes, the mist swirls and seethes.

We were mistaken, the night is not yet over. When, oh, when will you come, day for which we wait so anxiously?

ABOUT THE AUTHOR

Joachim Maass was born in 1901 in Hamburg, Germany, and was educated at the University of Hamburg. He was editor of the magazine *Die Neue Rundschau* and is the author of twelve books, two of which have appeared in the United States—*The Magic Year* (1944) and *The Weeping and the Laughter* (1947). Mr. Maass left Germany in 1939 for political reasons. On board ship coming to this country he began writing *The Gouffé Case*, which he worked on, with interruptions, for the next thirteen years. *The Gouffé Case* was widely acclaimed in Germany, and has also been published in England, France, Italy, Norway and Sweden.

Mr. Maass now lives in New York City. He is a Lecturer at Haverford College at present, and from 1940 to 1952 was a Lecturer in the rank of Associate Professor at Mount Holyoke College.